IN PURSUIT OF THE PERFECT PLANT

A Business and Technical Guide

Pat Kennedy, OSIsoft
Vivek Bapat, SAP
Paul Kurchina, KurMeta

Evolved
Technologist
Press
New York, NY

In Pursuit of the Perfect Plant
A Business and Technical Guide

Pat Kennedy, Vivek Bapat, and Paul Kurchina

Published by Evolved Technologist Press, an imprint of Evolved Media Network, 242 West 30th Street, Suite 801, New York, New York 10001

This book may be purchased for educational, business, or sales promotional use. For more information contact:
Evolved Technologist Press
(646) 827-2196
info@EvolvedTechnologist.com
www.EvolvedTechnologist.com

Editor/Analyst: Dan Woods
Writers: Dan Woods, Dan Safarik, D. Foy O'Brien, Emma Johnson
Production Editor: Deb Gabriel
Cover and Interior Design: 1106 Design
Illustrator: Tory Moore
First Edition: April 2008

ISBN: 978-0-9789218-6-6; 0-9789218-6-0

Contents

Acknowledgments

The creation of *In Pursuit of the Perfect Plant* took place through an unprecedented process of collaboration that involved a group of more than 100 experts. The authors and sponsors used their personal networks and the resources of their companies to reach out to invite people to participate in the book and the response was overwhelming. Dan Woods and the team from Evolved Media orchestrated the interviewing and writing process, but the true stars of the book are all of the generous people who helped provide ideas for the book and also carefully reviewed the content. Their names are included below.

The authors would like to convey special thanks to Ian Ryan and David Katona for coming up with the "Perfect Plant" concept in the first place and their continued efforts to push this forward

We also thank:

Ian Achterkirch	Kahn Ellis	HaJo Lockermann
Mukesh Arora	Ashtad Engineer	Krish Mantripragada
C. Edward Boddington	Marty Etzel	Colin Masson
Andy Bellagamba	Elizabeth Given	Paul Maurer
Jeff Bonnell	Kumad Goel	Jim McCoy
Paul Boris	John Harrison	Steward McCutcheon
James Breeze	Carol Jackson	Bimal Mehta
David Brousell	Carter Johnson	Charlie Miller
Rick Bullotta	Charles Johnson	John Mitchell
Connie Chiu	Alan Johnston	Charles Mohrmann
Tony Ciliberti	Gary Johnston	Chet Namboodri
Chris Colyer	David Katona	Kevin Parker
Paul Didier	Dan Knight	Owen Plowman
Marc Dillon	George Kube	Norm Poynter
Thad Dungan	Winston P. Ledet	Alan Preston

Derek Prior   Prasad Satyavolu   Steve Tonissen
Mark Pyatt   Frank Schuler   Ganesh Wadawadigi
Nand Ramchandani   Manfred Schulz   Michael Wendell
Stuart Robinson   Don Shobrys   Richard Wernsing
Carlos Rojas   Phanibhushan Sistu   John Wheeler
Richard Ross   Kristian Steenstrup   Terry Wireman
Sunil Roy   Eric Streed   Matthias Wobbe
Ian Ryan   Phil Tencer

This book was truly a community effort, experts coming together to share their knowledge, experience, and passion for the topic of this book. We hope that this community experience continues on after you read the book at *www.pursuitoftheperfectplant.com*.

Foreword

Flat world dynamics have rapidly given way to a new world order in business. The days of a single company competing against another company, or a single region competing against another region are over. The evolving rules of business mandate that business networks that cut across multiple organizations and geographies must now compete against other business networks. This new dimension of competition is changing the pressures on manufacturers, dispelling the traditional notions of quality, delivery, and costs metrics. Virtualization of manufacturing increasingly means that the individual plant may have to become part of one or more business networks, groups of separate companies that assemble and reassemble to meet market demands. Specialization means that the core competency of each plant must be precisely defined and meet ever-increasing regulatory and customer standards

The disaggregation and localization of supply and demand, combined with the virtualization of manufacturing, means that manufacturers must do several things at the same time. They must run responsive supply networks in perfect synchronization with their customers, suppliers, and partners; ensure operational excellence throughout the value chain; and extract the optimal value across distributed assets and energy bases. Furthermore, manufacturers must do all this while maintaining product and service leadership to provide differentiated value to the customer.

The need for rapid change arrives at a time most plant managers are beginning to understand that the extreme heterogeneity of plant systems architecture is a significant barrier to progress. Yet rip and replace is not a workable strategy. Rather, multiple players inside an organization must work together in concert with the appropriate vendors and partners to move incrementally toward a flexible architecture. The gaps between enterprise processes, operations, execution, asset management, quality management, and energy management must be closed rapidly. Granular information must be made available in the right context and at the right time to support proactive decision-making across plants and operations.

Against this back drop, the book that you are holding in your hands has been in the making for decades. The goal of the book is quite simple: to examine the most important aspects of the journey towards the perfect plant and to show how companies can use the vision of the perfect plant to help them make hundreds of incremental improvements that are unique to their own environment and corporate strategy. For the first time, authors have successfully put together a roadmap for designing and operating manufacturing operations for the new era, offering both a methodology as well as best practices to help you design your own perfect plant. This book shows how to combine new elements of information technology with time-tested production technologies and best practices. Instead of presenting this information in a dense textbook, the authors bring these ideas to life in a conversation. The result is a book that is easy to read and accessible to senior management, plant managers, staff, and IT personnel at all levels.

The world is full of books that provide hundreds of pages on micro topics in manufacturing. Lean manufacturing, Six Sigma, and other improvement initiatives have ornate methodologies that work wonders in the right hands. Instead of taking a deep dive on individual topics, the authors, Pat Kennedy, Vivek Bapat, and Paul Kurchina, have focused on a wider view, concentrating more on the essence of improving each area discussed. The business novel *The Goal* provided a general sense of how to go about change. *In Pursuit of the Perfect Plant* provides a general view like *The Goal* but with specifics in key areas relevant to improving manufacturing operations in today's business environment.

I am doubly excited to support this book because of the very collaborative nature of the project. It exemplifies how a business network of participants can come together to provide unique value. This book is the work of a network of participants from leading vendors such as SAP, OSIsoft, Cisco, and TCS combined with individual contributions from hundreds of industry experts. This diverse group came together as partners, each bringing their unique competencies to produce a guide that focuses on helping manufacturers anticipate and solve the next-generation challenges in manufacturing operations.

The networked partnership that this book represents brings to the table all of the people who will help create a perfect plant: plant executives, domain experts who work on plants, consultants, vendors, and analysts. I am proud that SAP has joined in this effort and I hope that you will be as pleased with the result as I am. Most of all, I hope that this book will inspire companies and help them accelerate their journey toward the ever-elusive goal of the perfect plant.

Richard Campione
Senior Vice President
Suite Solution Management
SAP

Introduction – The Transformation Challenge: Reaping the Rewards for Managing Change

I f you spend your days in the Byzantine world of manufacturing—making products, fixing equipment, supervising quality, implementing software, analyzing planning data, or managing the big picture—this book is for you. Our goal is simple and direct: provide information and suggestions that will help you improve the quality of your plant.

Making any one part of a plant work better is difficult, but hardly impossible. The real challenge facing most companies today is how to create a blueprint for an entire plant, or portfolio of plants, that integrates all strategies and processes to function under a single, consolidated plan. In the face of continual change, you need a vision to guide you on the path to achieving this plan. You must know where you want to go, and, just as importantly, how you would like to get there. What do you want your plant to accomplish? How can you coordinate all of its operations to work in concert toward that goal?

Local optimization—focusing on improving just one area—is a losing proposition. To succeed, your plant must improve as a whole, not just in one aspect. For example, if you reduce unplanned outages through more frequent maintenance, the plant's output may be diminished. If, on the other hand, you run a plant to avoid shutdowns for maintenance, the lifetime of your equipment may be shortened. Trade-offs like these abound in any plant and cascade into problems of mounting complexity.

What keeps you in the game is the knowledge that, although there are no easy solutions to such difficulties, solutions do exist. The first thing to recognize is that the modern manufacturing plant is a complex, interrelated system. For better or for worse, changing one part always affects those around it. When all the parts are working to benefit the others, you have achieved a vision of what we call the perfect plant.

To really make a difference in improving the operations of a plant to meet its owner's goals, you have to have a comprehensive vision of what the plant should accomplish and how every aspect of the plant's operations can help in the face of continual change. While each perfect plant meets the needs of its owner in a unique way, at the end of the day, each is still like all the others: every perfect plant is an extension of the financial and business strategy of the company that owns it, and every perfect plant produces certifiable business benefits and does not seek to meet KPIs for their own sake.

In *Part I: Pressures on the Plant,* we look at the big picture. We examine the payoff for improvement, the cast of characters and systems that run a plant, the pressures required to generate positive change, and the shape and requirements of a comprehensive vision.

In *Part II: Making Progress Toward Perfection,* we examine each of the plant's primary concerns, from traditional challenges like planning and asset management, to newer issues such as energy management and sustainability. We study the history of each, investigating who is involved, how to keep score, and what information is needed to succeed. We take a detailed look at how every perfect plant advances from one level of maturity to the next, undergoes transformation through patterns of success, and evolves a culture of reciprocity and tribal awareness. Further, we examine how each of a plant's various functions interacts with its counterparts, and then suggest methods that will help you improve all those functions in concert, while keeping the plant running smoothly.

Part III: Making It Happen addresses the problems of change management. Having envisioned the perfect plant, how do you move toward it quickly and efficiently? What are the best methods and techniques to communicate your vision to the vast mix of people who run your plant? What motivates these people, and what are the most effective incentives to change their behavior? These are just a few of the quandaries to which this book provides a series of well-considered, holistic solutions.

The Perfect Plant Is Not a Methodology

The past 20 years have seen a blossoming of new theories about how to run a manufacturing plant that meets the highest levels of efficiency and productivity. From Lean Manufacturing, to Six Sigma, to the Theory of Constraints that is set forth in the novel, *The Goal,* the suggested methods of improvement are as rich as they are abundant. While each has been proven in practice, it is important to note that they are sometimes applied ineptly.

It is not our intention to supplement the already exhaustive literature on plant methodology. Every company must deploy its own process of analysis. Until you see your plant as a single unit of finely tuned, complexly interrelated parts, your efforts to marshal all those parts will likely be frustrating. As we have suggested, a vision of the perfect plant infers a vision of the big picture. Once you hold this picture firmly in mind, your task lies in sharing it with as many people as possible.

This book will be of assistance in spreading an understanding of the big picture throughout the plant. For instance, it can be a fantastic vehicle through which to educate the people with whom you want to share your vision and to raise the consciousness about your plant across the enterprise. Consequently, you increase the chances that everyone has a clear idea not only of their role and its effects, but also of the role of those around them. Whether you are employing new methodologies or revamping established ones, they will all work better as a result of expending the effort to deepen your collective awareness.

How Perfect Is the Perfect Plant?

The perfect plant is one that knows how to achieve business goals with minimal resources. Sometimes this means prudently pushing everything to the limits to achieve objectives, with full knowledge of what those limits are.

If the perfect plant were a high-performance racing car, everyone in that car and on the pit crew would be focused on how to make sure that the car was moving as fast as possible without taking unreasonable risk. To do this, you must know a lot about how the car is operating and the track conditions. You must know how fast the engine can run, how much wear is on the tires, and what the tire pressure and oil temperature are. In short, you need instrumentation and the means to analyze what the instruments are telling you.

Many plants are struggling today because they lack a clear and precise vision for their future state. Without it, they cannot explain where they want to go and how to get there.

Another related concern pertains to employee motivation. If a business has not taken care to conceive a vision for what it wants to achieve, and then convey this vision to its employees, why would the employees care about improving their performance? The experts we consulted repeatedly explained that the most important contribution this book could make would be to show people how to create a workplace culture that is founded upon a clear vision of the perfect plant.

The drive to improve manufacturing processes and optimize return from resources is nothing new. However, the industry has seen astonishing change and growth, much of it driven by technology that makes it easier to execute processes that were once incredibly difficult, if not impossible. Today, for example, cheap, reliable online spectrometers can provide analysts with readings of chemical processes that only a short time ago were unattainable without engaging manual lab procedures that were time-consuming, costly, and error-prone. Many organizations balk at techniques that are now either proven or promising simply because they remember how difficult they were in the past.

Many plants, too, are not attempting to understand their limits and push toward them. This leaves money on the table and reduces the probability that the plant will survive. Let's look at various industries for a few examples of the challenges facing different types of plants:

✔   Paper mills must be pushing the limits of cost and efficiency given their market context.

✔   Refineries must increase asset utilization because demand and prices for their products are high.

✔ Power plants must meet financial, regulatory, and reliability requirements to maximize return.

✔ Discrete manufacturers must deal with balancing the needs of a large workforce, competition from abroad, and consumer demands for more products, higher quality, lower prices, and customization.

✔ All manufacturers must make the right products at the right time with minimal rework and resources.

This book attempts to survey the range of difficulties every plant will encounter on the path to meeting these challenges, from choosing the right objectives to understanding the performance of the plant, from sales and operations planning to quality, asset, and energy management, among a host of others.

Where We Found the Wisdom

We set out to examine every important facet of manufacturing across the process, discrete, and utility industries. As such, this book's scope is broad, and yet we have strived to ensure that it is also deep.

Imagine that you had time to do a research project whereby you personally interviewed the experts and specialists of every aspect of the manufacturing industries, learning the secrets to achieving superior performance in all that you do. Well, we had time, and we used it to interview over 100 people renowned by their industry peers for their proven expertise. Of course, we added our own insights to this collective wisdom, then boiled it all down to 13 chapters of approximately 25 to 30 pages each. (Some of the people we consulted are noted as contributing authors to one or more chapters, while others contributed to parts of one or more chapters, or provided comments as reviewers. Please see the acknowledgements for a comprehensive list of who contributed.)

The following list provides a few examples of how to best use this book:

✔ Senior management at the corporate level can read it to refresh their knowledge about the details of each important area in a plant.

✔ Plant managers can read it and help educate others in the plant about the bigger picture.

✔ VPs, managers, and operators in the plant can read it to learn better ways to communicate with other departments in the plant.

✔ Operators, engineers, and technologists in the plant can read it to understand the implications of their actions on the plant and on the business as a whole.

✔ New employees at any level can read it to gain an understanding of any plant's general and specific operations.

A number of the people involved with this project are affiliated with companies that sell technology or other services. Regardless, we have worked hard to guarantee that the book remains free of marketing messages or specific product promotion.

This book, like the perfect plant itself, is but a journey. Each of its chapters was improved through the input of people who read the content at *www.EvolvedTechnologist.com/perfectplant.* The same site will also be used to discuss issues that arise after publication. We invite you to drop us a line to let us know if our book has made a difference at your plant.

The Authors:

Pat Kennedy, CEO, OSIsoft
Vivek Bapat, Vice President, Solutions Marketing,
    Manufacturing, Supply Chain, and PLM, SAP
Paul Kurchina, Principal, KurMeta

Part I
Pressures on the Plant

··

Part I sets the scene for the book. John Mulcahy starts off introducing the training project to the team with a lecture on the nature of the world of manufacturing and why continuous improvement toward a comprehensive vision of perfection is so important. In following sessions, Mulcahy describes the people and processes used to run most plants and the challenges plants are now facing. In the last lecture of Part I, Mulcahy takes a close look at what it means to create a vision for perfection.

Chapter One
The Payoff from the Perfect Plant

. . . .

"**S**ince this is our first team meeting, we should start by coming up with a name for our team," said John Mulcahy, the newly promoted Executive VP of Manufacturing Operations for Wolverine, Inc. "We are going to oversee the operations of seven different plants that make over 200 products. Our job is to see that they all do what our strategy demands of them." Mulcahy looked at Joan Bonhoffer, Krishna Balasubramaniam, and Peter Moulton, the three analysts he'd selected to manage the relationship with the plants. They each had an engineering degree followed by an MBA and two or three years of experience in other parts of Wolverine. But, what impressed Mulcahy the most was their curiosity and raw thinking power.

"What about the 'Manufacturing Operations Team'?" suggested Balasubramaniam.

"I was hoping to have a little more fun than that, Bala," said Mulcahy, referring to the analyst by his nickname. "The relationship between plants and corporate is not always so peachy. The name should help people to understand that we are going to do things differently from now on."

. . . . ◀ 3

"Perhaps you can enlighten us a bit more about our mission before we try to put a name to it," said Mouton.

"You're right," said Mulcahy, "And while I'm at it, I'll tell you more about the roles I want you all to play, and a bit about myself, as well. The right name for the team will follow."

Mulcahy approached the double whiteboard that covered the wall of the conference room, grabbed a marker, and then froze, his mind whirring. With his shock of disheveled grey hair, nondescript business-casual clothes, and high-tech walking shoes, he looked more like an absent-minded engineering professor than a typical executive. His three new analysts munched on the last bits of donuts and bagels while waiting for him to snap out of his thoughts.

"Twenty years ago," he said at last, "I was a plant manager. I ran our Dearborn facility for five years before moving on to corporate troubleshooting and special projects for the CEO. I helped put all the lovely ERP software in the plants and then worked on the supply chain software to keep track of the flow of goods to and from the plant. Most recently, I was working on the M&A team. Do you guys know all these acronyms?"

"ERP is Enterprise Resource Planning," said Bonhoffer.

"ERP is Quick Books for the enterprise," said Mulcahy, "with lots of extra stuff slapped on. SCM tracks the extended flow of goods to and from us. All of this stuff is a general-purpose model that you can put to work to track what's going on in your business. So far, so good."

Mulcahy turned around and began to write. "Let me tell you what many years making all this stuff work has done to me," he said, and stepped aside. On the whiteboard, in huge letters, he had written:

I AM SICK OF SOFTWARE

"I took this job for one reason—to get back to being responsible for making our plants work better. Looking at the changes over the past 20 years has made me realize there's a huge opportunity to crush the competition by using our investment in software and technology to run the plants in a new way. I call this idea the Perfect Plant."

"Perfect?" asked Peter Moulton. "Isn't that setting the bar too high?"

"Not if you think of perfection as a target that you're always moving toward," said Mulcahy. "The idea is that to reduce complication in a plant, you need to clarify which goals are important to the enterprise and how those goals are affected by the activities engaged to reach them. Then you can figure out how the tradeoff between improving one aspect of a plant, like cutting maintenance costs, can be at odds with others, like reducing unscheduled downtime and improving plant availability to the corporation. If you have a vision for what perfection means at your plant, and an accepted measurement and visualization of your progress toward perfection, people won't do things that hurt another area's performance without getting it involved first."

"So the one of the goals of the perfect plant is to create and shape a shared vision," said Bonhoffer.

"Exactly," said Mulcahy. "So the first part of our job at corporate is to ensure that each plant has a clear idea of what we expect from them."

"That makes sense," said Bala. "But how much detail do we provide? I hope you're not suggesting we micromanage."

"Our job," said Mulcahy, "is to improve communication and sort out problems. That's why I became sick of software. Software is like electricity. Used properly, it can move the earth. But touch the wrong wire and destruction can result. Some of the IT guys haven't been able to grasp this. That's why there is a massive conflict between the way software is applied and the way it *should* be applied to make plants run better."

"I know what you mean," said Bonhoffer. "It seems to me that a lot of IT people live in an information world and see things as simpler than they are, without practical constraints or a clear understanding of the facilities. They throw software at problems without considering how it will improve the business."

"And manufacturing has cascading depths of complexity," said Mulcahy. "Software exists usually because some common way of doing things has been discovered that is embedded in the software. In the world of manufacturing, at each level, the complexity seems to grow. Plant equipment is controlled by programmable logic controllers that are controlled by supervisory systems that are communicating with execution systems that are linked with ERP, which is communicating with the supply chain. And to make things more exciting, if you get something wrong, equipment blows up and people get hurt. So when you throw software at something without careful consideration, the plant guys feel powerless to help guide the effort. They end up resisting new ways of working, until some executive gets angry and inflicts a system on them. In most of our plants, this process has been repeated so often that our systems have become isolated. In general, they function in mutual exclusivity, focused on specific activities. Some work well and perform vital tasks. Others don't work as well as we'd like. Either way, nobody can see the big picture— at corporate or at the plants. To run a plant well, you need to see the whole picture. That is why…" Mulcahy turned and wrote on the board:

> I AM SICK OF SOFTWARE FOR ITS OWN SAKE.
>
> I LOVE SOFTWARE WHEN IT SERVES THE BUSINESS.

"The good news," Mulcahy said, "is that in almost every one of our plants there has been significant investment in all sorts of technology and software. The bad news is that sometimes it doesn't work very well, and when it does, it is rarely coordinated to address the big picture. That's where you guys come in. "

"I've only spent a little time in the plants compared to you," said Bonhoffer, "so I don't want to go anywhere and pretend I can tell someone what to do based on knowing nothing. If I wanted to do that I would have gone into management consulting."

"Hey, not all management consultants are completely clueless," said Bala. "I—"

"Don't worry, Bala," Mulcahy said. "Some of my best friends are management consultants. In any case, I have no intention of sending you guys out to order people around. The people in the plants know their business—our job is to enable communication so that we can learn from them."

"That," said Moulton, "sounds like we've got a lot of listening and studying to do. Before we can help them to do a better job, we've first got to understand their needs. Running a plant has probably changed in a huge number of ways since the early 1980s."

"In more ways than one, too," said Mulcahy. "For instance, Just In Time, Six Sigma, Lean Manufacturing, Continuous Improvement, Kaizen groups for collaboration, and Balanced Scorecard are just a few of the methods now being used to improve manufacturing that have been developed in the last 20 years. There's also fresh technology in sensors and catalysts, along with a host of newly implemented process designs. But, whereas some of these are worthwhile, often the consultants were just trying to find a problem for their solution. External pressures are mounting, now. Nobody used the expression 'carbon footprint' back at my plant in Dearborn, and nobody threatened to send the CFO to jail for inaccurate numbers or to start a criminal investigation for sending the wrong equipment to the wrong country. It's a new world. We're going to learn about it together, discover the leading methods, and then apply them across the board in all of our plants."

"I feel like I'm back in business school," said Moulton, "except my professors were younger than you and better dressed. What's your plan for educating us?"

"First, instead of you paying for the privilege of learning, *we* are going to pay *you* to learn the business of running a plant and creating some credibility with our production people. Next, I'm going to assign you areas to study, and then I'm going to ask you to summarize what the experts recommend. Afterwards, we will unleash you on the plants. Before going, however, you'll study their capital requests to understand their impression of their needs. Once on site, you'll assess their problems. Finally, when you return, we'll engage in a series of conversations about how they can move toward the perfect plant. This method works. You will have the time that I don't have to spend with people and really listen. That will get the flow of communication going and lead to many good things."

The Payoff

"Let's assume," said Bala, "that you can educate us well enough to understand the workings of a plant. What makes you think that we can actually make a difference? The people you've already got can't be a bunch of dolts."

"You're right," said Mulcahy. "We've definitely got people who want our plants to excel. No matter how badly they want it, though, there are things they simply cannot do without cooperation from corporate. Before modern logistics and communication, these plants didn't serve a global market. Each plant was built and run with a command and control mentality. The idea was to carry out orders, and the orders lent themselves to this approach. Plants were isolated and autonomous. This created a macho culture that didn't encourage collaboration. That's one of the reasons the Japanese have made such rapid gains. They have a culture of cooperation and collaboration that allows steady progress into the unknown."

"Why is our project worth doing?" Moulton asked. "What's the payoff for teaching us how to work with plants to improve operations?"

"Count on the finance guy to get to the heart of the matter," said Mulcahy. "The ROI is huge. If you ever pull some benchmarking numbers from Stratuscope or Solomon or one of the other benchmarking outfits, the difference between the top performers and the bottom performers is massive.

"If you take such numbers to a plant and show them they are below the industry norms, they would tell you there's a barrage of unassailable reasons for that. For example, it could be because their products are more difficult to make, or because they have not been given the capital to improve a plant, to name a few. And they could be right. You don't have to be an industry leader in every metric to have a great plant. In order to reward innovation, benchmarking numbers have to be interpreted properly for each site. If we can just give each plant meaningful enough measures to allow them to move a small way up on the most important metrics, we'll usually see a remarkable payoff. In some cases, we could change this business dramatically."

"In financial terms," said Moulton, "if we use the assets we already have to move each plant up just one quartile, we can see millions in return."

"You got it," said Mulcahy.

"That's enough to grab anybody's attention!" said Bonhoffer. "How can we get started?"

"Before we go further I'd like you to focus on one aspect of looking at numbers that gets forgotten," said Mulcahy. "A lot of the time, when we look at benchmarking numbers, we get caught up in the variety of numbers that are available and lose sight of what we're really trying to do. I try to keep this in mind by distinguishing between measures and metrics. Measures are any number that tells us something. How much energy we are using per product, the percentage of maintenance done on schedule, that sort of thing. A metric to me is a number that indicates value from the perspective of the customer. A measure would be the relative cost of manufacture but a metric would be price and on-time delivery to the customer. If corporate is trying to maximize customer value, we must focus on metrics, not measures. It doesn't make sense to optimize a measure and sacrifice a metric. What if lowering the cost of manufacturing, for example, by running energy consumers at night, degraded the metric such as on-time delivery time? The key is to do the best you can on measures that are important to the plant without sacrificing metrics."

"So this is your own way of using these words," said Bonhoffer.

"Well, perhaps, but now that you know them, it can be your way too," said Mulcahy.

The Nature of the Plant

"Now let's start thinking about how to understand a plant. The first thing you need to do," said Mulcahy, "is learn how to think about the plant in both abstract and concrete terms. Groups of people operating these plants are theories brought to life, and once they have a life, they evolve in unexpected ways. Before we look at the new ways of doing things, I'm going to run you through the way I was taught to think about the plant as I came up the ranks.

"Back the late 1970s, my teacher was Thomas Mattern, who ran the Dearborn facility where I started. He was from the German academic tradition and always tried to ground what we were doing in one sort of theoretical framework. It was as if we had an engineering professor as a plant manager. For instance, he would refer to specific chapters in obscure books, which is exactly what I'm going to do to you.

"Our first stop is a book called *Computer Control of Industrial Processes*, by Emanuel Savas, which came out in 1965. In the opening chapter, the one I recommend you read, he describes plants as flows of materials, flows of energy, and flows of information. I've always found this useful when I walk inside a plant. You can pretty much see the flow of materials by standing and watching or looking at a floor plan. The flow of energy requires a bit more work. You must find out what type of energy is needed, where it comes from, and how it is transformed from electricity to motion, from oil to heat. Seeing and understanding the flow of information is both the most critical and the most difficult, largely because it happens in so many ways. Some plant managers like to go into the plant when they are thinking about problems. They want to 'feel the heat.'"

"Why don't you just look at the IT systems?" asked Bala. "Shouldn't all the information flow through reports, spreadsheets, and operator consoles of some kind?"

"Actually," said Mulcahy, "it's better to think of information flow as knowledge. The IT systems have important information, but they never tell the whole story. Brains have the context that makes information meaningful. For instance, consider what happens if a main crude pump is scheduled for maintenance just hours before a large tanker comes in to port. In our personal lives, we have all seen brand new streets torn up to run a new water line. These are examples of interrupted information flow. There are all sorts of information forms and flows—official and unofficial, formal and informal. The cast of characters in a plant and the way they interact is a world unto itself. I think we need a session on this topic alone, so let's make that the next meeting." Mulcahy went to the whiteboard and wrote:

PERFECT PLANT RESEARCH MEETINGS

CAST OF CHARACTERS:
Who's who in a plant and how do they work together?

"The flow of materials and energy are not easy to change in a plant. However, since both of these things are largely governed by the flow of a plant's information, improving that flow is critical.

"I need to teach you to assess whether everyone in the plant has the information they need to do their jobs. You'll find that in many cases they don't. In the absence of the right information, they run the plant based on practices established long ago, frequently by people who have long since retired."

"So, plants are operating equipment to fulfill historical goals that don't yield full benefits," said Bonhoffer. "It's sort of like running a new Ferrari at 30 miles per hour because you're afraid of the trouble you might run into at higher speeds."

"Exactly," said Mulcahy. "We have great managers at our plants, but to break through their limitations they need information about the real capacity of the equipment. They need to see exactly how much money is left on the table at the end of each day, when they operate within conservative limits."

"This is where the fragmented IT systems become a problem," said Bala.

"Sometimes," said Mulcahy, "you'll find that the information you need is easy to access and assemble. Once it's in the right hands, of course, the plant runs better. That's an easy case. The more difficult case might entail extracting, correlating, analyzing, and contextualizing information from five or six different systems. By then, it's stale, and that's not good. Plants are quintessential real-time operations. Data after-the-fact is useful for analysis but not for operation. Other times, the measurements might even be entirely missing, or not yet converted into useful knowledge. Instead of simply saying that you have lost heat, for instance, you need to come up with a hard exhaust temperature. The point is, no matter what the circumstance, people can't improve operations until they've determined a plan of action that is founded on reliable information."

"Can you please clarify what you mean by 'contextualizing information'?" said Bala.

"Let me give you an example," said Mulcahy, "that's related to one of the key processes in the plant, asset management, which is the practice of making sure the equipment is maintained and operating properly. Asset management information must be interpreted in the context of the goals of the plant to make good decisions. If certain conditions are met, then maintenance is needed."

"But doesn't that require shutting down the line?" said Bonhoffer. "I mean, you don't do that just because new measurements have been added and someone sees that a condition on a piece of equipment requires maintenance, right?"

Mulcahy smiled, glad for the question. "Not if it doesn't present danger to equipment or people. There are other factors that have to be considered in real time. But if the condition is really serious, it may be worth it, or indeed required, to shut down production to complete the task and thus avoid injury or perhaps even a longer outage later.

"Let me give you one more example, to solidify the concept of contextualizing information. There was a power boiler in one of our plants that developed a leak in the boiler tubes during a time of maximum production. Fortunately, new microphones had recently been installed in the unit; so that by examining the historic noise or hiss, you could see that the leak was on the low pressure side—a relatively insignificant problem that enabled the plant to run with the condition until it could take the outage. Had the boiler had a high-pressure leak, the plant would have had to implement an immediate shutdown. The savings that resulted from this information were immense."

Mulcahy turned back to the agenda on the whiteboard and added a few more items.

> ## PERFECT PLANT RESEARCH MEETINGS
>
> | CAST OF CHARACTERS:
>   Who's who in a plant and how do they work together?
>
> | SYSTEMS IN A PLANT:
>   Enterprise Architecture on the shop floor
>
> | PRESSURES ON THE PLANT:
>   Internal and External forces for change

"Have you guys heard of the book titled *The Goal*, by Eli Goldratt?" asked Mulcahy.

"We read it in the manufacturing class at B-school, but it's been a while," said Bonhoffer.

"If I had realized I would be taking this class now, I would have taken that class then," said Moulton.

"The book," said Mulcahy, "describes a great example of a plant that runs better because the information starts flowing in new ways. It also discusses an analytical framework called the Theory of Constraints. *The Goal* has sold in the millions, and Goldratt has a successful consulting business and lots of other books, as well. You'll find it relevant to our work because he makes a big deal about knowing what you are trying to do. That's "The Goal": making money in a plant. The book shows how this concept is frequently never in place or gets lost. Naively applied cost accounting techniques are a big barrier, too. One way we will succeed in what we're doing is to find ways for everyone in all of our plants to clearly understand our goals."

"This seems so obvious," said Mouton. "Isn't knowing what you are trying to achieve a basic principle?"

"Don't confuse a clear view with a short distance," said Mulcahy. "MBAs and IT guys are alike in doing this. It's easy to say that a plant should have a clear goal. It's wickedly hard to estimate what that goal is and then communicate it so that that everyone knows what they should do."

THE GOAL

The Goal by Eliyahu Goldratt is probably the most widely read book on manufacturing. The book tells the story, in the form of a novel, of UniCo, a manufacturing firm that is beset by problems and is in danger of being shut down. Alex Rogo, the plant manager, attempts to solve the problem with conventional thinking but is stymied until an older professor friend of his starts him thinking in a new direction. As the story unfolds, Rogo learns how to discard conventional notions of cost-based efficiency and reorganize the plant to reach the goal, which is to make money. As the story unfolds, Goldratt's continuous improvement philosophy called the Theory of Constraints is explained. While the goal is focused on manufacturing, Goldratt has written a series of other books that show how the Theory of Constraints can be applied to marketing, project management, and other areas.

Setting Each Plant's Goal

"Let's take a step back and look at some first principles," said Mulcahy. "Why do we have plants anyway? Let's hear what your MBA-trained minds have to say."

"To make things," said Bonhoffer, as all three analysts immediately reverted back to MBA-style competitive brainstorming.

"To create products to sell," said Moulton.

"To get an edge on the competition," said Bala, "in order to create a sustainable advantage."

"To allow the enterprise to make money," said Moulton.

"You all are on the right track," said Mulcahy. "Wolverine assembled these plant assets because it has a strategy for making money that involves making products. Wolverine wants to create products and run its plants so it has a competitive advantage—in the best case a defensible and sustainable one. That's the beginning of what a plant needs to do."

"What's the ending?" asked Bala.

"You've read the corporate history of Wolverine as part of your orientation," said Mulcahy. "What have you noticed?"

"Wolverine started making three kinds of parts for the auto companies," said Bala. "Then it acquired a supplier of the high temperature resistant plastic used in the parts. This led to a new line of consumer and industrial products, some sold to businesses and others through the retail channel. Right now the original parts business at the Dearborn facility makes up only 20% of the company's business."

"Very good," Mulcahy said. "So what's your conclusion about the role of plants based on this history?"

"Times change, companies grow," suggested Bala.

"Meeting customer demand is the key, and the ability to change with that demand is part of it. Obviously some changes are too large to contemplate. But as a general rule, the plant that can change, and change quickly, is the one that succeeds. The one that can't is the one that gets shut down in the next cycle. Arie de Geus talks about this in his book, *The Living Company*. For instance, the longest-lived company in history, Stora, has lived since the Middle Ages because it has totally changed its business multiple times. But all you have to do is take a look around the Dearborn facility to see what I mean. It's surrounded by empty buildings that were once thriving plants.

"So the mission of a plant," said Bonhoffer, "is to fulfill the strategy of the corporation, but to do it in such a way that increases the chances of the plant surviving when the next storm hits."

"There are a huge number of examples of the sort of gear shifts that happen," said Mulcahy. "The steel industry in the U.S. had the market to themselves for the 1950s and 1960s, but the Japanese started from nothing and kept coming. Most of the industry couldn't make the changes needed fast enough. Now all that's left are mini mills that are low energy and flexible. The oil industry is currently in a phase where their capacity is sold out at high prices. And even though most of a refinery optimization comes from flexibility in product mix—not production—for 15 years before this run-up, all the margins were spent on compliance and cutting costs. Paper mills in the U.S. are the opposite case—a specific mill makes only one product class, such as tissue, or white paper, or linerboard. Plus, since they do it with finite demand, they focus on being the low-cost producer that they feel comes with the highest product. For corporate, it's a bizarre game in which each plant is fundamentally competing with the other plants to avoid being the one that gets shut down or sold off. This has only been made more interesting due to the rise of contract or toll manufacturers, factories that can be rented to build products to specifications."

"I imagine that plants are also focusing on environmental and energy usage issues these days," said Bonhoffer.

"Either do proper compliance reporting and minimize waste of resources," said Mulcahy, "or the rest is moot. There is a rising tide of compliance coming from everyone that can pass laws—environmental legislation, increased trade restrictions for certain types of equipment after 9/11, and Sarbanes-Oxley to scare CFOs. Plus, there's the rising oil and electricity prices that are causing massive changes and, at times, even determining the way plants are run. In California they just passed a law that dictates how much carbon dioxide can be created from the megawatts of used power. So when we set goals for the plant, we have to help them navigate all of this and create the products we think will sell in the right volumes, frequently in response to demand signals. Remember, we hold the purse strings. They cannot make major changes in their equipment without making a capital request to us. We are the gateway to funding. That's why you generally get a good reception when you go to the plants."

"You mean we'll never have to buy our own lunches?" said Moulton.

"Never once," said Mulcahy. "People will see you as a way to increase their share of money sent to the plants, which only makes it harder to do the job I want you to do. Every year we get requests for 10 times more capital improvement than we can afford. We have to decide which plants get that capital and why. If we see a certain plant making product for a growth market, we may want to invest in reducing bottlenecks by upgrading equipment. If another plant is in a fading market, perhaps we want to prepare the facility for sale, or invest in extending the life of existing equipment, or change its product mix. What I want you to do, is to understand what is going on in each of these plants so we can make intelligent decisions."

"But the people at the plants will be putting on the best face for us," said Bonhoffer. "They'll be in major sales mode. We won't get the real picture at all."

"That's the problem," said Mulcahy. "And much of it is the fault of people who do my job. Decisions about what investments to make in plants are often made without any meaningful input from the plant. Frankly, that's standard practice. Systems are inflicted on a plant supposedly to solve problems that they may or may not have. Sometimes they are software, and sometimes they are procedures related to safety, audits, and inspections. For this unwanted investment, the plants are expected to improve performance. But frequently the systems provided are inappropriate or cause more work than they're worth. I have heard of cases where experienced maintenance people are creating reports and entering data for HQ instead of supervising the mechanics. I don't want to be that kind of EVP of Manufacturing Operations. I want to be the kind that actually helps, so the plants can succeed in their mission and help the company. But to do that, I need to know what's going on in them.

"That's where you fine people come in. You are going to be my eyes, and more importantly, my ears in the plant. I want you to do two things. First, research how people are succeeding in improving management of each important area of the plant, and summarize it so that the plants know all the ways they could possibly move forward and the tools that could help. I hate to use the term 'best practices'—what I want are best questions with the outline of answers that seem to work based on established experience. Second, I want you to find out what's going on in each of the important areas in the plants we own and then help the plants communicate to us about what investments would actually help them do what we are asking them to do."

"Not the easiest of assignments," said Moulton.

"That's why I chose the most polished, nerdiest MBAs I could find, ones that all have undergrad engineering degrees," said Mulcahy. "You will be ambassadors of my office, meaning you will represent the possibility of investment. But you also must be empathetic investigators who find out what is actually happening. To do that, you must know how plants work."

What Goes on in a Plant?

Mulcahy moved to open space on the whiteboard, drew with a marker for a while, got caught in one of his mental eddies, then quickly finished writing with a spurt of energy.

STRATEGY AND COORDINATION

PLANNING

EXECUTION

ASSET MANAGEMENT

ENERGY MANAGEMENT

QUALITY MANAGEMENT

VISIBILITY, COMPLIANCE, RISK, AND OPPORTUNITY

ARCHITECTURE, STANDARDS, AND INTEROPERABILITY

CHANGE MANAGEMENT

"This drawing is a dramatically oversimplified view of the plant," he said. "There are key processes such as procurement, profit management, supply chain, and others that are vital parts of running a plant that we will not focus on right now. The areas I've chosen represent the core flow of materials, energy, and information through the plant. They also offer the biggest return if you can improve them. There are many other important areas we won't cover such as human resources, labor relations, environmental compliance, warehouse and inventory management, and so on. We can do those next year.

"At the top of the chart is strategy and coordination, the process whereby Wolverine figures out what products to make and how to help the plants to make them efficiently, when they are required. I am part of the strategic process that formulates the plan. I hope to provide that process with more detail about what is easy for plants to do and what is hard. Right now, we do that planning without much input from the plants. Once the plan is in place, we then need to implement the plan with the plants. This is another area in which corporate can get snotty. We often don't spend enough time talking to the plants to meet these goals. It's an area in which I expect you to help me improve communication."

"So you want to be a kinder, gentler EVP?" asked Moulton. "An EVP who listens and communicates. The Oprah of EVPs?"

"Ah, grasshopper, wise man say talking is easy, but living is not," Mulcahy said. "These are not just platitudes, and it won't be easy to make this communication happen. For example, if we plan on having our Dearborn facility produce at a certain level of output, we might find that we're pushing the plant too close to the limit and that we need to set up a relationship with a contract manufacturer for part of the production. Or we might find that one plant is better at making a certain product than another, but they haven't gotten that message through to corporate because nobody was listening. If you think these are unrealistic examples, they're not. Screwing this up costs millions. If I have to drag you cynics through the swamp of my optimism to save the company big bucks, I am going to do it."

"I can put on a happy face to save a few million bucks," said Moulton.

"Once the plants get their marching orders, what's the planning process at the plant level?" asked Bonhoffer.

"At the high level, this process is all about planning how the materials will be transformed as they flow through the plant," said Mulcahy. "The details differ widely depending on the type of plant. For a process manufacturer like a refinery, the plant planning model tracks chemistry and physics and, since the crude oil is purchased according to HQ, the plan is more about inventory management. For a discrete manufacturer, the planning mode tracks a flow of work in progress through stations on an assembly line. There's an obvious problem here, though, that I think you'll snicker at. It is very seldom that results are derived as originally planned. More often, the plan gets changed along the way, as it is being executed, so that by the time it has been completed, it no longer resembles the original. The planning department, of course, has no way to improve their models, either, since frequently they don't receive the actual field results."

"Do you think that's because the execution process takes the plan and then makes products based on an automated process?" said Bala.

"It is true that execution is more automated than ever," said Mulcahy. "The one wave of investment that has pretty much succeeded is the introduction of more process control equipment into the plant. So, when you go to most of our plants, you'll find operator consoles for the largest equipment that show what is going on and allows the operators to control the equipment. But the automation is only a part of the whole process. You don't just flip a switch and watch everything happen. Automation is focused. Anyhow, in the same way that these three processes form a group, so do the next three—quality management, asset management, and energy management."

Mulcahy drew circles around three sets of three boxes and labeled them.

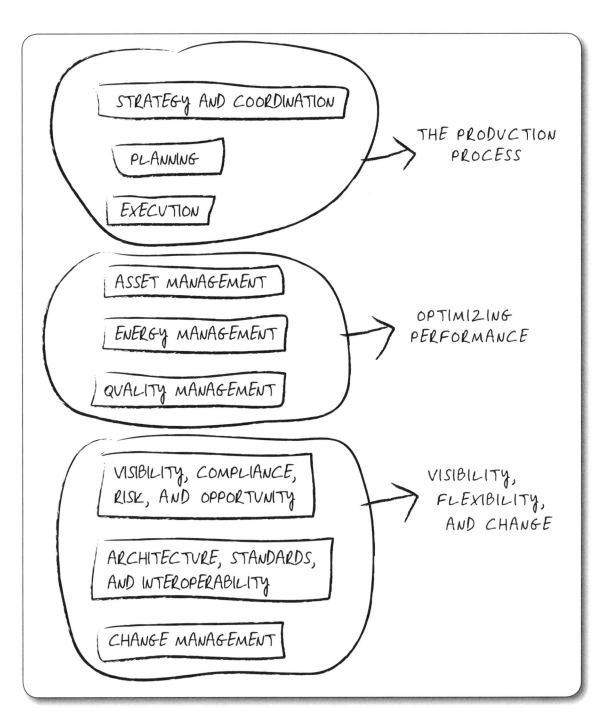

"We lump together the next three processes under 'optimizing performance,' which is about taking care of the plant from the inside. Asset management is my favorite because it's such an interesting balancing act. Asset management, as I suggested earlier, is all about maximizing the return on the equipment in the plant by caring for it through maintenance, replacement and reconfiguration, and improving its performance so that you can avoid unplanned outages. Plants that do the worst job of this run everything until it breaks. This is a recipe for lots of downtime. The best plants have a different strategy for maintaining each type of equipment based on its characteristics. Some equipment has a schedule based on time or usage, other equipment receives maintenance based on conditions that indicate a problem. There are many more complex strategies we will learn about."

"I imagine there are some interesting conversations," said Bonhoffer, "when the asset management team wants some downtime but the production team doesn't want to give it."

"That's when the big picture needs to be in everyone's mind so the conversation isn't just about power," said Mulcahy. "The other two areas, quality management and energy management, are fascinating, as well. Quality management is hugely important for consumer products and pharmaceuticals. Regulations require that extensive documentation be kept. Energy management is becoming increasingly important as energy prices rise and the incentives to conserve rise with them."

"I actually did some case studies in school on energy conversation efforts," Moulton said. "The upside potential is pretty impressive. There is huge money to be saved in this area."

"What about visibility, flexiblity, and change?" asked Bala. "It looks like a grab bag."

"There is a theme," said Mulcahy. "Each of these areas is broad and looks at the big picture. Visibility, compliance, risk, and opportunity, is a mini grab bag, but in each of these areas you must gather data and make sense of it across all the processes of the enterprise. Architecture, standards, and interoperability is about how you bake in flexibility and improve the flow of information. Change management is about how you face and overcome the barriers to transforming a plant."

How the Team Will Work

"I'm starting to understand why you brought us together," said Bonhoffer, "but what will we be responsible for?"

"Here's what's going to happen," said Mulcahy. "First, we'll spend a lot of time together getting smarter about the way plants work. I'll work my network and reach out to experts to train you in the topics in the agenda and also update my decades-old understanding of the plant. Sometimes we'll interview these people together, other times I'll send you on missions to get more info. But we will always get together like this to talk about it and make sure we all understand things the same way. Then, we'll add one more item to our agenda—describing the shape of a complete vision for the perfect plant."

Mulcahy turned and added one more item to the agenda.

PERFECT PLANT RESEARCH MEETINGS

| CAST OF CHARACTERS:
  Who's who in a plant and how do they work together?

| SYSTEMS IN A PLANT:
  Enterprise Architecture on the shop floor

| PRESSURES ON THE PLANT:
  Internal and External forces for change

| VISION OF THE PERFECT PLANT
  How to move close to perfection

"What happens once we're smart and you've programmed us?" asked Moulton, who let his voice slip into a robotic tone. "Do we get to leave the Borg cube and assimilate others?"

"Resistance to the perfect plant is futile," said Bala, copying Moulton's voice.

Mulcahy laughed. "Not quite. I'll send you on two-fold missions. You'll visit the plants to find out what their problems are. You'll also talk to experts in each area assigned to you. Bonhoffer, you're the most technical, so you get the activities inside the plant—asset management, quality management, and energy management. Moulton, you have the financial analysis and modeling background, so you get to work on strategy and coordination, and planning and execution, which is technical, but we'll help you. Bala, your comp-sci undergrad degree will prepare you for architectural analysis and the visibility topic, and your management consulting expertise will help you with change management.

"The goal here is to explain the marching orders for this year and get the communication flowing between the plants and this department and then to deliver back to them the results of this research. When you visit them, I want you to know what you're talking about."

"How will we deliver this information?" asked Bala.

"I'm sure you've heard of wikis," said Mulcahy. "We're going to create a manufacturing wiki as a resource, and a series of white papers that summarizes your research and provides guidance about the kinds of questions they should be asking and the patterns that seem to work to improve performance."

"This will be fun," said Bonhoffer. "Nerds love learning new stuff. No detail too small. But you know that already."

What's in a Name?

"So what should we call what we're doing?" asked Mulcahy.

"How about the Perfect Plant Borg Unit?" said Bala. "Everyone knows Star Trek."

"What about just the Perfect Plant Team," said Moulton.

"I think we have to be more descriptive than that without being too earnest," said Mulcahy.

"How about the Perfect Plant Research and Communication team?" Bonhoffer suggested. "PPRC is an acronym with a nice ring to it, and the name describes what we're up to."

"It's not as fun as the Borg idea," said Moulton. "But it does make sense."

"I like it. PPRC it is. At the next meeting, we'll cover the cast of characters," said Mulcahy. "Come ready to learn."

Chapter Two
Cast of
Characters

Contributing Author:
Charlie Miller, Praxair, Inc.

John Mulcahy began to write on the whiteboard. "These are the people we are going to be discussing today." He finished the list and continued, "This is probably one of the most important hours of your education with me," he said to the three MBAs assembled before him. "We're going to talk about a day in the life of a typical plant manager.

CAST OF CHARACTERS:

PLANT MANAGER

"Of course, in today's business world," he continued, "with the myriad practices and processes developing all around us, there is no true typical plant manager. Still, I want to make sure you know what makes these guys tick. What are their passions? What are their pet peeves? To start us off, I thought I'd describe my friend, Danny, one of the best plant managers I've ever known."

The Plant Manager

"This guy grew up in the plant, starting as an engineer," Mulcahy continued. "Like most other plant managers I know, he loves his work so much he rarely wants to leave the floor, though in his early years, he did drag himself away to study for his MBA. This guy is smart, ambitious, tough, and, most importantly, results-driven. He has little sympathy for missed objectives or mistakes. Danny's like the captain of a ship. He interacts with nearly everyone, from the operators on the floor all the way up to the suits on the corporate board, including the COO, the VP of Manufacturing or the Regional VP, legal, plant, and supply chain managers, service providers, union officials, and people from EH&S.

"As if that's not enough, since his plant is one of the community's major employers, and everything it does impacts that community, Danny is also the face of the company in it. He's a member of the Chamber of Commerce, he attends Rotary every week, and he's on the board of the local hospital."

"Wow, he sounds like a superhero," said Bonhoffer. "One guy responsible for thousands of employees and billions of dollars of assets. With so many responsibilities on so many levels, who holds Danny accountable?"

"Every month he reports the status of his plant's production and profitability to his business unit's senior VP," said Mulcahy.

"How does his interaction with corporate affect the way he manages the plant?" Mouton asked.

"The best way to answer that question," Mulcahy said, "while elaborating on Joan's, is to talk about the monthly corporate meeting. As I said, whether Danny does it in person or through a teleconference, he has to answer for his performance every 30 days. His monthly report sums up the plant's latest activities—production, output, shipments, costs, any safety or environmental incidents, and so forth."

"These meetings must be real pressure cookers," Bonhoffer said.

"Sometimes yes, sometimes no," Mulcahy said. "Most of the information is in the report, which everyone sees before arriving in the boardroom. It depends on the organization, too. Sometimes Danny gets chewed out for poor numbers, and sometimes he enjoys a pat on the back for goals met. Once he told me that presenting to the monthly corporate meeting was like drinking a glass of sand. In any case, these monthly reports provide crucial snapshots of two things—the plant's status and Danny's goals. They also offer a lens through which the plant manager can focus his crew."

"If you had to say Danny is a good old boy from the plant or a corporate schmo," Bala said, "which would it be?"

"That," Mulcahy said, "is a fine line that Danny has to walk every single day. He's frequently very hands on, so he spends large chunks of his time in the factory, working with managers and foremen and really seeing what's going on up front. This isn't as easy as it sounds. Plants can be rough places, and the majority of the workers are not highly educated. Some have substance abuse problems and come to work drunk or high. While Danny's dealing with matters like these, he's simultaneously nurturing his relationships with the people in corporate, even when they give him a hard time about his plant's performance. Many of his best friends are on that side of the line. All in all, the difficulty of his job is plain. However, neither he nor any other plant manager would excel at it if they didn't really enjoy it."

"My understanding of the relationship between the plant and corporate is that there is the same sort of divide between them as there is between church and state," Bonhoffer said.

"It's definitely an aspect of the culture that's worth keeping in mind as we go through these various job titles," Mulcahy said. "For instance, the plant people appreciate corporate for what it is, but they also know the suits at headquarters won't ever truly understand the day-to-day challenges of running a plant. Danny's job is to be the person who understands what it means both to run a plant and to lead it. He initiates and leads plant changes that benefit the company, which makes him look good to his bosses. In addition, he wants to protect his people by fighting for budgets and reasonable expectations from corporate.

"Layoffs or, God forbid, a plant closing, are about the worst things that can happen to a plant manager. He's the caretaker of the people who work in his plant. As a result, he's frequently a caretaker of the community, as well."

"I'll bet we could learn a ton from following him around for a day," Bala said.

"If you understand the dynamics the plant manager deals with," Mulcahy said, "you'll likely understand not just the plant, but the entire company. Imagine that production demands higher output, but maintenance says that added input will probably damage the equipment. Resolving the matter practically and diplomatically is Danny's job, even though the decision may conflict with a goal requirement from HQ."

"So how does he balance these daily disputes with keeping an eye on the big picture of the plant's goals?" Moulton asked.

"At this point," Mulcahy said, "it might be helpful to talk about cycles for a minute. Plants have either three- or five-year cycles and one-year budgets. Usually, once or twice per year, you have a 'roll down,' starting with the corporate strategy and action plans. This might be called a 'long term' or 'medium term' plan, and is oriented to the management of capital: which assets, what kind of assets, where to position the assets, organic growth of the assets, acquisition growth, to name just a few. These plans also address fundamental aspects of the plant's performance, like costs and productivity. Typically, the technical manager and plant manager are very involved in this exercise.

"The plant production costs are part of the yearly budget cycle, which is managed on a monthly basis and is more management oriented. Many plants use a bottom-up approach once the targets have been 'rolled down' from senior managers to plant managers. For instance, I rolled down to my plant managers the targets for the next year, which are in line with the long- and short-term plans laid out for the whole company. Perhaps costs are too high, productivity too low, reliability too inconsistent, or quality too poor. Targets would be set, and then the plant manager would have to roll down these to his managers. The next step is a series of 'roll ups,' which pertain to the strategy and action plans to meet the targets. After that comes the 0–365 day optimization. This is more tactical, given the condition of the asset and looking at it from an overall supply chain point of view, determining the optimum output for the manufacturing asset on a month-by-month, week-to-week, or day-to-day basis. Some plants have a day-to-day philosophy at the levels of foreman, manager, and plant manager, and a week-to-week philosophy at the executive level. All of these targets are reviewed in the morning meeting." Mulcahy turned and wrote "Morning Meeting" on the whiteboard.

CAST OF CHARACTERS:

PLANT MANAGER   MORNING MEETING

"The big boss runs these meetings and gets an update on what everyone is up to. This is not a place to report data but to discuss actions. It's where people can report problems and work out issues—and sometimes get in each other's faces, a little like the locker room meeting before the big game. The morning meeting usually happens early, at 6:30 or 7 a.m. Sometimes there are two meetings: one for the foremen types who give raw updates of the previous day's activities, and a second for department managers—operations, technical, maintenance—to put things in perspective. The focus is on the day-to-day operations of the plant. One machine breakdown or injured person can mean huge problems for the whole company. That's really the nut of the plant manager's role—running the plant with the entire company's interests in mind."

"With so many topics and departments to cover," Bala said, "how do they decide who goes first?"

"The very first things on the list these days are EH&S oriented—environmental, health, and safety issues. In the refining and chemical industries, there is a clear reason why: non-compliance with laws such as the Clean Air Act of 1990 and OSHA Safety Management can shut down the plant and even make people criminally liable. Regulators discovered that fines weren't very effective at keeping companies from breaking rules for a profit, so they added criminal penalties. Most jail time comes from putting the public or your workers in jeopardy, for example, by knowingly shipping hazardous material through a city without appropriate permits. Prosecutors, too, have taken the approach that there is no such thing as a 'renegade employee,' which is why criminal penalties can be pressed for lack of good oversight, diligence at self-investigation, or failing to act once information is known."

"I used to think all that was just political posturing to make environmental activists shut up," Moulton said. "But from what I've read, more than a dozen managers have faced jail time for screw-ups at their plants. The laws have made a huge impact on manufacturing."

The Safety Manager

"Some managers I know in California," Mulcahy said, "where the laws are toughest, say that as much as 60% of their time is occupied with satisfying community and government agency inquiries and regulation. That's why the health and safety manager is usually up first in these morning meetings." He added Safety Manager to the list.

CAST OF CHARACTERS:

PLANT MANAGER   MORNING MEETING

SAFETY MANAGER

"I'm friends with a safety manager out in Rochester, whose reputation in his industry is spotless. His chief duty is to conduct audits and inspect equipment, but he also investigates any accidents or unusual incidents. Once he has his data, he makes recommendations to various departments for changes, updates, and maintenance of equipment and procedures. One of his days in the plant could include all or any combination of these duties. Make no mistake: the safety manager's recommendations frequently have a gigantic impact on those around him. If he suggests changes that will decrease the chance of a fatal accident, people listen.

"His effect on decisions in the plant is the main reason many of the other managers view EH&S as their biggest ally. Any time operations or maintenance managers have trouble convincing their crews to follow or change procedures, the safety manager is the go-to man."

"What sort of EH&S issues are people likely to bring up at morning meeting?" Bala asked.

"Updates on any releases, emissions, or waste issues usually start the show," answered Mulcahy. "Everyone also wants to know whether the production line is emitting more than the company's or the government's standards allow. Most importantly, there will be a report on any lost-time accidents or near misses that require an investigation, or reasons any worker had to seek medical care. Of course, if someone was injured or there was an environmental spill, the plant manager would already know about it before the meeting and a special team would have begun investigating. This stuff is taken seriously enough to warrant a phone call to the plant manager's home, even in the middle of the night. People can lose their jobs over these things, which is why any incidents mentioned in the meeting are followed by lots of discussion—people defending themselves, placing blame, and figuring out how to prevent another incident."

"Whose butt is on the line?" Bonhoffer asked.

"The manager of the department where the incident took place will be at the center of the discussion," Mulcahy said. "This person will come to the meeting prepared with info on what happened, what went wrong, who was involved, and, most importantly, why it won't happen again. But since an EH&S screw up can impact yearly bonuses for the entire plant, everyone has a vested interest in resolving this problem."

The Production Manager

Mulcahy wrote "PM" on the whiteboard. "Once safety matters have been covered, the conversation is usually picked up by the production manager."

CAST OF CHARACTERS:

PLANT MANAGER   MORNING MEETING

SAFETY MANAGER

PM

"These managers want to see high-quality product come off the end of the line and ship to the customer. That means they'll do what it takes to ensure that the plant runs at maximum efficiency while budgets are met and costs held down. To increase overall efficiency, for instance, they may drive such team building programs as Lean, Six Sigma, or Instigate."

"My understanding," Bonhoffer said, "is that since PMs are at the top of the plant's personnel hierarchy, they really tend to know what they're talking about."

"Not only are they smart," Mulcahy said, "but they're also ambitious. Many PMs want to become plant managers. Often they have backgrounds as chemical, electrical, or mechanical engineers. If they don't have an MBA yet, often they're pursuing one."

"How do they coordinate with others?" Moulton asked.

"Production managers coordinate with managers of every department," Mulcahy said, "and are involved in the budgeting process for plant capital spending, and general budgeting for raw material spending. Frequently, they oversee several hundred people and interface with first- and second-line supervisors, as well as with the business offices that give them directives for how many units to produce, and so on. To meet the company's goals, they must rely heavily on other units around them—maintenance, quality, inventory."

"That's a lot people and personalities to contend with," Bala said. "They must have to be really good at juggling multiple tasks."

"That's why they give a run-down of the previous 24 hours at each morning meeting—how many units of each product were produced, which systems have a glitch, any major problems with production, quality, supply, or output," Mulcahy said.

"So they're the ones," Bonhoffer added, "who can provide a snapshot of how the previous day turned out and what's likely to happen in the new one."

The Maintenance Manager

"And once we have that snapshot," Mulcahy said, writing "Maintenance Manager" next to "PM," "the meeting gets handed over to the maintenance manager."

CAST OF CHARACTERS:

PLANT MANAGER   MORNING MEETING

SAFETY MANAGER

PM   MAINTENANCE MANAGER

"That makes sense," Moulton said. "Any slowdowns or halts in production are often blamed on maintenance problems."

Mulcahy continued, "These are the people who oversee all scheduled and emergency upkeep and repairs on equipment and are involved in system and product updates. This includes maintaining and monitoring the plant's preventative and predictive maintenance programs, and using that data to adjust maintenance work procedures to meet scheduled production levels. They interact with equipment vendors, too. If a major machine is on its last leg, or a critical component is down, they'll provide an update at the morning meeting. They'll also brief the team if there is a scheduled maintenance that might disrupt production or require rescheduling of workers. They inspect any completed work for conformance to blueprints, specifications, and company standards.

"Both production and maintenance managers are on call 24/7. At the very least, their foremen are, depending on the level of their empowerment and capabilities. Maintenance managers assure mechanical integrity and 'uptime,' so they are often risk-adverse. It behooves them to have a plant that runs like a charm. That way, they can spend more time leading, rather than managing, the hundreds of staff and contractors that they oversee. They also work with Engineering to consider long-term fixes to troublesome problems."

The Inventory Manager

"The inventory manager is up next," Mulcahy said, adding "Supply Chain Manager" beneath the other roles listed on the board.

CAST OF CHARACTERS:

PLANT MANAGER   MORNING MEETING

SAFETY MANAGER

PM   MAINTENANCE MANAGER

SUPPLY CHAIN MANAGER

"They're also known as supply chain managers. These people—who oversee warehouse and expediting functions that can involve up to 50,000 materials—are critical in maintaining the flow of the plant by ensuring a sufficient supply of equipment, raw materials, parts, and the like, and that shipments are made on time and transportation runs on schedule. As you can imagine, to make sure everything runs smoothly, they must connect with several departments, including production, maintenance, quality, and the business department at headquarters. They'll also interact with drivers and forklift and crane operators, among others, to ensure that stockpiles meet specified levels and that trucking, crane, and other transport services are in line."

"So if production was off," Moulton said, "the operations manager might blame inventory, right? After all, if raw material isn't available, you can't make widgets."

"I wouldn't necessarily use the word 'blame,'" Mulcahy said. "But yes, supply can throw off the entire plant, including production goals."

"All these managers sound like they need to have Type A personalities," Bala said, "in order to handle multitasking all over the place while managing tons of people. That's some serious pressure."

The Quality Manager

"Yet another important, high-pressure role," Mulcahy said, "that doesn't have a high profile is the quality manager. Most of these people took undergrad degrees in chemistry or mechanical or electrical engineering, and then began their professional careers as chemists, laboratory analysts, or process or control engineers. Not to over-generalize, but these guys can tend to be on the geeky side."

CAST OF CHARACTERS:

PLANT MANAGER   MORNING MEETING

SAFETY MANAGER

PM   MAINTENANCE MANAGER

SUPPLY CHAIN MANAGER

QUALITY MANAGER

"Geeks rule the world," Bala said. "Everyone had better get used to it. Power to the geeks!"

"As quality managers," Mulcahy said, "they may not be very dynamic leaders but they usually have a deep respect for competence in others and tend to run regimented departments. Many quality managers really love the science behind what they do, even though nowadays they have to manage big labs of workers and interact with the technical manager—who is basically their boss—as well as the inventory guy. After all, if one production line is producing lousy, below-grade product, that throws off inventory. When something like that happens, the QM has to step in, perhaps going so far as to halt the production of the entire plant."

"In addition to managing lots of people," Bonhoffer said, "don't they also have to be competent schedulers and cost controllers?"

"No doubt," Mulcahy said. "And QMs have to know enough about statistical and sampling methods to assist in troubleshooting. That being said, most of their time is spent in the lab, running routine tests on product, looking for defects, and certifying that product is suitable for shipping and sale."

The Union Officer

Mulcahy wrote "Labor" on the whiteboard. "Now we get to the other characters who impact the lives of plant managers but who aren't likely to be at every morning meeting. First on that list is the union officer."

CAST OF CHARACTERS:

PLANT MANAGER   MORNING MEETING

SAFETY MANAGER

PM   MAINTENANCE MANAGER

SUPPLY CHAIN MANAGER

QUALITY MANAGER

LABOR

"Ah," Moulton said, "the bane of every manager's existence."

"Yes and no," Mulcahy said. "The plant manager sees the union guys about once a month at a meeting that's also attended by an HR manager and the operations and maintenance managers.

"Unions are present at almost all plants. They're powerful in heavy industry—especially auto manufacturing—though less so with lighter industrial. They're frequently contentious and have a long legacy in the Midwest and in the Gulf Coast area. The East and West Coasts have fewer unions, with 'milder' cultures.

"As for the union officers, aside from their normal duties as operators or mechanics, they're allowed about 20% of their weekly hours to devote to union issues. At these times they can be found in a designated office to receive visitors. The various issues that arise in a given month are what the officers discuss with the plant manager at their meetings. Occasionally, the union will bring in consultants from their national or regional offices, but most plants' union officers have the power to handle matters locally.

"Essentially, this is the way workers obtain an avenue through which to confront issues without putting their jobs in jeopardy. The union officer's focus is to ensure that his members get everything promised in their hard-won contract."

"A large percentage of union leaders," Bonhoffer said, "are part of a long family legacy of union members and leaders. It makes sense that their passion for the organization would run deep."

"That's why most officers take the time to do things right," Mulcahy said. "Many companies have clearly defined protocols for dealing with routine grievances like failure to report to work and incorrect call outs. This involves filing grievances with direct supervisors, then HR, and so on. Only more serious things, such as health and safety issues, discrimination, or breaches of contractual issues, would be taken to the union at all. A typical topic raised by the union officer might concern whether someone was forced to work OT when it wasn't his turn, according to the contract. Or they get involved if someone gets injured on the job or a worker is having medical bill issues. In these cases, the union officer takes up the issue with the maintenance manager or the human resources director. When meetings involve the plant manager and the union officer, most of the time they're in virtual fisticuffs with each other, engaging in a nice little dance routine they pull out for the benefit of all in attendance."

"I don't get it," Bala said. "Why do they have to fight all the time?"

"It's all a power struggle," Mulcahy said. "If the plant manager gives the union guy exactly what he wants—say, the promise that no one will ever have to work overtime without it being exactly by the books—then he has a chit in his corner when it comes to a bigger issue or when it's contract time. If the union guy feels that he and his union have been slighted, then, believe you me, that issue will be documented and used at an opportune time. It's politics in its rawest form, really."

"Sounds totally annoying and inefficient," Bala said.

"Most union officers are really nice guys," Mulcahy said. "Despite what can be perceived as pettiness, they have their people's best interest at heart, and if management learns to work with them, it's a good thing for everyone. If you stay in this business long enough, you'll see quite a few cases in which the plant manager and the union officer can be nasty to each other at meetings in the morning, and then hang out at lunch like best friends. They know that it's business, not personal. I guess we could all learn something from that."

"Spiritual enlightenment through labor relations," Moulton said.

"Something like that," Mulcahy said, and wrote "Planning Meeting" on the whiteboard.

The Plant Manager Revisited

CAST OF CHARACTERS:

PLANT MANAGER   MORNING MEETING   PLANNING MEETING

SAFETY MANAGER

PM   MAINTENANCE MANAGER

SUPPLY CHAIN MANAGER

QUALITY MANAGER

LABOR

"The meetings and duties we just discussed do not constitute the plant manager's only responsibilities. About once a month, Danny also holds a planning meeting, called the sales and operations meeting. This is a broader-based discussion of where the plant is in terms of sales and how that relates to the plant's physical capacities. At this meeting, Danny typically coordinates with a wide range of people, including purchasing people from headquarters, who help provide raw materials. The economics and planning folks—sometimes called 'pilots'—will be in attendance, as well, and so will the optimization people. He will also see the operations and tech managers there, along with the maintenance manager if the plans include a major shutdown. The heavy hitters at this meeting are the economics and planning people, who come prepared with a clear idea of what needs to be accomplished.

"This meeting matches up sales and shipping goals against plant capacity, and maps out any improvements or physical plant changes that are needed to meet those goals. The engineering department plays a critical role in this meeting.

Again, these job titles vary—sometimes engineering and technical or project management get lumped together. For now, let's go through all the separate roles so we have a more granular understanding."

The Technical Manager

"Technical managers," Mulcahy said, "sometimes have backgrounds in chemistry, but more often their histories lie in mechanical or industrial engineering. Their chief duties are to keep an eye on efficiencies—energy flow, air and stack emissions, and waste disposal. They also set all equipment parameters and coordinate with other managers to establish ambitious operations goals. Ensuring compliance with governmental regulations, and reporting if anything is amiss, is another of their responsibilities. These people understand the technical status of the plant and often foresee issues long before the maintenance or inventory departments."

CAST OF CHARACTERS:

PLANT MANAGER   MORNING MEETING   PLANNING MEETING

SAFETY MANAGER

PM   MAINTENANCE MANAGER

SUPPLY CHAIN MANAGER

QUALITY MANAGER

LABOR

TECHNICAL MANAGER

"How would you characterize their role at sales and operations meetings?" Moulton asked.

"They need to be especially aware of new projects that are brought to the table," answered Mulcahy. "If there are chemical trials, for instance, or any other procedure that aims to improve efficiency or quality, they need to ensure that all standards are met. They also let everyone know what's come up at morning meetings. They may discuss whether they're meeting efficiency goals, or perhaps they have detected some unusually high emissions or vibrations that operations and maintenance need to know about. All in all, while maintenance is on top of the more routine cleaning, fixing, and upkeep, the technical manager heads off any issues and gets a big-picture snapshot of the mechanics of the plant. When the monthly planning meeting rolls around, everyone pays close attention to the technical manager."

"I was speaking with a plant manager the other day who told me that technical managers also field and fix customer complaints," Bonhoffer said.

"Right," Mulcahy said. "When a customer complains that a shipment is late or that quality is off, this poor chump gets the call and figures out how to remedy the situation. This is why a technical manager needs to be very personable and have good historical production information at his fingertips, in addition to all his others strengths and skills. This position is another one that naturally feeds into the plant manager position."

The VP of Corporate Engineering

Mulcahy added "VP Corp Engine" to the whiteboard.

CAST OF CHARACTERS:

PLANT MANAGER   MORNING MEETING   PLANNING MEETING

SAFETY MANAGER

PM   MAINTENANCE MANAGER

SUPPLY CHAIN MANAGER

QUALITY MANAGER

LABOR

TECHNICAL MANAGER

VP CORP ENGINE

"Very large plants also have corporate engineering execs who attend the monthly planning meeting. These people usually hold an engineering degree and a VP title, and report to the COO. Their role tends to be more project-oriented, but always with the goal of measuring ROI, whose results go straight to corporate. Projects might include capital-project engineering, quality testing, asset reliability oversight, mechanical or instrument control, and research and development work. Though they have a team of engineers under them to make those projects happen, that doesn't mean they're necessarily great at managing. These are geeky, detail people who got their corporate titles by being a cut above their peers in having an eye for plant improvement. When it comes to personality, they're definitely more technical than managerial."

The Chief Technical Officer

CAST OF CHARACTERS:

PLANT MANAGER   MORNING MEETING   PLANNING MEETING

SAFETY MANAGER

PM   MAINTENANCE MANAGER

SUPPLY CHAIN MANAGER

QUALITY MANAGER

LABOR

TECHNICAL MANAGER

VP CORP ENGINE

CTO

"Depending on the size and type of the company," Mulcahy continued, "another role that may or may not be lumped in with others is the CTO, or chief technical officer. These people all have engineering degrees, and most of the younger ones have MBAs. Sort of like technical managers on steroids, they balance technology against ROI against plant processes and objectives. They serve as the permission clearinghouse for big overhaul projects and offer guidance and direction along the way. If a company hires both a CIO and CTO, the CTO will act as more of the day-to-day project manager. In other words, CTOs get their hands dirty interfacing with all levels of the plant. These guys are usually as strong with people as they are with technical concerns."

Making It All Work Together

"So how do all these projects fit into the regular, scheduled, day-to-day operations of the plant?" Bonhoffer asked. "That has got to cause conflict."

"All the time," Mulcahy said. "For instance, engineering might hire a crane at $2,000 per hour to install a new compressor in the same area where operations and production are overhauling the existing compressor. But since operations is under the jurisdiction of the plant manager, and production answers to corporate, and since neither is communicating with the other, no one has a clue about the other's plans until some morning meeting when it becomes clear they both need this pricey crane, which is sitting there unused because everyone wants his project to have priority. Engineering might say, 'Listen, we have this project approved all the way through corporate, and we're spending five or six figures for this crane to sit on the lot, so let's get things going.' But operations have the plant manager on their side, right there in the meeting, and it's his plant, so they win. It can get ugly. Usually, the wrestling match is won by whoever has the plant manager in his corner."

"It's like a mini Capitol Hill in each and every plant," Moulton said.

"Some days," Mulcahy said, "I think morning meetings should be broadcast live on C-Span. It would be much more interesting.

"Speaking of capital, once a month or so there is usually a capital planning meeting, frequently chaired by the technical manager and attended by his or her top crew members and the project people—the money folks and bean counters. They help determine if proposed projects jibe with the budget, if they make sense from an investment standpoint, and how any plans fit in with larger corporate goals. Other attendees might include the maintenance and EH&S guys. This is where decisions are made about big investments in the plant."

"It looks like the maintenance and EH&S managers need to be everywhere," Moulton said. "They touch on pretty much everything that goes on at a plant."

"Exactly," Mulcahy said. "The EH&S guys might be called in by the tech manager who says, 'Listen, we've got a big waste water treatment project,' or, 'We've got a project that will require some extra special interest because we'll be working in an operating unit, which is particularly dangerous, and we need your counsel on what safety precautions are needed.' Their expertise is required at just about every level in the plant."

The Chief Financial Officer

"We haven't talked much about money," Moulton said, "and of course it's all about money. Who and where are the money guys?"

CAST OF CHARACTERS:

PLANT MANAGER   MORNING MEETING   PLANNING MEETING

SAFETY MANAGER

PM   MAINTENANCE MANAGER

SUPPLY CHAIN MANAGER

QUALITY MANAGER

LABOR

TECHNICAL MANAGER

VP CORP ENGINE

CTO

MONEY GUYS

Mulcahy smiled and wrote "Money Guys" on the board. "I was just getting there, Peter. The controller will definitely attend the capital-planning meeting. In many plants, the title of 'controller' has been replaced by 'CFO,' but the job function is basically the same. These are usually accountants or IT professionals who also have MBAs and at least 20 years experience. They hold the purse strings, overseeing the general ledger activities and keeping an eye on the company's day-to-day financial situation. Even so, they don't have a say over how *much* is in the budgets, only how those budgets are used and accounted for. In Europe, and in truly decentralized companies, it's common for a plant to have its own accounting structure. In integrated plants and many U.S. organizations, on the other hand, the plant accounting staff is minimal and most accounting functions are handled at corporate, especially with the advent of the ERP systems. If there is both a controller and a CFO, the CFO receives the controller's reports while the controller receives his from the accountants and auditors beneath him."

The Chief Information Officer

CAST OF CHARACTERS:

PLANT MANAGER   MORNING MEETING   PLANNING MEETING

SAFETY MANAGER

PM   MAINTENANCE MANAGER

SUPPLY CHAIN MANAGER

QUALITY MANAGER

LABOR

TECHNICAL MANAGER

VP CORP ENGINE

CTO

MONEY GUYS

CIO

"Plants," Mulcahy said, "don't always have CIOs, or chief information officers, but when they do, CIOs usually have a strong IT history behind them, along with an MBA. These people nearly always have hands-on plant experience in areas such as heading the supply chain or purchasing departments, and often have been plant managers. Armed with a staff of IT professionals, the CIO is charged with advancing the company's technological front via cutting edge computer and hardware systems. This is a person with vision. As such, she must be able to interpret the ROI of moving technology and translate that value to senior management. In recent years, the CIO's duties have grown to include setting data protection policy and other information security issues, as well. At the end of the day, the CIO reports to the company's 'Big Kahuna.'"

The Maintenance Technician

"So those are the core people the plant manager interacts with each day," Mulcahy said. "The last few dynamics on the plant floor involve the operators and the maintenance technicians. In many ways, these guys are the heart and soul of each plant.

CAST OF CHARACTERS:

PLANT MANAGER   MORNING MEETING   PLANNING MEETING

SAFETY MANAGER

PM   MAINTENANCE MANAGER

SUPPLY CHAIN MANAGER

QUALITY MANAGER

LABOR

TECHNICAL MANAGER

VP CORP ENGINE

CTO

MONEY GUYS

CIO

MAINTENANCE TECHNICIAN

"Maintenance technicians don't always have degrees," he said, "though nowadays many do have some college experience. Mostly, they are people who love taking things apart just to see how they work. My friend's brother has been a maintenance guy his whole life. He started taking apart televisions, toasters, and blow-dryers when he was a kid, and then moved on to things like diesel engines. Lots of maintenance technicians begin as mechanics and then develop specialties as welders, machinists, electricians, boilermakers, and so forth. On the whole, they are disciplined, well organized, logical, and methodical. Another key trait is their independent nature, which is why they tend to work in teams of two. Group any more together, and you can get some negative fireworks going.

"As you can guess, maintenance technicians are responsible for maintaining the plant's equipment and fixing it when it breaks. Compared with an operator, this job is more physical and suits those who like to get their hands dirty. As for their schedule, it's fairly traditional. Without natural daylight, repairs become increasingly difficult and dangerous."

The Operator

CAST OF CHARACTERS:

PLANT MANAGER   MORNING MEETING   PLANNING MEETING

SAFETY MANAGER

PM   MAINTENANCE MANAGER

SUPPLY CHAIN MANAGER

QUALITY MANAGER

LABOR

TECHNICAL MANAGER

VP CORP ENGINE

CTO

MONEY GUYS

CIO

MAINTENANCE TECHNICIAN   OPERATORS

"Operators," Mulcahy said, "generally possess very specific skill sets that have taken years to acquire, from the time they were apprentices. These guys know what it takes to run the machines hour by hour, and how to make sure they are running within safe speeds and temperatures. Once in a while a big shutdown will require emergency work, so they will be involved in flushing pipes and recalibrating controllers. Operators normally interact with their foreman and other operators, though in a breakdown situation they work in conjunction with maintenance. They're famous for giving engineers a hard time. Engineers have all the formal education and big earning potential. What they don't have is the years of experience that the operators have, or the intimate knowledge of the plant's equipment and history. The engineers need all of that information to do their jobs. Believe me when I tell you that the operators know this very well. They resent the heck out of having to train some of the cocky young engineers they encounter. The stories of operators challenging them are legendary."

Mulcahy capped his pen and placed his hands on his hips, grinning at his pupils. "So kids, what do you think?"

"Sounds like the interpersonal complexity," Bala said, "is as intense as the plant itself."

"Definitely," Mulcahy said. "It takes real cooperation and consideration, to say nothing of talent and capacity, to make a crazy, complex plant work day in and day out. When there are difficulties between people in the plant, it's usually because they care deeply about the jobs they're doing."

Chapter Three
Processes, Systems, and Networks in the Plant

Contributing Authors:
Chet Namboodri, Cisco Systems, Inc
Derek Prior, AMR Research

"I'm sure you've all seen or read *For Dummies* books," Mulcahy said as he called his team to order. Joan Bonhoffer, Krishna Balasubramaniam, and Peter Moulton shifted in their chairs, ready to listen. "This session will be the equivalent of reading *Manufacturing for Dummies,* if such a book existed."

"So you think we're dummies," Moulton said. "I knew it."

"If the shoe fits…" Mulcahy said, laughing. "But seriously, I really am going to copy the method of learning that has made the *For Dummies* books so successful. They present in a simple fashion the landscape of a field, the important concepts, and the categories and terms that help make sense of a topic."

"My favorite is *Wikis for Dummies,*" Bala said.

"And mine," Mulcahy said, "is *Yoga for Dummies.*"

Processes Surrounding the Plant

"My goal today," Mulcahy said, "is to explain the anatomy of manufacturing, specifically the processes, systems, and network infrastructure that are involved in the entire manufacturing cycle. If I can get these basic ideas across, then your research will go a lot faster. I will introduce you to a lot of things, explain them briefly, and then you'll be able to dive deeper in your research. Let's start with some basic concepts." Mulcahy drew a diagram on the whiteboard.

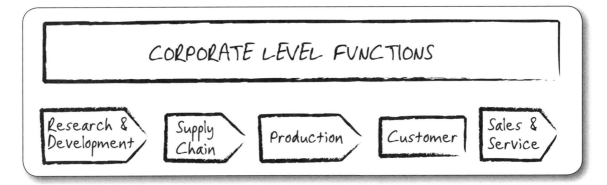

"Here's an oversimplified view of the manufacturing enterprise and its chain of value-added processes," Mulcahy said. "The corporation that owns the manufacturing facility establishes the business strategy, arranges financing, allocates capital, executes sales and marketing for the projects, coordinates the activities of all the manufacturing plants and suppliers, and distributes the products to customers. Nowadays a company almost certainly doesn't have all of these functions in-house. More frequently, the company doesn't own any of the assets or employ any of the people directly associated with production. Instead, it contracts other companies to manufacture and distribute goods to the customer. But it doesn't really matter who owns what. There is a basic set of duties that must be performed to manufacture product, regardless of industry—discrete, process, utilities, or combinations thereof. Here's a sampling of what sorts of manufacturers fit in each category."

DISCRETE	PROCESS	UTILITIES	HYBRID
Automotive,	Primary Metals,	Power Generation,	Food & Beverage,
Aerospace,	Mining,	Transmission & Distribution,	Pharmaceuticals,
High Tech (Semiconductor, Electronics),	Pulp & Paper,	Municipal Water,	Fine Chemicals,
Medical Devices,	Bulk Chemicals, Petrochemicals, Refineries	Gas Pipelines and Distribution,	Consumer Packaged Goods,
Other Assembly		Other O&G	Packaging Materials,
			Metals Fab,
			Plastics

"So the corporation," Bonhoffer said, "is the conductor of all of this activity whether it owns its plants or not. Either way, the same fundamental processes, flows, and systems are involved."

"Let's go through them one by one," Mulcahy said, and drew another diagram.

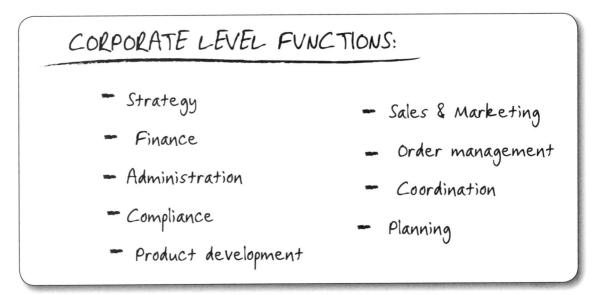

CORPORATE LEVEL FUNCTIONS:

- Strategy
- Finance
- Administration
- Compliance
- Product development
- Sales & Marketing
- Order management
- Coordination
- Planning

"The corporate entity in manufacturing," Mulcahy said, "which is the enterprise that controls the whole process, performs each of these listed functions. The corporation has a reason they are in business that involves manufacturing something, and a strategy for success. The company raises money, performs administrative and management tasks, develops the products, sells and markets them, takes orders, and coordinates both the supply chain and all of the plants that make the products. Usually there is some sort of planning cycle through which the company communicates to the plant what it is expected to make. The formal name for the planning cycle is Sales and Operations Planning, and goes by the acronym S&OP."

"That seems pretty straightforward," Moulton said.

"The supply chain function is pretty simple in the abstract, as well," Mulcahy said. "The corporation must contract for and coordinate all of the material required by the plant to make the products. The challenge here is that the company wants to keep costs low, quality high, and avoid paying for huge piles of inventory at the plant. So, modern supply chains attempt to work as much as possible on a pull model, one driven by customer demand, delivering goods to the plant just when they're needed. Much of the reward for implementing concepts like Lean Manufacturing comes from squeezing excess inventory and other forms of waste out of the system." Mulcahy drew another diagram. "Supply chains can be lean by reducing inventory that is held in the factory. Factories are lean by having less inventory and also by reducing waste and inefficiency in every way."

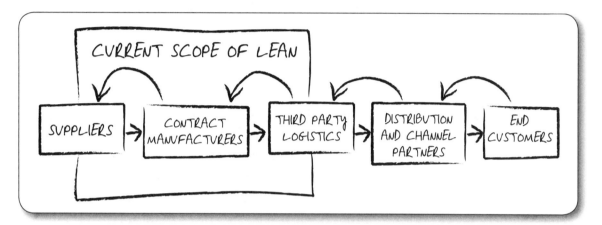

"This diagram is just to give you the gist of how Lean works," Mulcahy said. "We're going to discuss it in a bit more detail at one of our next meetings. (See Chapter 5, "Vision.") For now, suffice it to say that its chief characteristics include reduced inventory buffers and levels, analytically sized reorder points, planning forecasts that are based on real orders, and radically simplified processes."

"That all makes sense," Bonhoffer said. "The lower the inventory levels, the less money is tied up financing them. What's the downside?"

"Lower inventory levels can put a plant at a greater risk of having to shut down to wait for materials," Mulcahy said. "But this is a well-known risk and modern supply chains are amazing. Companies like Dell have things so finely tuned that they actually get paid by their customers before they have to pay their supplier, so instead of having to finance inventory, they have money in hand."

"The cost of reducing inventory, then, is increased skill required for planning, coordination, and risk mitigation across the entire supply chain," Bonhoffer said.

"The supply chain downstream from the plant, the way that products flow through distribution centers to the customer," Mulcahy said, "has also been the focus of incredible innovation. Wal-Mart, for example, pioneered the Vendor Managed Inventory model, through which manufacturers monitor the inventory in distribution centers and stores. When the manufacturers learn that the inventory has reached a certain level, they generate purchase orders to themselves and deliver the goods. Ideally, the plant manufacturing the products is aggregating these signals so that the production schedule is adjusted accordingly.

"Cisco is another company that has gone to great lengths to improve the flexibility and transparency of its supply chain. Like so many other companies, it began work with stand-alone functionality. Soon enough, though, Cisco realized that the brittle nature of this method would prevent it from evolving, so it expanded to enterprise-wide systems. From there, it was a natural leap into a collaborative supply chain model. Today, 95% of its manufacturing is outsourced to over 50 locations in 17 different countries. Cisco has over 1,000 suppliers and nearly all of their production is high velocity and configure-to-order."

"With so many suppliers and most of your work based on real-world orders, it's hard for inventory to build up at the distribution centers," Bonhoffer said. "At the same time, you always have what you need to avoid running out of product, the dreaded stockout."

"Depending on who you talk to," Mulcahy said, "there are a lot of names for these concepts. AMR, the research firm, labels it as, 'Demand Driven Supply Networks.' ARC uses the terms 'Collaborative Production Systems' and 'Collaborative Manufacturing Management.' SAP uses the term, 'Adaptive Business Network.' Procter & Gamble talks about 'Responsive Replenishment,' and I'm sure there are many others I don't know about."

Mulcahy began to write on the board. "The other idea you should all know about is mass customization. This is the notion that you manufacture to meet the demands of specific orders, not standard products.

MAKE TO STOCK
Create products to be sold from inventory

MAKE TO ORDER
Create products when they are ordered

ENGINEER TO ORDER
Design products to fit customer requirements
when they are ordered

CONFIGURE TO ORDER
Assemble components into a configuration chosen
by the customer when they are ordered

"Make to stock is the old way of doing things, where you make products to have them in inventory because you believe somebody's going to buy them. Make to order is newer—you don't make your product until after it has been ordered. Engineer to order is much more refined. It involves actually reengineering a product to meet a customer's particular specification. Configure to order is also cutting edge, and it's what Dell does, for example, when your order a PC. Everything you've ordered has been engineered and built, but all of the parts are put together in the configuration of your choice. 'I want a hard drive with so many gigs, I want so much RAM, and I want a processor whose clock-speed is over 2 GHzs.' More and more products are being created this way. The Toyota Scion is a great example. Local dealerships and auto shops finish your car with customized detailing and other features after you order it. This isn't exactly manufacturing to order, but it gets the same result. You get just the car you want."

"But if a plant is going to react to the pull of demand," Bonhoffer said, "that means it has to be able to move faster or slower based on what its customers are asking it to do. Which means the supply chain has to be able to do the same thing."

"You've just described the perfect plant, Joan," Mulcahy said. "It's the only one that has a chance of playing the game you just described. And while the theory of lean and demand-driven manufacturing is a reality in some of the leading firms, many other plants in operation today are simply not that flexible. For most companies, including Wolverine, I am sorry to say, plants are just big black boxes—orders and supplies go in and products come out, but nobody on the outside has a clue about what's going on in there. If you want to change something, you have to wait until all the orders are done, because you just don't know what's up on the plant floor. If a sales rep has a big order and wants to know if it can be rushed, he doesn't have the necessary transparency to actually promise it. A plant does not become 'perfect' until it has flexibility and visibility. You have to be able to see everything and change your plan in a heartbeat. Only then can a plant move quickly enough to deal with problems on the supply side or to react to changes on the demand side."

"How is what you've asked us to do," Moulton asked, "going to get Wolverine closer to the perfect plant vision?"

"It's not going to be easy," Mulcahy said. "There are layers of people, processes, information, and machines in a plant. To rapidly optimize things or change direction on the fly, everyone has to have a high level of awareness and as much help as possible from technology. You will work with me to help our plants understand where they need to go in all sorts of dimensions so they can start incrementally moving there every week, every month, every quarter. That is the only hope we have of making substantial progress. If we made a master plan and imposed it on the plants, our plan would fail. They know better what they need to do. We must help them create a vision for the perfect plant and provide as much help as possible in getting there."

Processes Inside the Plant

"You've described what's to the right and left of the plant and what's on top," Moulton said. "Are you saving the best for last?"

"That's right, we're actually at the plant itself now," said Mulcahy. "Here are the key aspects we'll consider." He wrote the following points underneath a box labeled, "Production Functions."

PRODUCTION FUNCTIONS

- Planning
- Execution
- Asset management
- Energy Management
- Quality Management
- Visibility, Compliance, Risk, Opportunity

Planning

"Planning in the plant gets the ball rolling," Mulcahy said. "In most plants there is an annual cycle in which people like us at corporate tell the plants what we expect them to make for the next year. This, of course, is driven by the overall corporate strategy. The CEO decides what the company's financial targets are going to be, the head of sales, CFO, and line of business VPs all figure out what that means in terms of how much product will have to be sold. Then this plan is delivered to the plant and the plant manager figures out how to do it and also how to interweave all the other activities such as fixing plant equipment or performing upgrades or expansions that may require downtime."

"In other words," Bala said, "the plant manager takes the high-level plan and turns it into something that can be executed."

"The plan usually goes from an annual or quarterly description of what needs to be manufactured down to a monthly, weekly, or daily plan," said Mulcahy. "There is, of course, some deal making. If the plant manager thinks the plan is too aggressive, he or she may push back."

"And then you then negotiate to come up with something that everyone can live with," Bonhoffer said.

"This can be a difficult process," Mulcahy said. "Once relationships are in place and people trust each other, it tends to go much more smoothly. An unrealistic plan doesn't do much good. As actual production is reported and the deviation from the plan becomes obvious, unrealistic plans become apparent. Or the plant manager gets fired. But your research will bring more light to this story. Let me write the key concepts on the board for you."

KEY CONCEPTS FOR PLANNING:

- Sales and Operations Planning (S&OP)
- The slow loop and the fast loop.
- Closing the loop: improving planning models based on production results.
- KPIs

Execution

"Execution," Mulcahy said, "is the next process. Once the plans are set, they must be translated into instructions for the plant to make the products. The first part of this is a process called an MRP run. MRP means 'Materials Requirements Planning.' This process ensures that all the materials needed to make the products are on hand or will be on hand on time. If you are in the discrete industry, once an MRP run has been conducted, a production order is created. If you are in the process industry, a process order is created. This describes just what the plant is being asked to produce. There may also be something called a batch record that sets forth the specific characteristics of what's going to be produced."

"These are the basic terms we'll hear people talk about when they describe execution, right?" asked Moulton, scribbling notes on his legal pad.

"This is just the beginning of the process," Mulcahy said. "As we'll see when we get to the systems part of this discussion, the production or process order gets exploded into a massive number of precise instructions to all sorts of equipment that involve cascading levels of standards. But in terms of the high level process, execution proceeds as follows. As the production run continues, work in process is reported and then the results of the run are reported at the end. Then the product is packaged and shipped to distribution centers or customers. The key concepts for execution are as follows."

KEY CONCEPTS FOR EXECUTION:

- Materials Requirements Planning (MPR)
- Process orders and production orders
- Manufacturing Execution Systems
- Purdue manufacturing model
- ISA S95, ISA S88, and OMG standards
- SCADA, PLC, DCS, HMI
- MESA model

Asset Management

"Now, I want to look at the processes that Joan is going to explore, ones that keep everything running efficiently and protecting quality: Asset Management, Energy Management, and Quality Management," said Mulcahy.

"Asset management is pretty simple in theory, but hard in practice. It's about maintaining all the equipment in the plant and keeping everything running. There are thousands of pieces of equipment in most plants. Just like a car, plant equipment needs the equivalent of oil changes, tune-ups, overhauls, and diagnostic check-ups. To do this you need to have a strategy for how each piece of equipment is maintained. Some types of equipment wear out based on use, others based on the passage of time, and still others based on less predictable factors. Advanced techniques can help predict failure once you know what you want to fix and when you have to fit any downtime into the production schedule. Much of this has to do with safety, so there are lots of records to maintain. Another big challenge is keeping the right parts on hand. The ideal is to have everything planned and avoid unscheduled downtime."

"It sounds like asset management is all about maintenance," Bonhoffer said.

"It's really about more than that," Mulcahy said, "the term 'asset management' stresses the bigger picture. Maintenance is just about fixing things. Asset management is more holistic—you consider all the assets in which you've invested, including your equipment, your networks, and your buildings, as a portfolio in which you want to maximize the return. Here are the key concepts."

> ## KEY CONCEPTS FOR ASSET MANAGEMENT:
>
> - Asset management KPIs
>
> - Maintenance Strategies
>
> - Reliability Centered Maintenance

Energy Management

"Energy management is something I really didn't consider as one of my top priorities when I was running a plant 20 years ago. It was an important cost, but not the top priority it is today. Now, making sure a plant uses energy efficiently in every way is on everyone's mind," said Mulcahy.

"Rising prices must be one factor," Bonhoffer said. "Environmental consciousness of global warming and the way it affects regulation must be another. The idea of sustainability has become quite prominent, too. It's been gaining steam in Europe for some time, and increasingly in the rest of the world, as well."

"The reaction," Mulcahy said, "has been a variety of techniques and methods to measure energy usage and to find ways to reduce consumption. Companies are installing meters so that every action taken in the plant can be seen in terms of its energy consumption. Refineries have always kept good track of how much energy goes in and out of the plant, but now the manufacturing industries have begun to do the same. Today, just about everyone in manufacturing keeps much closer track of energy used per unit of product produced. Some companies are creating an 'energy bill of materials' for products, which is a specific description of the energy used on each part of a production process. Joan, I'm going to send you to talk to Kodak about this—theirs is a fascinating story. Here are the key concepts."

KEY CONCEPTS FOR ENERGY MANAGEMENT:

- Energy bill of materials
- Evolving a culture of energy conservation
- Measurement and visualization of energy usage

Quality Management

"The last topic for you, Joan, is quality management," Mulcahy said. "Running a line at full speed doesn't mean much if what comes out fails to meet specifications and thus needs to be scrapped or fixed. There is a large body of knowledge and a complex set of processes around ensuring quality in manufacturing."

"Six Sigma is a big part of this, isn't it?" Bonhoffer asked.

"Six Sigma," Mulcahy said, "is about reducing variation, which can have a lot to do with quality, but there are all sorts of other methods like Good Manufacturing Practices and Statistical Process Control. In some industries, like pharmaceuticals, quality is the primary consideration, and they have to keep extensive records about everything that happens. But it is important in every plant. It involves the basic manufacturing processes as well as other systems for testing products and reporting defects. The key concepts for quality management are as follows."

KEY CONCEPTS FOR QUALITY MANAGEMENT:

- Statistical Process Control
- Good Manufacturing Processes
- Failure Modes and Effects Analysis
- Hazard Analysis and Critical Control Points
- Six Sigma

Visibility and Compliance

"Bala, your topics start with one I call Visibility and Compliance," Mulcahy said.

"Sounds like a hodgepodge to me," Bala said.

"While most people wouldn't recognize this process by name," Mulcahy said, "every plant does the things suggested by it. In this context, visibility pertains to the process of collecting information and synthesizing it such that it is both available and useful throughout the business. Much of the time this involves taking data from many different systems and using it to create a model of some activity. Remember, each system in a plant is based on its own model. A big part of gaining visibility is bringing together all the different parts of those models to create a bigger picture. Where recalls are concerned, for example, this is vital. If you don't know what raw material went where, you have to recall way more product to cover your bases. To get more visibility, usually you use some high-end data warehouse that can handle real-time data or near real-time data. You can then use your model to create a bigger picture of what's going on in your plant. This sort of system can be used to notice when certain important conditions have been reached and generate events or warnings. It can also play a role in reporting on the activity of the plant to meet compliance obligations. Here are the key concepts for visibility."

KEy CONCEPTS FOR VISIBILITY:

- Information integration and modeling
- Traceability
- Analytics
- Recognizing events
- Network mining

"This is more like a system than a process," Bala said. "Lots of different processes could be run through such a data warehouse, from safety to environmental monitoring to financial optimization."

"The reason I think of this as a process and not a system," Mulcahy said, "is that you could use lots of different systems to implement what I consider the overall process, which is the process of monitoring and analyzing your operations.

"I'm going to switch gears now to analyze the systems used in plants to automate various aspects of all of these processes. Before I do, I want to point out that there is a lot of stuff I didn't mention. Processes for safety, human resources, accounting, environmental compliance, and many other areas are important. We're focusing on the areas I've outlined so far because I think that's where the biggest return will come from. If we can get these processes working better and synchronized, then we will truly be helping our plants."

Systems in the Plant

"When you say 'systems,'" Bala said, "what exactly do you mean? And how are they different from processes?"

"Systems," Mulcahy said, "are the technology that help you execute your processes. Processes are what happen. A sale gets made, a product gets created, inventory is accepted in the warehouse. A process could be carried out inside someone's head or in a completely automated fashion inside a computer. The systems are the technology that supports processes either by automation or by providing and capturing information. Before we get too deeply into the world of systems, though, you need to understand that I think of everything in the plant in terms of brains and machines. By machines, I mean software and hardware. Here's the drawing I use to get this across."

"Every action in a plant takes place because of a flow between brains and machines," Mulcahy said. "The processes we just mentioned happen because people look at information and equipment and then decide to take action, usually with the help of some system or another. The key is to have the people do what people should do and the machines do what machines should do."

"What is an example of a mistake in this regard?" Bonhoffer asked.

"Over-automation," Mulcahy said. "Sometimes people put in systems that try to track everything. They want the system to run the show instead of letting it work as a record keeping device. In this situation, everyone ends up doing lots of data entry instead of their jobs. And to do their jobs, they have to get around the system, rather than using it to help them. Under-automation might occur when you have a lot of copies of a spreadsheet that does a key calculation running on different PCs. Because the spreadsheet is distributed, it can't be controlled or tested for quality. If it were part of a central system, it could be managed and improved. The key is to have a process flow naturally between the person and the system in a way that helps get work done faster and better."

"I'm sure this is harder than it sounds," Moulton said.

"The job is made more complex," Mulcahy said, "because plants have many different generations of equipment and software. The best way to understand these is to use the Purdue Reference Model for manufacturing. We will go over this again in the session we do on architecture that Bala will lead. The Purdue model identifies six levels of systems. Let me draw it for you."

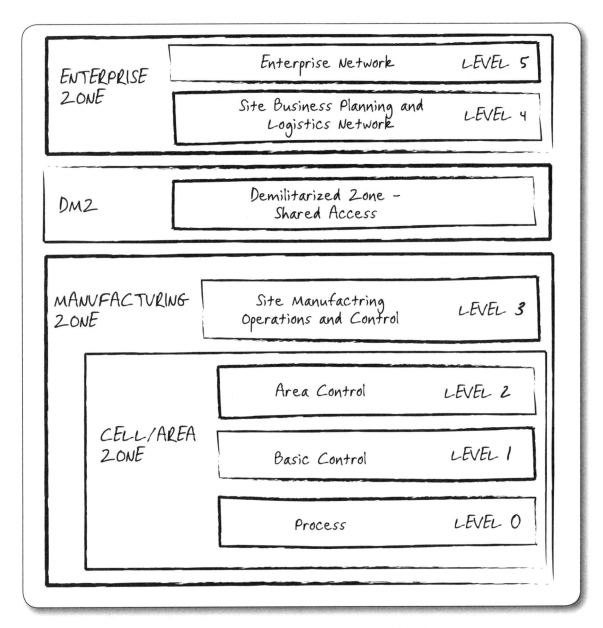

"This model," Mulcahy said, "is extremely important for the execution research you'll be doing, Peter. But it also very quickly helps us understand what sorts of systems are in a plant and can clear up one of the largest areas of confusion."

"Which is?" Bala asked.

"What sort of system does what," Mulcahy said. "Almost every plant now has an ERP system. This is used for all sorts of finance, budgeting, accounting, and so forth. It is also used for key processes of the plant, like tracking orders, planning, and MRP runs, which, as I noted earlier, are conducted to determine if everything needed for a production run is on hand or will be on hand. ERP vendors are always expanding their products, so much of the time there will be something in the ERP system that is related to other systems. For instance, an ERP system can track assets for depreciation purposes. Some newer functions are able to help do maintenance, as well."

"So why is this confusing?" Bonhoffer asked.

"Much of ERP operates at level four of the Purdue Reference Model," Mulcahy said. "Most of the processes at this level are part of enterprise architecture, a software term for processes and systems that run a business, and yet other ERP processes, such as the MRP runs, are on level three. An MRP run is clearly a manufacturing process, which is part of Plant Systems Architecture, the processes and systems that run the plant. Many processes are split into two aspects, one of which concerns the enterprise while the other concerns manufacturing operations. Frequently there is a separate, third-party system that controls the manufacturing operations, whose functionality is far more detailed than the ERP system's. The vendors of the manufacturing operations management software, on the other hand, often extend their products upward and add enterprise-like functionality because their customers want it. Not everybody has ERP, after all. So, there is a lot of overlap.

"It gets confusing because one person might talk about quality management in terms of how some of the information is tracked in an ERP module, while someone else talks about quality control in a specialized system. MRP happens in ERP but the manufacturing execution system, MES, runs the process of pushing an order through all the steps of production. There is a system for every process we mentioned above. Much of the visibility research, for example, involves taking information from a variety of systems and creating a single model. Some folks refer to this single version of the truth as Enterprise Manufacturing Intelligence, or EMI."

"That sounds like a fascinating integration problem," Bala said.

"The next layers down are interesting, as well," Mulcahy said. "Level zero concerns the equipment and level one the controllers for the equipment. The acronyms here are PLC for 'programmable logic controller' and DCS for 'distributed control system.' These systems control equipment or groups of equipment. The OPC standard allows you to talk to PLCs and DCSs. The convergence of Human-Machine Interface software/GUIs with Supervisory Control and Data Acquisition systems—using the combined acronym 'HMI-SCADA'—is what coordinates plant equipment activity. When this coordination gets advanced it moves up into level two, which is about higher level coordination and aggregation of data from equipment. Level three, as I said, is about managing it all."

"That's a lot of acronyms," Moulton said.

"This is just the beginning," Mulcahy said. "One of the things you'll do in your execution research is learn about the ISA S95, ISA S88, and the OAG standards. These standards provide a way to model the higher-level flow of activity through a plant, which is what ISA S95 is all about. ISA S88 is about modeling what goes on in a localized group of equipment for batch processing. ISA S99 models structures for sensor networks, typically within process manufacturing. OAG has created standards for messages between these layers. MISMO is another standard by which a piece of equipment can report any problem it may be experiencing, and whether it needs maintenance."

"You've got systems and standards for modeling and communication at all levels," Moulton said. "But I can't imagine everyone has all this working perfectly. If they did, we wouldn't be doing this project."

"These standards are new," Mulcahy said, "and just starting to affect the way products are created. In the supply chain world, standardization is ahead of what's going on inside the plant. People can exchange purchase orders and invoices and track products much better than we can exchange information within the plant. But we are making rapid strides, and the important thing is to have an idea of what you want to do. This comes from turning the lights on.

"By which I mean that every system at every level has information about what's happening in the plant. If you invest in infrastructure that extracts and analyzes that information so people can understand what's happening, then you are turning the lights on. The goal is to provide people access to as much information as possible so they can learn ways to improve the plant's speed and efficiency. Unifying your infrastructure is the first step toward realizing this objective. Once you see what's happening, you can automate still more processes. Vendor products usually play at both of these levels. Every plant has a different layering of everything I've just described with various generations of technology at each layer."

"And the standards provides the means by which all these layers talk to one another," Moulton said.

"They are doing that slowly, with improvements every year," Mulcahy said. "There is also a push to increase the use of standardized services, sometimes called Manufacturing SOA, which stands for Service-Oriented Architecture. In corporate computing there is a big push to allow everything to be accessed through services. The same thing is happening in manufacturing. As we consider both software and infrastructure architectures, the Service-Oriented Network Architecture (SONA) prevails. The idea is that all these ways of providing information can use the same standard and web services. For example, some people claim that the existing standards I mentioned, OPC, actually do a better job of sharing information in the plant than web services do in corporate computing. But it's clear that we can get more information if we try just a little harder to unlock it. Once we have it, the question will be, 'What do we do with it?'"

"We can't answer that until we improve our understanding of the processes in a plant." Bonhoffer said. "We need to learn how they flow through the systems and where the opportunities are. Sometimes more information will be needed to allow people, the brains, to make better decisions in real time. Sometimes automation is needed when you can boil something down to an algorithm and there is no reason to bother people with it. You have the org chart in play, the processes, the systems, a changing competitive environment, and the need for capital improvements. No wonder you like your job."

"It's a fiercely competitive and complex world," Mulcahy said, "but a fascinating one. But we're not done yet. We've introduced the plant network but haven't finished talking about it. It is another world altogether."

Networking in the Plant

"Most people who have some familiarity with IT," Mulcahy said, "wonder why we have to talk about networking at all in manufacturing. We don't talk about it much in corporate computing except to assume that there is a network, and that it works."

"So it's different in the plant?" Bala asked.

"The network in the plant is like everything else there, a hodgepodge of layers installed back when technology was less advanced and the needs of the plant were different. Ironically, however, very little of this has changed. Networking in the plant was urgently needed long before it was needed on the corporate site. The telephone, faxes, and FedEx helped people communicate before email and cell phones arrived. Then corporate networks arrived and people started using email and IM over a variety of different networking standards. Finally everything was standardized on Ethernet for the local area network using the Internet Protocol, or IP. And this is the way we live today."

"But the plant doesn't use IP?" asked Bala. "That seems sort of strange."

"Ethernet and IP are used in the offices of the plant, just like everywhere else," said Mulcahy. "Yet on the plant floor, you'll find a legacy of network layers. Remember, when you have a programmable logic controller in charge of a high-speed conveyer belt or a robot or some other device that's whipping metal from place-to-place, the network that connects these two devices must work well. A lot of this equipment dates back 15, 20, 30 years before Ethernet and other forms of IP networking equipment could handle speeds like this. A lot of this equipment relies on protocols designed by a single company, as opposed to protocols based on a converged set of standards."

"If that's the case," Bala said, "why is it still there?"

"Here's where we run into a huge difference between the plant and the corporation," Mulcahy said. "It's all still there because it works. Putting something new in production means going through the trouble of making it work, and plant managers and engineers know how hard that can be. They are not eager to upgrade anything unless there is a clear payoff. If it ain't broke, don't fix it."

"Don't the legacy layers of network topologies hold the plant back?" Moulton asked.

"In short, yes. But that's not all," said Mulcahy. "As time goes by, the heterogeneous network can become a much bigger headache. Look at it this way: with the Perfect Plant we seek more visibility into what's going on, which means we want more information from as many spots as possible in the plant. If the network doesn't block visibility, then it isn't a problem. But when it does, it is."

"So the vendors of this sort of technology aren't improving their networks and supporting IP?" Bala asked.

"They are making improvements," Mulcahy said, "but for a variety of reasons the mentality in many plants is firmly set against a common network. In many plants, there is no common network infrastructure. There is only the networking of pieces of equipment together. When plants put in a common network infrastructure, they can start doing all the things that we do in the company, including support wireless networks for mobile workers, run a host of devices off of the network, deploy voice-over IP, access the Internet, use video surveillance, and so on. The main reason against connecting a network like this to the plant equipment is that it freaks out some of the engineers."

"Why is that?" Bala asked.

"Some of the older PLCs and DCSs in the plant are Window NT, Windows 95, or even OS/2 machines that were created to do one job only," Mulcahy said. "They don't have virus or firewall protection, which potentially presents a major security hazard. A virus bringing down my PC is one thing. A virus wrecking a PC controlling a high-speed robot is quite another. Reliability is paramount."

"But that still doesn't mean it makes sense to not have a network infrastructure in the plant," Bonhoffer said.

"You're right," Mulcahy said. "Increased visibility depends on increased access to information. An infrastructure is required to collect that information, and a converged, common network is key to such an infrastructure. Once we get a common infrastructure we can do all sorts of things to help us see what's going on. When IP traffic converges on an IP network you can use filtering devices to notice patterns of behavior and generate events or warnings or do other things to optimize performance. For example, you can make certain traffic higher priority than others, or if your security system notices that someone has broken in, you can send a warning out to shut down the lines or take other action. Or you can look for patterns of activity that represent inefficiencies. There are many ways to work with wireless networks, as well. Bala, I expect that you will find a lot of information about networking for use in the architecture research."

"It sounds like we all stand to learn a ton," Bala said.

"As you can see," Mulcahy said, "the world of the plant is complicated and has many layers. Moreover, it's a complexity that never seems to stop. The standards for reliability and safety are higher because plants are dangerous places. Mistakes can hurt or kill people. The challenge is to find a way to rise above this complexity and create a vision for moving forward. I'm counting on you guys to get smart and then help the people in our plants raise their level of understanding and see the bigger picture. If we can do that, this project will be more than worth all the time we are putting into it."

Chapter Four

Pressure on the Plant: Forces Demanding Improved Performance

Contributing Authors:
David Brousell, Editor, *Managing Automation*
Kevin Parker, Editor, *Manufacturing Business Technology*

"Hello, again, everyone," said Mulcahy, EVP of operations, to Joan Bonhoffer, Peter Moulton, and Bala, his three MBA protégés gathered around the conference table. "I want to use this session to describe to you the pressures being visited upon manufacturing plants worldwide. Having spent 20 years on the floor and refreshed myself recently with a couple of tours, I've come up with a pretty stark and crisp picture of what those pressures are.

"We are working in a world where the forces of globalization are creating all kinds of new pressures on manufacturing plants. Increasingly, we need to think of plants as part of a business network extending all the way from product design, to development, to marketing, to sales, to orders, to manufacturing, to delivery. To some degree, that chain has always been there. But, now there are many more moving parts that have to move faster than ever before and stay in close synchronization with each other. With the rising trend of outsourcing, manufacturing processes have become decentralized, and corporate management has different levels of authority over, and visibility into, different nodes on the chain. Unlike in the past, the average global manufacturer today has to coordinate activity across more than 40 different plants.

"As these corporations grow and acquire more plants, they're also acquiring the install base of different types of equipment and software, and they have to figure out how to make them work together. Here are some of the drivers." Mulcahy turned to the white board to draw up a graphic summarizing the forces increasing complexity.

COORDINATION	VISIBILITY	EXECUTION
Increasing number of plants to manage	Numerous systems and applications in use	Increasing demands for better performance
High supply network inventories	High TCO-multiple systems	Increasing defects, high WIP
Poor asset utilization	Multi-plant deployment difficult	Poor compliance, recalls
Delayed product introductions	Data redundancy and latency	Missed customer due-dates

"The one word that best summarizes the source of pressure on most plants today is 'complexity.' There's more complexity in plant equipment, in the business models being pursued, in the products being manufactured, and in the relationships between plants and the rest of the supply chain. All of this complexity is managed and tracked more completely—but not perfectly—than ever before by software and technology, and that technology is all relatively new compared to much of what has been in the plant."

"How can we even begin to get a hold on this, John?" asked Bonhoffer. "It sounds pretty daunting."

"I'll break it down into some digestible pieces," said Mulcahy. "First, let me point out that not all industries are changing as dramatically or at the same rate as others. Most companies are heterogeneous—they are multinational, but not global companies. Some aspects may be global, such as product design and marketing, but many others, including production planning, are more regional. For example, you'd need quite a differently configured plant to make a Toyota for Japan than you would for the U.S.—to start with, the location of the steering wheel is different, not to mention the way work is organized. We are moving from the multinational corporation of the 20th century to the globally integrated enterprise of the 21st century—but we aren't there yet. Also, the difference between process and discrete industries is so large that it's hard to have a meaningful conversation that covers both of them. We'll try to qualify the broad statements whenever we get to an exception.

"We'll start with the internal pressures on a plant, then look at the external pressures," said Mulcahy. "Then I'll break down the challenges the plant manager has to deal with at his level, and finally I'll look at the pressures from the perspective of the line operators and the other rank-and-file workers.

"First, though, let me take you through the cast of characters and the hierarchies at play."

Cast of Characters: The People Under Pressure

Mulcahy turned to the board and wrote:

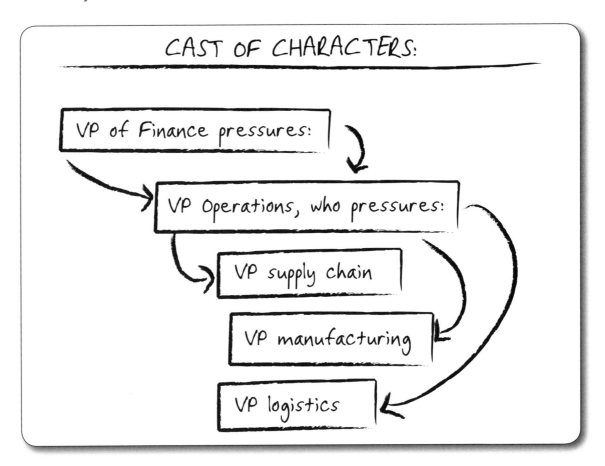

"At the top of the heap we have the vice president of finance, who is responsible for translating the strategy into a plan with financial targets for sales. Then, under him, we have the vice president of operations, who handles transforming those targets into operation terms; that is, specific amounts of products that will be created in each period to meet the sales targets. He supervises the vice presidents of manufacturing, of the supply chain, and of logistics. Remember these guys, because they're going to get into some tussles later."

"I'm starting my fantasy vice presidents league right now," said Moulton. "What's the over-under?"

"Before you start placing bets, let me tell you a little about the internal pressures on the plant, and the implications those pressures have on the plant manager," said Mulcahy.

Internal Pressures

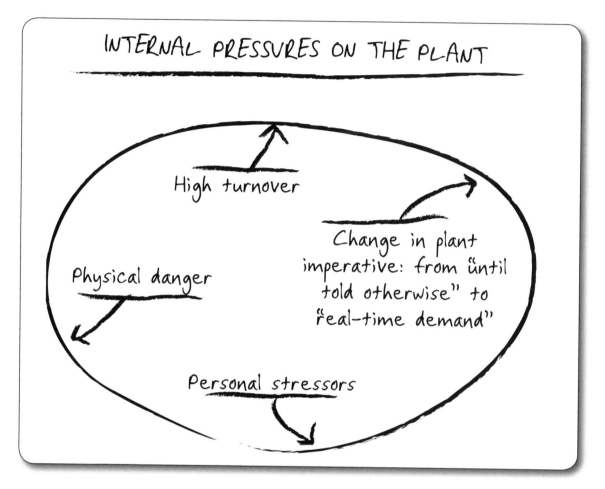

INTERNAL PRESSURES ON THE PLANT

High turnover

Change in plant imperative: from "until told otherwise" to "real-time demand"

Physical danger

Personal stressors

"Looking at internal pressures brings us a little closer to the people on the ground," said Mulcahy.

"First there is the subject of turnover. Some industries have high, unionized wages and a loyal workforce that spans across lifetimes and generations. Many do not. Although it varies greatly across industries and regions, manufacturing can be subject to high levels of turnover. Most positions are pretty monolithic, and job responsibilities are quite fixed. But you can be promoted swiftly, from shift duty as an operator, to unit engineer, and up into management after that. If you start right out of high school, you can be up in management before you're 30."

"Sounds great," said Moulton. "Job mobility."

"One of the reasons there is so much mobility, though, is because, at least in the more dangerous industries, people don't want to stay on the floor very long," said Mulcahy. "That means heavy re-training expenses and safety and efficiency risks from putting new people on the floor. But this isn't always the case, and longevity creates its own problems. There is a huge worry now about workers who have stayed on the job for a long time who will retire soon and take a lot of knowledge about how to run the plant with them."

"Additionally, we're moving into a new paradigm for manufacturing operations that focuses on just-in-time and demand-driven manufacturing. Companies are shifting their plant-operation directives from, 'produce X quantity of product Y until told otherwise,' to, 'we want you to be responsive to daily changes in supply and demand and to be flexible.' That's easier said than done."

Implications of Internal Pressures on the Plant Manager

"I'm going to try to tell this story from the perspective of the plant manager, since he's caught in the middle of all this," Mulcahy said. "His job is changing from ensuring the machines keep running to managing multiple plants from a distance—sometimes from overseas—all while keeping his eyes on the KPIs."

Operational challenges

PLANT MANAGER'S CHALLENGES:

OPERATIONAL:

- MULTIPLE PLANT COORDINATION
- OUTSOURCING
- HIGH INVENTORY IN NETWORK

FROM MANUFACTURING TO PLANT MANAGEMENT

- ☐ Pressure from corporate to create reports
- ☐ Poor demand management
- ☐ Corporate seen as meddling in daily operations
- ☐ Inventory piles up/workers idled
- ☐ How to coordinate partners?
- ☐ How to co-innovate with partners?

"A lot of tension can develop between the plant manager and all these other players because of the changing character of production today," continued Mulcahy. "Many companies haven't set up their communications and inventory systems to facilitate efficient logistics. So, there are serious coordination issues that can cause a lot of tension.

"It wasn't that long ago that manufacturers almost exclusively used historical data to determine the demand picture for the end customers. They would use past sales and gross estimates from regional sales offices to determine the amount of forward supply they created over a given period of time, tweaking the model slightly to meet current conditions. But now, demand is registered in real time, and manufacturing has to respond to that.

"A common and recurring problem is hiccups in inventory, which happen when companies are not set up to respond to demand in real time. So the VP of finance is barking at the VP of operations, saying, 'Inventory levels are too high. You guys aren't doing your jobs. We've got inventory building up on the books and we're not responding to demand signals out there.' Meanwhile, the stores are running out of stocks.

"Operations gets into trouble when a sales rep calls and says, 'I sent you this information two weeks ago and told you what the customers need. Where is it?' The process failed. So, he calls down to the VP of Production, who says, 'guess what?'"

"Not my problem, man," said Bala.

"Right," said Mulcahy. "The VP of Production says, 'I created the supply based on those demand signals, and now the stuff I produced is sitting on a truck that's parked somewhere.' So then it becomes the VP of Supply Chain's problem, or the VP of Logistics' problem. A lot of this interplay is related to inventory issues, and the inability to get the product to the right customer at the right time."

"It probably gets even worse when you're trying to deal with these issues across more than one plant," said Bonhoffer.

"Yes," Mulcahy said. "Suppose these plants are in more than one country, and you just acquired a bunch of them, or even better, you outsource to them and they're not even legally part of your company. This is a reality in today's manufacturing world.

"The challenges are substantial because businesses, and manufacturing in particular, are so interdependent upon the global network of customers, suppliers and partners. Very few manufacturers are vertically integrated anymore. About 90% of manufacturers, at least in the consumer-products space, have outsourced a major portion of their manufacturing—they don't literally own or participate in the day-to-day running of their plants, but they still have to manage the outsourced plants and partner plants along with the plants they operate directly.

"The questions these companies are asking, which their plant managers must effectively answer, are, 'How do I distribute manufacturing across multiple plants? How do I work with my collaboration partners?' and, ultimately, 'How do I start co-innovating with those business partners?'"

"And I bet coordination across those plants is silky-smooth," said Moulton, smiling.

"It all comes with more hiccups than a pediatrician's office," said Mulcahy. "The repercussions of a poorly managed acquisition or partner network are well-known. Typically, what happens is that companies end up with very high supply-network inventory. They don't utilize their global asset base effectively, and ultimately they're not able to introduce products in time. If you look at each one of these factors, every one is tied to a pretty significant dollar amount.

"Cisco Systems, in the mid-2000's, was both a manufacturer as well as a software-plus-infrastructure provider. Because they did not read their demand signals well, they ended up with tremendously high amounts of inventory in their network. They had to write off inventory to the tune of $2.2 million in one year.

"Since then, Cisco Systems has significantly invested in getting the coordination and visibility in execution across all of these plants tied together, such that if there is a problem on an assembly line in any plant that Cisco runs today, they can detect it remotely, shut down the line remotely and take immediate action across their supply chain, and coordinate, and maybe even move production to a different plant. That's the kind of environment that we're living in today.

"Although the long supply chain seems to be the way of the future, it is not a panacea and there are many kinks still being worked out."

"Would it be fair to say the job of the plant manager has moved from being a pilot to being an air traffic controller, turning knobs in a tower watching everything happen on a screen?" asked Moulton.

"Actually, Peter, it's more like he's had to become both pilot and air-traffic controller," said Mulcahy. "You definitely don't have to look hard to find the stressors.

"Its funny you should mention airplanes, because two of the most highly-touted airliners in recent memory both had rocky starts due to the extreme complexity of their supply chain.

"The Boeing 787 Dreamliner's maiden flight was set back six months when the company realized it had spent so much time and energy perfecting its fuel-efficiency, that it hadn't invested enough in getting its first-ever majority-outsourced production process into shape. The first Dreamliner that showed up on Boeing property was missing tens of thousands of parts. The company faced the threat of millions of dollars of penalty payments to customers and had to 'parachute in' hundreds of its own employees to supervise production at the outsourced plants, many of which had done their own outsourcing, unbeknownst to Boeing.

"Over at Airbus, a company whose corporate organization is already a global affair, they also decentralized tough-to-manage operations. The result was different fuselages from different companies, and guess what?"

"They didn't fit together," said Bala.

"Bingo," said Mulcahy. "A global supply chain for a huge discrete product like a jetliner is an extreme example, but it provides a poignant example of the challenges and limitations of the outsourcing model that is increasingly being used in manufacturing."

"I'll take my Xanax now," said Moulton.

"You may want to take two, plus an aspirin," said Mulcahy, turning from the whiteboard. "Because now we're going to talk about corporate myopia—another big headache for the plant manager."

Corporate's obscured view

> ## LACK OF CORPORATE VISIBILITY:
>
> - Local point problems "solved" with applications
> - Corporate pressures IT to create integrated solution
>
> Composite applications could help

"Many are the woes of today's plant manager," said Mulcahy. "We've talked a little bit about the inventory pile-ups and the lack of integration across the company and its partners. This comes down to a lack of visibility into operations from the corporate side. It ends up making a lot of work for the people working in the plants—they spend a lot of time compiling reports when their time would be better spent manufacturing. Add this to the pressure corporate places on the plant to both 'innovate' and 'be lean' at the same time, and you can see why it's a tough relationship.

"For years, plant managers have essentially tried to deploy systems and applications to solve functional problems. Let's say the company has five different plants, and there is a plant manager for each of those plants. In one of those plants, maybe quality was an issue, so that plant manager went ahead and purchased something to solve the quality management problem. In another plant, maybe asset management was an issue. So that manager went ahead and purchased an asset management solution.

"When companies solve their functional problems locally, it leads to a situation where there are hundreds and hundreds of applications and IT functions deployed all across the plant floor, and they may vary from plant to plant.

"So, when corporate actually wants to extract the data from those applications, the information generated on the plant floor is locked within these application silos or they just are not collecting the data that would help, or it is being collected but it is trapped inside a special-purpose network. It's very difficult for an organization looking for visibility across its manufacturing base to do point integrations into every one of these systems."

"That does sound time-consuming," said Bonhoffer.

"Not only is it time consuming, it's extremely expensive and not scalable," said Mulcahy. "So now corporate IT is saying, 'How do we get some level of standardization across our plants, such that we're able to coordinate and execute better, and we're able to make additional multi-plant deployments easier?'"

"I know that point-to-point integrations are a nightmare," said Bala.

"The best-case scenario here is to avoid doing point-to-point integrations between each data source and each application," said Mulcahy, "because that's too expensive and not scalable. Having some kind of central aggregation of the information feeding a composite application that can support the applications is the best way to reduce your cost of ownership."

"So why doesn't everybody just buy this architecture?" asked Bala.

"Well, many do, but as I have mentioned in previous sessions, composite applications are kind of like, 'part of a healthy breakfast' but they are not the whole meal," said Mulcahy. "There are structural issues in plant operations that need to be resolved alongside, if not prior to, the introduction of composite applications."

External Pressures

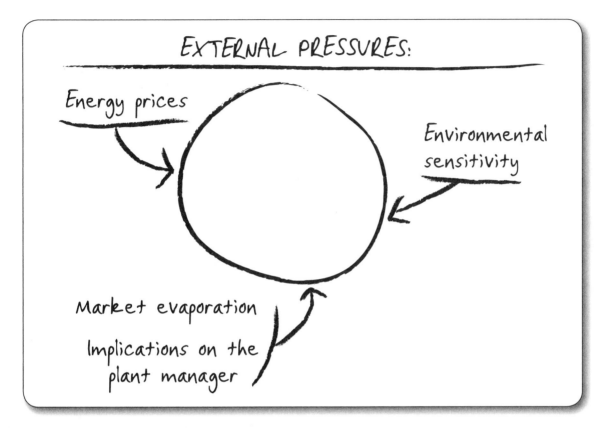

EXTERNAL PRESSURES:

Energy prices

Environmental sensitivity

Market evaporation

Implications on the plant manager

A Demand-Driven Economy

"Let me set the stage a little bit," said Mulcahy. "One of the biggest pressures on the plant comes from the transition of the manufacturing economy from a supply-driven to a demand-driven business. Companies that used to produce to stock, manage, and maintain inventories have essentially decided to change, or have been pressured to change, to a demand-driven approach. You used to be able to say, 'I will produce 50 widgets and they will sell, and they are all blue, because nobody cares about the color.' Until they did care. Now you have to figure out how to make 20 blue, 10 pink, 5 orange, and one each of four more colors.

"That leads to shorter cycle times. It places the emphasis on improved management of work and processing, and it allows manufacturers, particularly in industries where there are fast-moving products, to be able to really bring new products up to speed as fast as possible. And it makes 'inventory' an especially bad word. You don't want to sink a lot of cost into your operation only to have it sit around not recovering any revenue. If you don't understand what your demand is, then you most likely overproduce, leaving you with a lot of overstock that you have to manage.

"Along with the demand-driven economy, comes this idea of mass customization. Dell Computer is the best example of that, with their just-in-time model. You can now get the individual customer order from the Web site and then manufacture to that series or to that group of customers. You aggregate demand so you can produce to different categories of demand signals coming in.

"The mobile telephone market is another good example. So you've got several different new models released every month, and somebody's manufacturing all this stuff, right? It has to be very responsive to trends and keep up with advances in the technology as well as changes in taste and style, in a much more accelerated way than in the past. Every time a new product is introduced, you have to retool your lines and shift the sequence of operations. That's like a brand-new assembly line every few months.

"The third and most recent category of the new manufacturing paradigm is mass personalization. That means you can take an individual order and create a product that is customized only for that person."

"You mean like this?" asked Bala, waving an iPod with the words "Great Balas of Fire" etched on it.

"Precisely," said Mulcahy. "It wouldn't be so complicated to deliver all of the above if we were still on a centralized manufacturing model, where the company that owned the name owned all the means of production and it produced for a small localized area. That's no longer the case. Now obviously, not all of these pressures apply universally to both process and discrete industries. Nobody asks for personalized gasoline. But there's no doubt the demand-driven economy is having its effect on both types.

Energy Prices

"Obviously," he continued, "we're living in a time when the price of energy is a big concern. It's important to consider the scope of that statement. When we talk about energy, we're not only talking about electric power, but, particularly in the case of process industries, we're also talking about raw materials. There are many products whose original materials depend on crude oil supplies.

Then there are steam plants, dry air, water, solvents, and other materials—all of which are closely tied to the cost of producing and supplying energy. The cost of these resources can vary from region to region quite rapidly, even, in the case of electrical power, hour by hour. In Upstate New York, for example, the wholesale price of power can vary every 10 minutes. With today's fluctuating oil prices, plant managers are tearing their hair out trying to determine how to do forward planning for the next quarter, much less the next year."

Environmental Sensitivity

"Environmental sensitivity is another big issue," Mulcahy went on, "one tied closely to your choice of energy sources, in terms of their effect on your immediate neighbors as well as the globe at large. Within this category, I include regulatory pressure to limit consumption of scarce resources and emission of harmful agents. It could also run to issues like your immediate neighbors complaining about noise or odors from machinery or from workers leaving the plant on the late shift. In those instances, the plant manager becomes the first line of defense in public relations.

Regulations

"Let's take a look a related theme: the regulatory environment," said Mulcahy.

REGULATORY PRESSURE:
MAJOR NEW JOB FOR PLANT WORKERS

- "Top 3-5 regulatory/compliance edicts"
- TREAD
- FDA
- SARBOX
- Consumer product safety standards
- Single-outlet requirements (Wal-Mart)

"We can expect a barrage of new regulations from recent U.S. energy legislation and many of the State legislatures, such as AB32 in California, which restricts the development of new sources of electricity.

"Particularly in Europe, environmental regulations have become more stringent. Companies have to accommodate these from both a process and an information-systems point of view. That means altering your physical processes and then altering your systems to control and report on those processes. The effects are not limited to process industries and smokestack emissions, either. Think about how many products have electronics embedded in them. Because of increasingly stringent regulations regarding the disposal of electronics waste, the discrete industries have to plan more carefully with respect to the end-state of their products."

"Great," said Bala. "So the electronics revolution has opened up all these new markets, but it also makes it harder to throw things away."

"Welcome, Bala, to the Hall of Mixed Blessings," said Mulcahy.

Market Evaporation

"Another issue affecting the plant's survival is the potential evaporation of the market," he continued. "For example, the paper industry has undergone a lot of cyclical movements as people have, every few years, predicted the 'paperless office.'"

"Oh yeah, now that we have computers and the Internet, there's no paper in my office," chortled Moulton. "If anything, there's more. I print out everything to read it."

"Nonetheless, the movement of news consumption to the Web has lowered demand for newsprint and paper, so a paper plant must adapt from a full-on production mode to a cost-cutting mode pretty quickly," said Mulcahy. "That can cause some pretty tough disruptions in the operation of the plant.

"Another example is the oil-refining business. The price of oil is not only a pressure on the supply side, but internally represents the refinery's biggest source of production costs. Most refineries operate on a 'margin,' which means that some of the products, such as asphalt, sell for less than the crude oil itself.

They must produce the products, because there is nothing else to do with the heavy byproducts of refining that make up asphalt, and purchase of lighter crudes is expensive. Rapid price changes are usually beneficial, however, because plants can continue to process cheaper crude in the 'pipeline,' but hikes in gasoline prices occur right away, and take much longer to come down after crude prices drop again. That's when they make their money. If the margins are narrow, then you have to cut costs very quickly to get the margins up. If the margins are wide, then you have to be able to swing quickly into full-bore production mode and change the product mix. That's not always an easy transition to make."

Manufacturing Malaise

"While we're on the subject of 'market evaporation,'" Mulcahy went on, "it's not surprising that there is a sort of pervasive psychological malaise at U.S. manufacturers. It is about 30% more expensive to produce a product in the U.S., on average, than elsewhere in the world. There is a sense that the center of gravity of manufacturing is inexorably moving to the East."

"But that is what's happening, right?" asked Joan.

"It's definitely true that cost-cutting is of paramount concern," said Mulcahy. "But the situation isn't as bleak as people make it out to be, at least not across the board, though it does account for the popularity of Lean Manufacturing and Six Sigma, which we will discuss later. What you need to know for now is that there is a dual-headed, seemingly contradictory pressure on the plant where, on Monday, you could be told, 'be as lean as possible,' and on Tuesday, you could be told, 'you've got to innovate. Innovation is the key to the future.' And both are valid in their own right."

"Could the problem be cultural?" asked Moulton.

"I think so," said Mulcahy. "Everyone talked about the 24/7 business 10 years ago. Well, now we have it, and with it came the expectation that every solution we implement will have an instantaneous effect. In the U.S. in particular there is a tendency not to take the long view, but to focus instead on the short-term fix, which is why many attempts to implement Lean Manufacturing, for example, tend to fail, because it is a long-term philosophy that gets applied as a band-aid."

"So it's like, managers say, 'let's get lean, let's innovate,' and when someone comes back to them with a bill, they say, 'we need to be lean and innovative without money,'" said Bala.

"That's about right—we'll look at some possible solutions to that condition later on," said Mulcahy.

Evaporating Skill Pool

"There's also the issue of the evaporating skill pool," Mulcahy said. "Not only are the veterans retiring and taking their knowledge with them; kids who are graduating with math and engineering degrees often don't see manufacturing as a viable career option. Thirdly, manufacturing is now so technical and the degreed candidates are few and far between, many U.S. companies are forced to import people from overseas. It's a serious demographic problem. "

A Question of Scale

"Do different sized companies face the same pressures?" Bonhoffer asked.

"Not necessarily," said Mulcahy. "For example, the larger the organization, the more affected they are by the forces of globalization. The bigger you are, the more imperative it is to develop a global business model and invest in technologies that will allow you to collaborate across geographic boundaries, in different time zones, with different groups of people. That means hiring people with the knowledge of wikis, blogs and teleconferencing. It also means re-thinking your business model as a global entity—do you organize centrally, do you decentralize, or is there some kind of hybrid?

"A huge corporation like GE is able to realize high revenues per employee, because they have invested heavily in information technology that allows those employees to be valuable. But as the old saying goes, 'you've got to spend money to make money,' and that's easier for some than others—especially if they have just doled out a bunch of cash for acquisitions, only to find they face an integration nightmare that they must negotiate to get out of the woods and start seeing returns.

"Medium-sized manufacturers face different challenges. More often than not, medium-sized manufacturers are part of a business network, where they are part of a value chain and play the role of supplier, and that means conforming to whatever the top of the food chain wants to do. Wal-Mart is the most obvious example of this—it has inverted the retail model so that the store calls the shots and the suppliers have to fall in line.

"Improvements in technology have meant a lot more opportunities for medium-sized manufacturers to compete with more manufacturers in markets they've never competed in before. It also means that they will show a higher percentage of investment per dollar of revenue than their mega-corporate cousins, which is another turnabout from the typical trend. Technology also opens them up to competition in ways that may make them vulnerable, too. When the big kahuna in your supply chain, be it Nike or Wal-Mart, passes down a mandate that says, 'now everyone has to implement RFID,' you have to be prepared to do that, lest you be cut from the chain," said Mulcahy.

"It sounds like things are getting more ruthless," said Bonhoffer.

"You bet," said Mulcahy. "And it's far from over."

Technology Itself

"I have a sense that in a lot of your presentations, we're going to hear that the solution to many of these pressures lies in technology," said Mulcahy. "That's true. But keeping up with technological developments, and accepting that their effects may take time to manifest themselves, is itself a pressure, and can sometimes feel like a full-time job in and of itself.

"Technology is unquestionably part of the solution. But even in a world that always seems to move at light speed, the application of technology on good, solid industrial processes may take years to bear fruit, and there are many kinks that can develop along the way. That's why it's so important to first come up with a business process model that makes sense, and mold the technology to that—rather than letting the technology dictate how you do business. Leaders don't need to understand the minutiae of technology, but they do need to understand the big trends and be able to act decisively when they see these trends affecting their plants."

Implications of External Pressures on the Plant Manager

"With increased external pressure, particularly regulatory pressures, on a lot of industries, much of the responsibility for creating detailed reports for compliance purposes is given over to the plant, which may not be equipped to handle these requests," said Mulcahy. "The plant manager will get buffeted by requests from corporate for a lot of detailed compliance information on his production, and meanwhile, he's yelling back at corporate, saying, 'my workers are working overtime to produce all this stuff that just sits in a warehouse,' or, 'all of my workers are just sitting around, and I heard the other plant over in Kansas that makes the same product is overflowing with work—why hasn't the demand come to me?'"

"Gee, where do I sign up to be a plant manager?" asked Bala. "Don't everybody volunteer at once."

"I think a good subtitle for this section would be, 'playing nice,'" said Mulcahy. "Today's plant manager spends a lot of time appeasing regulators, the community, and the head office's need for information and compliance.

"First, there's the issue of getting along with the neighbors. You can imagine that if you have a plant in a town, the mayor is pretty happy to have those jobs and people paying taxes. You can also be sure that the mayor and the city council and the citizens in general want to know that everything is being run safely. If you are sewing together flags, that might not be too much of a concern. But the more dangerous the activities are inside your plant and the more flow of materials and waste there is, the more the community will need to be informed and reassured that everything is being run safely. Emergency plans will have to be in place with the local fire departments and police and so forth.

"Then, there is the issue of dealing with utility prices. Manufacturers are huge users of power. Plants frequently have power generation facilities as well, so in some cases they can sell power back to the grid. Electricity prices are part of a complex regulated market that a plant manager has to keep close track of. Rising oil prices may mean that the way power is generated or used has to change.

"Third, there is the increasing issue of regulatory compliance, especially where it intersects with environmental protection," Mulcahy said.

"The halcyon days, when we could freely produce acid rain with impunity, are gone," said Moulton.

"And I think that's for the better, Peter—but it does mean there's even more on the table to think about than before," said Mulcahy. "Let's look at the example of 'cap and trade.' We've all heard about greenhouse gases and global warming."

"Is all the evidence in?" said Moulton. "I'm not convinced."

"Well, the regulators aren't taking any chances—but they also haven't really decided on the best approach," said Mulcahy. "What they have settled upon for now, is a voluntary program for the measurement of your company's carbon footprint. Measuring that footprint creates a certain amount of work for the plants. That's one layer.

"The next layer is this concept of 'cap and trade.' The idea is that your company will cap its greenhouse-gas emissions at the level they were at in 2000, or 1990, or some point in the past. Chances are, if you've been expanding your business, you probably can't actually achieve those levels. So, instead, you trade credits with somebody who *can* produce emissions at that historical level. That sets up a market for greenhouse gas trading, and that trickles down to the plant manager."

"So now the plant manager has to be an energy trader, too? I hope these guys are getting raises," said Moulton.

"The trading is normally negotiated higher up the chain and is generally aggregated by third parties," said Mulcahy. "But the plant does have to deal with data for the computation of credits needed or created.

"That means that, as a manager, you're constantly looking at ways you can measure the footprint and then meet the requirements. The more you can modify operations to get close to the cap level, the less you have to spend to trade credits with somebody else. The good news is that if you can further lower greenhouse gases with plant modifications in excess of the emission levels to which you committed, you can sell the excess capacity."

Corporate/Plant Divide

CORPORATE VALUES:

Factors corporate monitors:

- Plant availability

- Cost of maintenance per ton of product
  (or per # of serial #s)

- Percent uptime

GOAL: MAXIMUM UPTIME AT LEAST COST

Corporate Values

"Having worked in manufacturing, it probably won't surprise you to learn that the corporate office and the plant approach operations pretty differently, and with a different set of values," Mulcahy said.

"I'm going to start with the corporate-level values, and the factors they monitor to see if those values are being fulfilled.

"Corporate is mainly interested in tracking how a plant operates, including production, energy cost, and availability. These metrics are preferably referenced to benchmarks, but in the absence of benchmarks, the historical values can be used. These include energy per unit of production, materials per unit of production, maintenance per unit of production, or plant throughput compared to maximum capacity. In order to get those answers, oftentimes corporate will install production management and asset management systems. Unless they are paid or judged based on these numbers, this is not necessarily what the floor people are looking for."

"I doubt anyone on the floor ever asked for an asset management program," said Bonhoffer. "They'd probably rather be excused from having to enter data into and maintain the corporate asset management system."

"It's definitely a concern," said Mulcahy, turning to the whiteboard. "And if the plant is really going to strive for perfection, there has to be some alignment of these goals."

Plant-Level Concerns

PLANT-WORKER CONCERNS:

- ❏ "No Thinking after 8:30"
- ❏ "Sheer terror"
- ❏ KPIs? Who cares?
- ❏ Compliance = paperwork
        - ERP: "Move information to the people,
        - not people to the information."
- ❏ Efficiency gains
- ❏ Short-term thinking

"A lot of the people working on the floor are not provided, or don't have much interest in, the big-picture goals that corporate has laid out—financial targets and the like—unless their pay is based on plant success," said Mulcahy. "Nor does corporate really understand what it's like to be on the floor of a factory, where equipment makes all kinds of noise, and everything is in a delicate balance, and only by way of extremely close concentration does the operation stay on the right side of entropy.

"The chemical industry, for example, has a list of stressors that affect behavior and morale in a plant: these include personal financial issues, lack of training, domestic issues—there are close to 50 that they've listed, and more.

"What's interesting about these factors is that they are additive—so if you've had a fight with your wife *and* you're fatigued *and* you're asked to do something for which you've not been trained, *and* you feel unsafe, then that's far worse than experiencing any one individual stressor.

"It's difficult to overstate the gulf between finance and operations. Corporate and production people are speaking two different languages. Right now, there is really no clear way to translate financial parameters into operations or vice versa, at least not in real time. After the first morning meeting, there is not sufficient time to put a lot of thought into what you are doing, other than executing on the task at hand—everyone is principally concerned with execution, and making sure nothing goes horrifically wrong. The KPIs that corporate uses are financial. The KPIs that operations people watch are related to specific production targets. It's very hard to keep those in sync. The financial KPIs corporate invents are pretty meaningless to a guy sitting over a vat of boiling oil—that guy doesn't want to hear about 'perfection'; he just wants to avoid spills, get paid, and live another day. If you're being hammered about some nebulous KPI, that's another stressor.

"When we talked about corporate values, we mentioned KPIs. Plant-level workers don't see a lot of value from the installation of corporate systems that provide a lot of nice numbers for corporate, especially when 10% of their day turns into entering numbers manually into those systems.

"Basically, anything that could reduce the amount of mind-numbing, repetitive, and autonomic things that plant workers have to do would bring a lot of joy to Mudville. You should all investigate the work of J. E. Rijnsdorp, a professor at Delft University in the Netherlands, who used to work for Royal Dutch Shell. He describes the life of the operator as one of '99% boredom and 1% terror' where somebody is sitting there, doing routine tasks, waiting for a failure and hoping they can cope with it. They're interested in things that make their life easier. They're not going to look at a display that shows a bunch of KPIs. They absolutely will monitor the systems that control their biggest and most troublesome equipment—primarily the materials levels, such as mass balance and pressure, which is part of the energy balance. These guys are principally concerned with smooth operations and leaving the plant with all the body parts they came in with—'striving for perfection' could sound pretty nebulous and canned to them.

"I don't want to make this sound as if operators are the problem. People often blame operators for defeating some brilliant project, but the converse is actually true—an informed and skilled operator can make a marginal project fly. They are interested in targets that they are given and they think of a KPI like they think of the production rate they are instructed to hold. If the information presented is useful to them, things go very well," said Mulcahy.

"Is there even a discussion of KPIs when they start the day?" asked Moulton.

"Generally there is a plant meeting in the morning, but the philosophizing stops there," Mulcahy said. "Once they hit the floor, the main concern is implementation of targets.

"Another thing that is perceived as 'getting in the way' of implementation is reporting. There's a lot of paperwork in a plant. You have to document every work order. These guys have a limited amount of time in which to get things done, and paperwork is seen as a time-waster if it is only for someone else to look at, and of no use to the author."

"But what about software? Won't an ERP system solve this problem?" asked Bala.

"It depends on how it's implemented," Mulcahy said. "We need to automate as many of the readings and aggregations as possible, but in some cases headcount on the floor goes up just to accommodate this new need for people to bang numbers into a system from which they never derive any benefits. You've just created more work, rather than less, without making the person's job easier or more fulfilling.

"Automated systems are appreciated on the floor to the extent that they can monitor equipment that would otherwise be obnoxious or hazardous to keep tabs on. The key phrase here is, 'move information to the people, not people to the information.' If you can centralize monitoring to a conditioned cockpit or bridge, rather than force some guy to put on his fireproof suit or walk ¾ of a mile just to get a piece of information, you're saving time and improving safety."

Communication Breakdown

COMMUNICATION BREAKDOWN

- The Plant/Corporate Divide
- Plant workers left out of corporate decision-making
- Plant people left out of corporate information
  ✘ Corporate view vs. plant view
- Corporate "second-guessing"
- Engineer-speak
- Corporate incentive (close the plant)
  vs. plant incentives (survival)

"Now I'll show you some of the critical communications failures that happen between the corporate side and the folks on the floor, and how that leads to poorly implemented solutions and unhappy employees," said Mulcahy.

"Part of the problem is that corporate has the advantage of the big-picture view across the entire company and the plant operators often do not. This can lead to very different interpretations of how problems should be solved, and can put the corporate incentive at odds with the plant or local incentive.

"For example, say that in a production facility you don't have as high a level of production as you should, and there's a work order submitted by the plant manager to de-bottleneck a pumping station. Now, from the corporate perspective it might make sense to say, 'for the long term, it makes more sense for us to jerk out this whole pumping station and put in a bigger one.' But the point of view of the plant is, 'We're going to be idled or at least inconvenienced for several days—why can't we delay until our turnaround?'

"So there are decisions that are made at a corporate level that require a viewpoint and resources that are not available at the plant level, and the plant understands this and will try to work within the constraints. It can only do de-bottlenecking projects and upgrades that do not require significant engineering. This is more difficult in a plant that processes highly hazardous materials and is covered by the OSHA Process Safety Management (PSM) standard, but it's still possible. There are options in how to pursue such a live changeover, however, including closer monitoring and changes in operational procedures.

"At the corporate level, they can look at the overall problem and say, 'Well, look, this plant is making a product that we're going to need more and more of as well as some products that aren't needed or can be made elsewhere, and if they're having trouble now, instead of just de-bottlenecking, why don't we actually solve the overall problem and maybe even convert one of the lines to produce the needed products?'

"So, when it is time to allocate money, there is competition from the localized view, which is a rather short-term view, but a very important one. It may be an immediate concern that this pumping station is failing. But corporate may take the longer-term, permanent fix and expand view, which you would get out of corporate engineering and the big capital budgets. Both have legitimacy—but they are different plans.

"To take it one step further, there may be many situations where it makes sense to corporate to shut down a plant, because regulations in that plant's jurisdiction are too constricting, or because it's cheaper to produce elsewhere. That's obviously a direct opposition of goals.

"There are other cases that are more nuanced," continued Mulcahy. "The corporate side has an incentive to keep their raw material prices down and their profit at a certain level. Some of that control comes from ensuring that the manufacturing process uses materials efficiently. So they pass that goal down to the plant operators—sounds reasonable, right?

"But there's one big problem. The guys on the floor don't know the raw material prices, yet they're being told to reduce costs. Corporate does not know where the materials are consumed, or the effect of shorting a batch with expensive material. For example, they don't really understand the effect on paper properties when substituting clay for titanium dioxide pigment, so allocation must be done on the plant floor—blindly.

"A third problem is something you all have probably seen before. There's probably nothing the plant manager hates more than people in corporate second-guessing him. Thus, managers will work very hard to only provide information that has been reviewed and reconciled, not the raw information. There are good technical reasons for this, in that the further away from the process you get, the less you are able to judge data. An operator may get a bad reading and, because of the history of the variable, local knowledge about the problem, and the relationship with the other variables in the unit, he or she knows if the value is good or should be rechecked. Corporate gets only one number, *after the fact*, with no ability to have the value checked. Bad data or ambiguous data can defeat a decision cycle. This makes plants want to control their information, but ultimately they must fully understand that all of the information is ultimately owned by the Enterprise."

"It sounds kind of like '*A Few Good Men*'—you know, 'let me operate on my own—you can't handle the truth!'" said Moulton.

"Pretty close, Peter," said Mulcahy. "I'll give an example: Maybe you have a broken feed pump, and that slows your feed down. Well, if corporate does not have the information system in place to know the feed pump is broken, then they look in and say, 'Oh, gee, you're not running fast enough.' Plant managers hate that kind of second-guessing, which corporate would call 'oversight.'

"If oversight is properly used, however, there are no objections *per se*. Many manufacturers have instituted centralized maintenance and diagnostics of their rotating equipment, because such an effort requires specialists who are not usually in the plants. This is done by actually bringing all of the real-time information back to a centralized facility. Because these experts are actually helping the people in the field, they are respected and assisted by the people on the floor. The key is proper use of information.

"Another issue is the timeliness of the information. If you ever see someone punished because they have been using data, it is a reflection upon the timeliness of the data. Although there is some friction, the people in a company genuinely want to work together, but if you only get the information a week later, you can't collaborate—all you can do is punish.

"There's another class of people who end up withholding information, although they probably don't realize they're doing it; in fact, they probably think they are being explicit. Any guesses?"

"Engineers!" Bala shouted, smacking the table with his palm.

"Gold star for you, Bala," Mulcahy said. "Engineers are deeply trained in analytics and sometimes work in a hermetic environment that leads to stubbornness. Around communications issues, engineers sometimes are not given the big-picture information available to corporate, and so they will often state the solution instead of the problem.

"For example, they will report to the manager that 'we need more people to fix equipment.' But what they're really saying is: 'we have equipment reliability issues.' In the perfect plant, corporate will be tracking the percent uptime, the availability of the equipment, and the cost of the maintenance. The requests coming in from the plant just help guide corporate as to what their thoughts are for the solution, but someone has to go out to those facilities fully appraised of the problem. And they have to be prepared for the fact that some people in the plant will already think they have the solution hammered out."

"But isn't corporate often guilty of imposing systems on plants that don't work?" asked Bonhoffer. "You make it sound as if plants get the systems and solutions they deserve because they are provincial and clannish, and don't provide the right information to corporate."

"Oh yes, there are often cases where the wrong solution is implemented because the problem is not well understood, but it is seldom because someone withheld the data," said Mulcahy. "My final example was going to be two phenomena that you've probably heard about: 'malicious compliance' and the 'indispensable man.'

"I don't think malicious compliance is a conspiracy, so much as the unfortunate consequence of an information gap," said Mulcahy. "'Malicious compliance' is the procedure of killing a policy or software solution that the implementer or user never wanted in the first place by doing *exactly* what was requested, no more, no less, rather than being an active participant in the solution. Sometimes the base cause of this could be that the solution was selected, designed, and implemented without fully consulting the user.

"So the result is that people are cooperative in the meetings. They answer every question honestly, but won't volunteer additional information or advice, and at the end of the day they deliberately let a poorly conceived project run its course and run aground.

"There's a poem by Saxon White Kessinger called 'The Indispensable Man.' Allow me to read to you for a moment:

> Sometime when you're feeling important
> Sometime when your ego's in bloom
> Sometime when you take it for granted
> You're the best qualified in the room,
>
> Sometime when you feel that your going
> Would leave an unfillable hole
> Just follow these simple instructions
> And see how they humble your soul;
>
> Take a bucket and fill it with water,
> Put your hand in it up to the wrist
> Pull it out and the hole that's remaining
> Is a measure of how you'll be missed
>
> You can splash all you wish when you enter
> You may stir up the water galore
> But stop and you'll find that in no time
> It looks quite the same as before
>
> The moral of this quaint example
> Is just do the best that you can
> Be proud of yourself but remember
> There's no indispensable man."

The group applauded, and Mulcahy looked up from his paper and said, "Bet you didn't think I was going to read poetry to you guys today. The moral of the story is that the plant has already laid out where they think they could use your help. And if you don't work to truly grasp the problem, you'll become the 'indispensable man.'"

"That was music to my ears, John," said Bonhoffer. "So you'd say the guilt for the corporate/plant disharmony lies on both sides. Maybe what's lacking is a shared vision, and that's because there isn't enough shared information."

"That's right, Joan," said Mulcahy. "Thanks everyone for a great session."

Chapter Five

The Vision of the Perfect Plant: Coordination, Planning, Execution, Integration, and Intelligence

Contributing Authors:
Ashtad Engineer, Tata Consultancy Services
Elizabeth Given, Cisco Systems, Inc.
Charlie Miller, Praxair, Inc.
John Wheeler, CIDX

Bonhoffer, Bala, and Moulton were knocking back their coffee, trying to jump-start the early morning lesson they were about to get with John Mulcahy. "I see you're all ready to drink from the overflowing cup of my wisdom," he said. "Today, I'll try to communicate my vision for a perfect plant. If you can absorb it, you'll be well prepared to perform the research for the second part of this project."

"Consider us ready for absorption, oh wise one," Moulton said, spreading his hands out from his forehead.

"Given the size and scope of what falls under 'Manufacturing,'" Bonhoffer said, "I'm not sure how it can be captured by one vision. So far, you've mentioned three major categories of manufacturing. Process industries include everything from refineries to paper mills. Companies in the discrete manufacturing industry, on the other hand, make laptops, washing machines, and other devices. In utilities, both process industries and discrete manufacturing industries generate power. So far as I can tell, the distinctions between these categories are blurry and overlapping, especially when you get into the details."

"For example," Bala said, "pharmaceutical companies produce lots of little bottles of pills. The creation of the medicine inside the pills is a process on the line, and all of the ingredients and batches that yield the medicine must be tracked. At the same time, each little bottle is a discrete unit that has to be tracked and correlated to the ingredients and batches inside the bottle."

"It's true," Mulcahy said. "Manufacturing is a huge world, loaded with incredible variation. But in our discussion of processes and systems, we heard that some basic processes are in play at all plants, and that the pressures on the plants are getting more intense. So let's start with why running plants is so difficult."

Balancing a Complex Act

"So far," Mulcahy said, and began to bullet some points on the whiteboard, "we've described a flow through the plant that involves the following steps, each of which is supplemented by two key activities."

- COORDINATION
- PLANNING
- EXECUTION
- INTEGRATION
- INTELLIGENCE

"Coordination," Mulcahy said, "is the flow of information from the corporation to and from all of the plants it owns or controls. Basically, my job as EVP of Manufacturing Operations is to direct the plants to do what the corporation needs. The planning process takes corporate goals and turns them into specific plans at various levels. Execution makes it happen."

"And integration and intelligence are supporting activities," Bala said.

"Integration," Mulcahy said, "is the way all the activities are synchronized at the levels of process, information, and automation. Intelligence is about making all this visible, and constructing models of what's going on to help run the business. All the areas you're researching in the next phase of this project fit into these dimensions in some way."

"But we're going to research areas that are much more specific than these broad categories," Bonhoffer said.

"That's partly true," Mulcahy said, "but as you delve into each area, you'll find that the complexity never stops growing. It's like a fractal. That's what makes improving plants so difficult. Let's go through some examples, starting with my job.

"A plant exists to carry out the corporate strategy. Another way of looking at it is that the plant fits into some sort of corporate-wide process that provides value to the customer. Nowadays, though, there are so many more choices for how we can make things. We can either improve our existing plants or build a new plant, or we can use an outsourced manufacturer for part or all of the process. When we look at the portfolio of plants, we have to decide who gets what. I only have so much capital to spread around. Everybody wants more. The amount is decided by figuring out what corporate needs each year from the plants. What is needed from the plants gets determined by corporate's long-term strategy."

"So you have to figure out which plants need to be more productive to meet growing demand," Bonhoffer said, "and which are nearing the ends of their useful lives."

"Exactly," Mulcahy said. "This influences how we allocate capital investment and our maintenance strategy. Planning goes deeper into detail. Once the corporate plan is set for the year, it's broken down into quarterly and monthly plans. There's quite a bit of back and forth between the plant managers and me in this process. After that, it's up to the plant managers to make it happen."

"That doesn't seem so complex," Moulton said.

"If you aren't worried about whether your plan is right," Mulcahy said, "and if you don't listen to your plant managers, you can whip something off pretty quickly. However, if you don't want the CEO tap-dancing in front of financial analysts, trying to explain revenue shortfalls, spikes in production costs, or the reasons behind massive accidents, it's much more difficult. Still, in a way you're right. The planning process is simpler than the operations inside the plant, where the number of moving parts dramatically increases.

"Say you're a plant manager and your maintenance manager reports that a pump looks like it's going to fail, a pump that's critical to keeping the line going. Do you keep the line running and hope for the best? Or do you stop the line and do the maintenance and blow that shift's schedule? When you do the maintenance, do you fix the pump or do you replace it with a more energy efficient model? Everyone has a dog in this fight. Sales will go crazy if a crucial order is delayed. Production wants to keep the line going. Maintenance wants to fix it. Those in charge of decreasing energy usage want a new pump, but what does that mean for the capital budget? If you're in a sold-out market, one set of decisions will seem right. If you aren't, then you'll lead in a different direction. All of this will be influenced by the plant's long-term plan. If you're building capacity and want this plant to run efficiently for years, then buy the pump. If you're at the end of life, fix it. Of course, the relative cost difference must be taken into account, which not only includes the cost of a new pump but parts and labor to fix the old one."

"Okay," Moulton said, "so you do have to make difficult decisions."

"It goes way beyond that," Mulcahy said. "The whole team is involved, everyone in the plant. When you run a plant, you're optimizing a massive multivariate, non-linear equation. You want to create products to a high degree of quality, for the lowest cost, meeting the plan, maximizing use of equipment, using energy efficiently, staying in compliance with environmental, health, and safety regulations, and adhering to labor union agreements. You have to keep a close eye on the stream of orders and supplies arriving at the plant even as you ensure that products are shipped and delivered on time. Oh, and, by the way, the costs of bad decisions or lapses in judgment are incredibly serious. Because of Sarbanes-Oxley, for instance, a CFO might go to jail for a bad financial statement. In a plant, a series of bad decisions means equipment can blow up and kill people, a thought that's never far from a plant manager's mind."

"Now it sounds intense," Moulton said.

"When you get it right," Mulcahy said, "it can be a thrill. But you have to get used to living in fear and taking action to prevent things from getting out of control. When you start trying to improve one area, like energy usage, your solution might affect quality or reliability or costs."

"When you push one knob in," Bonhoffer said, "another pops out."

"So how does this multivariate equation get optimized?" Bala said. "Anything easy would be done quickly, leaving you stuck with problems that are embedded with contradictory goals."

"Yes," Bonhoffer said, "like how to execute planned maintenance without interrupting production. Or how to save money without affecting quality."

"The short answer," Mulcahy said, "is that the plant gets better in a set of incremental steps carried out by a large team. So far, I've been somewhat romantic about the role of the plant manager, the heroic figure of the plant. Few plant managers would disagree with me that theirs is the key role, but if the plant manager doesn't create a team to run the plant, then he or she can quickly become a barrier to progress."

"But if each team is in charge of optimizing a different set of variables in this equation," Bonhoffer said, "and is motivated by different key performance indicators, or KPIs, then how do you resolve all that tension?"

"This is perhaps the most challenging part," Mulcahy said. "You have to somehow create a culture that is able to see the big picture and take into account what's best for the plant. And each area has its own culture. In your upcoming research, pay careful attention to the culture of success. Joan, you'll be looking at energy management and quality management. Moulton, from you I need to know how teams involved in coordination, planning, and execution work successfully. And Bala, I want you to explain the culture that helps plants successfully transform themselves."

"Solving these problems sounds like a tall order," Bala said.

"I'm not asking you to figure this out yourselves," Mulcahy said. "You'll talk to the experts in each area to extract information and ideas and distill them into a form we can use to educate all the people working in Wolverine's plants. I chose you three for this task because this ability to synthesize is your strength.

"Before you can do any of that, however," Mulcahy said, and began to write on the board, "you'll need the vision."

WHAT IS A PERFECT PLANT?

A perfect plant is 100 percent on stream at full capacity producing consistently high quality product with no health, safety, or environmental incidents with optimal use of resources.

A perfect plant is a plant where everyone can handle change, where everyone is aware of the processes of the plant, aware of their role in them, and aware how their actions affect other people.

In a perfect plant, the lights are turned on, the right information is in the right place at the right time to increase the velocity and impact of decisions. Information flows so people can make the best decisions based on information not instinct.

"This description is pretty good but there are many ways to put it," said Mulcahy. "A perfect plant is one that offers a 360° view into all operations. It allows you to increase visibility and improve integration with business processes. It enables you to progress from reactive management of operations and maintenance to proactive management of operations and predictive maintenance. Your 360° visibility into all plant operations provides the ability to positively impact the business' bottom line. With it, you can plan and schedule in real time, and you can respond faster to operational issues and customer delivery targets."

"So you can see what's happening and react quickly," said Bonhoffer.

"But we need a *prescription* to help make our plants better," said Mulcahy. "The perfect plant is an ideal meant to serve as a blueprint for your own manufacturing transformation, helping you to prioritize when and where to devote resources to produce steady, incremental improvements to your manufacturing processes. In the perfect plant, you can optimize your use of manufacturing assets and drive increased production performance—all in concert with enterprise-wide plans and objectives. In a perfect plant, personnel no longer waste effort constantly reacting to line failures, supply network disruptions, and operations emergencies. As Bonhoffer pointed out, the vision can't be too specific, because the plants in our portfolio are so different from each other. But it can't be too general, either. While they're not all the same, there are finite numbers of business processes that most organizations run at the enterprise level that we can talk about. When you get into manufacturing, there are business processes at the operational, supply chain, and manufacturing levels that can be dramatically different, depending on the specific industry. As a result, one of the challenges you'll face in making a recommendation is whether to provide a lowest-common-denominator set of best practices, or to suggest implementing an industry-specific, next practice."

Assessing Flawed Approaches to the Perfect Plant

"I'm going to explain some things, now," Mulcahy said, "that do not work. I'm not pointing out these problems from some high place of scorn—over the years, I've made all of these mistakes myself at some point. I simply want to educate you about negative patterns so that you can recognize them in our plants and help to fix them."

"So we'll be sort of like medical interns," Moulton said. "We won't really know what we're doing yet, but we can propose a diagnosis now and then."

"Maybe by the end of this process, you'll be more like residents," Mulcahy said, and began to draw on the board. "Remember, the first rule of medicine is to do no harm, which is why it's important that you know what *not* to do."

"Everything that happens in a plant is controlled by brains or machines," Mulcahy said, expanding on his drawing. "And when I say machines, I'm including software. To make things work well, the brains have to know what's going on in the plant, and the machines have to have instructions to do what's needed. In our first meeting, we said that a plant can be thought of as a flow of materials, a flow of energy, and a flow of information. These flows run through the machines and brains in the plant. From the other side, products emerge."

"The challenge of running a plant is to have all the materials, energy, and information directed and transformed by the brains and the machines. The most common negative pattern, one that I fell into as a beginning plant manager, is the one-brain command and control model. I used to call this the military model, but I ran into someone from West Point who said the military doesn't work this way anymore.

"In the United States, when the modern world of manufacturing was created after World War II, many of the people who ran plants came out of the military. They brought that era's ideas of command and control with them. In other countries it was much the same way because hierarchical management ruled the day. The idea was that everyone would get general direction in the form of standing orders, which in the plant translated roughly into directives to optimize certain KPIs and specifically to how to do things. This seems like a good model in the same sort of way that a planned economy does, but it leaves little room for individual contributions and initiative. No set of rules can handle every situation in a plant, so either people act on their own, in violation of policy, or they send all decisions upstairs."

"Which is when the managers become the bottleneck," said Bala.

"That," Mulcahy said, "is because you have a much smaller number of brains working on your problems than you would using other models. But you do have clear lines of authority and a sense of control. This model is probably more common than most people acknowledge. The personality type that tends to become a plant manager can lead in this direction."

"It must be a tricky balance," Moulton said. "The plant manager has to understand everything, but not be involved in a way that takes responsibility away from the teams."

"Like most plant managers," Mulcahy said, "I'm interested in everything. So it was hard for me to step back and let the processes I'd set up resolve situations. But there are no panaceas—even when responsibilities are delegated, things can go wrong in different ways.

"Once you create a separate group to handle each major area—all of which are necessary to run a plant—sometimes they don't communicate. The teams devolve into what people usually call silos. The overly involved plant manager provides an important and often unacknowledged benefit—he or she acts as a conduit for communication. The cost of over-involvement is that it creates a bottleneck."

"What happens when teams are in their own silos?" Bonhoffer asked.

"All of the things you would expect that come out of a lack of coordination and poor communication," Mulcahy said. "Key maintenance is put off to keep the line running, or the line is interrupted for maintenance that could have been put off. Nothing, including planning, is optimized to maximize throughput. At its worst, lack of communication can lead to safety or environmental problems. Most large disasters are attributable to some sort of communication breakdown."

"But, you have to have focused departments and teams to run a large plant," Moulton said.

"Yes, but even then, they need to communicate," Mulcahy said. "A shared vision for how the plant is supposed to run can help resolve communication issues. Plants work better when people know what everyone is doing and how it all fits together. Without a widely shared vision, your plant may need more communication than is practically possible."

"So with the vision," Bonhoffer said, "teams communicate when needed, not just to check on Standard Operating Procedure."

"Even then, you can still have problems," Mulcahy said. "Some plants optimize in a pathologically focused manner. A friend of mine visited a plant that was dedicated to having the lowest possible labor costs. The plant manager had done everything to keep wages down and staffing levels low. Benchmarking showed that the plant was at the top of the first quartile in terms of labor costs."

"That would be considered a victory in most companies," said Moulton.

"Perhaps," Mulcahy said. "The benchmarking, however, failed to reflect another, critically important factor. Further analysis demonstrated that the plant was wasting huge amounts of energy across it entire operations. All of the savings from lower labor costs were being blown out the smokestack."

"It wasn't wrong to keep labor costs low," Bonhoffer said, "but that was far from the whole story."

"The moral here," Mulcahy said, "is that you must always balance your efforts."

"I see your point," Bala said. "But how do you do that when the balance is always changing?"

"When I talk about the vision of the perfect plant," Mulcahy said, "some people suggest that the best plant might be one that runs in lights-out mode, with no people in it. That's theoretically possible for a plant that makes the same thing over and over again for decades, but no plant is really like that. New products, new equipment, new ways of working, new regulations, and new market conditions all mean that balancing and rebalancing is in continual flux. The total automation vision is impossible, so we need smart people to run plants."

"But increased automation is a reality," Bala said. "In every area of the plant, more technology and software is being applied."

"Depending on the approach," Mulcahy said, "technology and software can help or hurt the plant. You can make the same mistake about automation in each department, too. At their best, technology and software provide people with what they need to make the right decisions and take the right actions. It opens up possibilities for enhanced information sharing and hence for innovation. At its worst, technology generates useless data, or a reliance on technology without an understanding of the process the technology supports or drives. Since there's no feedback about how things are working, or empowerment to do a better job, the technology gets in the way.

"The perfect plant is not a machine that operates in isolation, like a lawn mower or a tractor. It's a key part of delivering the value proposition of a company to a customer. The more often the plant, its operations, and its products provide high value to its customers, the more frequently you'll have a sustained and defensible profit margin."

Understanding the Duties of the Perfect Plant

"The whole notion of a plant as an isolated unit," Mulcahy said, "gets in the way of the idea model of the Perfect Plant. As we pointed out before, plants exist to serve the corporations that own them. There is a large-scale process of creating value for the end customer of the business that begins in the corporation, flows through the plant and all the suppliers, and then continues downstream as the product is distributed to the customer. Many of the important processes flow through the plant. Some processes are inside the plant, but increasingly even those involve communication outside the plant. Let's zoom in on some of those.

"If you look at the big picture, it's clear that the plant is part of larger processes that begin outside it and then continue after it has done its work. The sales and operations planning process, for example, starts at the board level, cascades down to specific goals for a plant, and then continues through delivery to the customer. A famous general once said, 'No battle plan ever survives contact with the enemy.' As sales proceed and production continues, the plan will have to be monitored and adjusted. Information about how well the production plan was fulfilled will flow from the plant to corporate, and adjustments to the plant will flow back. The same sort of communication has to take place between the plant and the customer receiving the orders. Can we deliver late? Can we deliver early? We have some extra capacity, do you want more product at a lower price?"

"But isn't this sort of communication routine?" Bonhoffer asked.

"The conversation with the customer may be routine or may not happen at all," Mulcahy said, "but constant communication about the plan is far more unusual than you might think. This is just the tip of the iceberg. If a plant makes standardized products that are also made elsewhere, the two plants could help each other by filling in gaps in each other's production plan. But to make this work, they must keep in close touch. They must maintain the standards that are the foundation of standardized products. If there are any problems with supply, they must be detected as soon as possible, hopefully before they can affect the process."

"It sounds like information must flow in and out of the plant all the time," Bala said.

"Communication is perhaps the most important aspect of a perfect plant," said Mulcahy. "As you do your research and visit plants, you'll notice that plants see themselves as self-contained islands. Inside the plant, we already talked about how silos can form that retard communication. The best plants have lots of communication: Everyone in the plant knows how the plant is performing, what is coming down the road, and what the effects of their actions are. The second part of being a perfect plant is pretty obvious—performance. The best plants optimize the multivariate equation at all levels."

"All business is about optimizing performance," Moulton said. "What you're saying is, if you want good performance, you have to find a way to measure it. There are all sorts of numbers to keep track of in a plant. To get good performance in a plant, it seems to me you need to follow your KPIs."

"But what if the KPIs are in conflict?" Mulcahy asked. "How do you sort that out?"

"I thought management was supposed to decide these things," Bala said.

"That's the point," Mulcahy said. "How do they decide?"

"ROI?" Bonhoffer asked.

"ROI is a fine thing," Mulcahy said, "but I'm looking for something more fundamental. If you consider all the numbers used in a plant, we can think of them in different ways. I call most of the numbers 'measures.' That is, they're numbers that indicate the performance of some activity—like the stats for baseball or soccer. On-base percentages or number of shots, or saves, or red cards are important indicators, but they don't win games. Scores wins games. I call the scores in the plant 'metrics,' and I define them in a special way."

"Most people would call your 'measures' 'metrics,'" Bonhoffer said.

"For our purposes," Mulcahy said, "'metrics' will be defined in a special way that I think is best for gauging the performance of a plant. A metric is the way the end customer recognizes the value created by the product, as we covered in our first session. On-time delivery, for example, of a complete order."

"How is this different from measuring ROI?" Moulton asked. "In my book, ROI is a fantastic way to keep score."

"Not for your customer," said Mulcahy. "If you focus on measures like ROI and profit in the absence of a focus on customer value, you may end up extracting more profit in the short term but abuse or anger your customers. If you focus on value and optimize everything else to meet that target, you'll keep your customers happy and create a strong position in the long term. Of course, the plant isn't completely in control of adopting this philosophy. Some plants will be run to maximize profit regardless of the effect on the customers."

"What about change?" asked Bonhoffer. "Hasn't that got to be a vital aspect of the perfect plant, too?"

"Yes," Bala said. "Nothing stays optimized for long. Products will have new requirements, customers will have new demands, supply conditions will change, and strategy will shift. Regulations will also come and go, and market conditions will ebb and flow."

"You're both right on," Mulcahy said. "The perfect plant reacts and keeps meeting the demands of customers, corporations, regulators, suppliers, and competitors. However, you can't expect change to happen by waving a magic wand. You have to have a culture to promote change in the right direction. That's what continuous improvement programs are about. But you also have to build the systems in the plant and design the processes in the plant with flexibility in mind. You can invest in technology in a plant and end up with a rigid, frozen structure, or you can end up with the ability to support rapid change and improvement. It's all a matter of your approach."

"These goals are fine," Bala said, "but frankly, they're sort of like Mom and apple pie—hard to disagree with. If we are going to help make Wolverine's plants run better, we have to give more specific advice than this."

Creating the Perfect Plant

"You're exactly right, Bala," Mulcahy said. "We can't just run around saying, 'Do better guys. Communicate. Perform. Prepare for change.' We need to dig in and come up with specific recommendations. That's what you'll do in your research." Mulcahy stepped up to the whiteboard and wrote the steps toward the perfect plant.

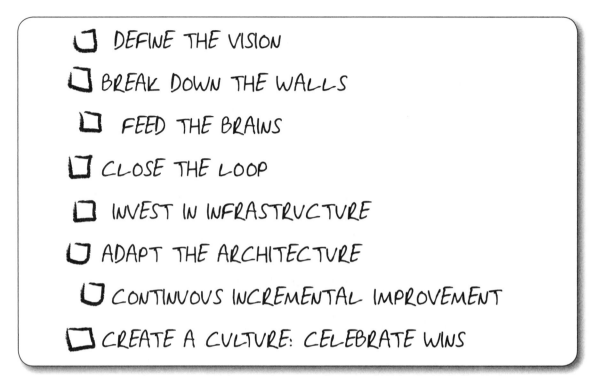

"By taking a closer look at each of these steps," Mulcahy said, "you'll understand more thoroughly my idea of a perfect plant. When you do your research, you'll have a way to organize the information you're hearing. If someone suggests a way to improve asset management, you'll be able to associate that idea with one of these steps. When you're done with your research, you'll be able to clearly describe what you found."

Defining the Vision

"To improve a plant," Mulcahy continued, "its leaders must develop a vision that is common and simple, one that is easily understood and seen as a picture that each employee can put into his or her own words. Until this happens, what you have isn't so much a vision as a dream. Leaders who succeed in transforming their companies understand their mandate. Not only can they translate their plan into an understandable vision, but also they can break it down into components that their teams can digest and own. In short, effective vision amounts to the perfect plant leader's translation from the corporate strategy into an ambitious mandate with deliverables that can be described, delegated, and digested by the plant leadership and employees.

"Once you have this vision firmly in hand, you will be able to understand where you are, how well you're doing, where you want to end up, and why. Manufacturing as an industry is better off than many other kinds of businesses because benchmarking statistics are well developed.

"These are like the stats in sports. There are companies that conduct annual surveys of what's going on in plants at a very detailed level. Some firms specialize in the refining and automotive industries. The participants who provide their data get a complete set of industry averages in return. You can then use this data to determine how well you are doing in key measures."

"Sort of like seeing how well you're hitting or pitching as a team compared with the rest of the league," Moulton said.

"But it's more complex," Mulcahy said. "In a way, each plant plays a different game because it serves the needs of a different owner. One plant may want to have the best pitching but not care too much about hitting. In a plant, the measures would be energy usage per unit of product or inventory level. The numbers don't tell the whole story, though they do help keep track of progress—you can see the trends. Are you getting better or worse?

"Perhaps the most important kind of vision is one that expresses the personality of the plant. Southwest Airlines is 'The Low Cost Airline,' and everybody who works there knows it. Most plants can't have a slogan that simple, but it helps to try. The more the personality of the plant can help guide decision making, the better. 'We are the safest, most profitable, most responsive refinery in the industry,' would be an initial attempt at such a vision. But a really excellent plant will then take that vision and translate it into a clearly defined way of working that everybody knows about. This is where the vision gets transformed into culture."

"A great vision will be industry-specific," Bala said.

"I can't tell you guys," Mulcahy said, "what vision to look for when you visit the plants. But when you are in a plant, you can ask: 'What is this plant all about? What are you guys trying to be? How do you do things around here?' At a great plant, you'll get clear answers to these questions, and there will be a sense that the vision is up-to-date. People do things a certain way because they learned from experience, not because a plant manager 20 years ago liked it that way."

Breaking Down the Walls

"The vision, then," Mulcahy said, "is just a target, as specific as possible, of where you want to go. The rest of these steps have to do with how well you get there. The next step, 'breaking down the walls,' is one of the toughest. When you start visiting plants, you'll find yourself really getting into the culture. You'll start to learn this huge amount of interesting stuff about each area of the plant. This creates a nerdish sort of isolation. The plant and each silo becomes a cult. There are those who know and those who don't. What naturally follows this is a communication barrier."

"But everybody can't know everything," Bonhoffer said.

"No," Mulcahy said, "but everybody can know more about each other, and how they're interdependent. They can also know that they can make better decisions if they cooperate. The best plants systematically work against isolation by setting up rewards for achieving common goals, locating departments that need to communicate in the same offices, and things like that. A common technique that helps break down barriers is visualization. When people see the effects of their actions on other departments and the big picture, they tend to communicate more and make better decisions."

"Won't this change as younger workers start taking responsibilities at the plant?" Moulton asked. "The digital natives, like us, are used to working in groups."

"The forces that create silos will work on younger people, as well," Mulcahy said. "Even with a bunch of people running around texting each other about mass balances and maintenance schedules, the cult of nerdism will create silos. You have silos of data, silos of workflows, silos of networks, silos of responsibility. Silos are embedded in the infrastructure, architecture, and networks in a plant. It seems strange to think of a network in a silo, but that's exactly how many plant-level networks work. Networking within a manufacturing cell is all about exchanging data between equipment and controllers at high speed, not about transmitting information to other parts of the plant or the rest of the company outside of the plant. Remember, much of the equipment and the systems in plants weren't built to be transparent. The architecture of many plants was created to allow each area to be separate. The need to communicate and perform in a more collaborative and transparent manner is an idea that came on the scene much later. None of these silos will go way by themselves or very easily. The best plants plan ahead and make a lot of effort to break down the walls."

"How can they do that," Bonhoffer asked, "if plants see themselves as isolated units cut off from the company and the rest of the world?"

"What happens at the silo level happens for the plant as a whole," Mulcahy said, "and can have an extremely negative effect, now that the need for transparency is growing faster than ever. For example, virtualized, outsourced manufacturing requires that the plant communicate lots of details to the people outside who are ordering the manufacturing. Nike doesn't own manufacturing plants, but it has an extremely detailed model of what goes on inside all of its contract manufacturers, so it can make adjustments as market conditions change. Companies like Cisco and Li & Fung operate the same way."

"So the factories," Bonhoffer said, "report the state of their production lines, materials inventory, their work in progress inventory, and so forth?"

"Inside Nike," Mulcahy said, "there is a massive model of all of the manufacturing that it's ordered. Nike monitors supply shipments to the factories and movements of products from factory to factory and to distribution centers. In order to be a Nike supplier you have to be transparent."

"Transparency, then, could be a competitive advantage," Moulton said. "It can make you easier to work with."

"Not just for contract manufacturing," Mulcahy said. "Most companies are working together more and more, in collaborative business networks, which requires more transparency so each company knows what's going on. The winners will be plants that can recognize problems early and react to market conditions. As EVP of Manufacturing Operations, I'll never argue against having a better window into what's going on in a plant. If I can see how well the plan is being fulfilled on a daily basis, I get a great sense of security."

"If transparency requires reporting information to those who need it," Bala said, "consuming information from others, and modeling activities outside the plant that you are relying on, like Nike does, must translate into a certain style of Information Technology."

"We'll explore the information sharing and IT requirements in a minute," Mulcahy said. "You'd be surprised how many plants are paranoid about sharing this information. I still run into plant managers who think it's none of my business what they're doing as long as they meet their objectives."

"Don't plants have to do a lot of reporting about safety and health and sustainability?" Bonhoffer asked.

"That's a domain of enforced transparency," Mulcahy said. "The other area of excellent cooperation industry-wide is safety. Plants generally share information about how to make things safer, or help each other, or police and fire departments, deal with chemical spills extremely quickly, with no questions asked."

Feeding the Brains

"The next step toward a perfect plant," Mulcahy said, "entails making sure people have the information they need to do their jobs. Since plants are run by brains and machines, you must feed the brains so they can make better decisions. Visualization is especially important. Simplified visual models that boil down lots of information into the essential trends and components make information more valuable. In addition to information, brains need tools to analyze that information and to communicate with other brains."

"So you're talking about defining a set of information," Bala said, "analysis tools, and ways to communicate and collaborate for each role in the plant."

"But doing this," Mulcahy said, "implies that the people filling those roles are empowered to actually do something with the information. In different industries, especially refining, the equipment operators play a hugely important role. They make decisions that have a significant economic impact on the bottom line. Ideally, you want that information and visualization to not just be about the physical processes, but also how that physical process is part of a business process with an economic impact.

"Visualization should not be about some abstract measure of efficiency, but about how much money the department or plant made in the past hour—focus on business impact. Make decisions with the lights on. In other roles in the plant, however, sometimes less is expected of the people. You want to make sure that if you have a person doing a job, they have a chance to make the best decisions."

"But this needs to be more than just about empowerment," Moulton said. "It's got to be about ownership, too. Nobody in the history of the world ever washed a rented car."

"That's true," Mulcahy said. "You want the reward structures to encourage the right behaviors, but you also want an element of flexibility. In some plants, working according to plans and procedures is so emphasized that people don't make suggestions for improvements, even when they are obvious and make sense. Sometimes people focus on instrumenting a problem to get more data but never ask the operators what they think should be done.

"The collaborative aspect is all about making it easy to get more eyeballs on the problem. Once you're looking at some data, how can you get others involved? Young people do this naturally with texting, email, wikis, all that sort of stuff. Those people in plants who aren't young need to be encouraged to collaborate. They need to be shown how to use the tools that get other people involved."

Closing the Loop

"There is another aspect related to feeding the brains that is crucial," Mulcahy said, "but hard to accomplish a lot of the time. Have any of you guys read that book called *Flow,* by Mihaly Csikszentmihalyi? He's a psychologist who explains this state he calls 'flow,' in which you become so engaged in an activity you lose your sense of time passing. To achieve a flow state, a balance must be struck between the challenge of the task and the skill of the performer. If the task is too easy or too difficult, flow cannot occur. Csikszentmihalyi makes a case that being in flow a lot makes you a much happier person."

"What does this have to do with a plant?" Moulton said.

"Flow happens," Mulcahy said, "when your skills are adequate to cope with the task at hand in a goal-directed, rule-bound system that provides clear clues as to how well you are performing. What's most important in this notion is seeing these clues. In plants, frequently people take actions when the effects of those actions are not clear. If you can see the results of your action through visualization, you'll change behavior."

"In other words," Bala said, "you want to turn the plant into one massive video game. Each person should be able to see the effects of their moves as soon as possible."

"The video game analogy applies to some processes in a plant," Mulcahy said, "but most of the time the effect of an action can't be visualized in real time. This is what I mean by closing the loop. This is where you must introduce discipline, to actually take the time to follow up and see what happened.

"Closing the loop on a planning process involves taking a look after the plan was executed to see how well things went. In refineries, they have models for chemical processes that predict how much gasoline will be produced from certain types of crude oil. To improve these models, you must see if your predictions were accurate and then either explain the differences or improve the model. Closing the loop applies to almost every process in the plant. It's not easy, but it's the essence of continuous improvement."

"You are playing the game to maximize some sort of score," Moulton said. "And if you can give that score actual business value, meaning money, then you can really get things humming along."

"In the best plants," Mulcahy said, "everyone's compensation is tied to the financial results the plant produces. In some plants, 30 to 40% of everyone's pay may be determined that way. People with this sort of incentive structure are highly motivated."

Investing in Infrastructure

"This next step is perhaps the most crucial," Mulcahy said. "Everything we'll talk about today implies a set of requirements for the systems in a plant.

"Consider what we've said so far. The vision step requires that you understand where you want to go. Breaking down the walls implies that communication and transparency must be supported. Feeding the brains means that information must be available, as must be tools for analysis and collaboration. Closing the loop means that these tools must be used in a certain way, to encourage better decisions and continuous improvement.

"Let's also include the steps that are to come—adapting the architecture, continuous improvement, and creating a culture. The first two are about flexibility and change. The last is about creating positive habits, a sense of the way we do things around here."

"So the systems in a plant," Moulton said, "have to provide information, networks to move it around, tools for analyzing that information, ways to visualize that information, and ways to collaborate. Oh, and it all has to be flexible."

"I think he's got it," said Mulcahy. He turned to the whiteboard and wrote the implied requirements.

INFRASTRUCTURE REQUIREMENTS

PROVIDE

- INFORMATION
- NETWORKING CAPABILITY
- ANALYSIS TOOLS
- VISUALIZATION TOOLS
- SUPPORT FOR COLLABORATION
- SUPPORT FOR FLEXIBILITY AND CHANGE

"Given all we've said about empowerment," Bonhoffer said, "it will be important to avoid installing systems that are too well-defined, too locked down. Otherwise the systems will restrict people. But if you put information in the hands of people in the plant along with tools for analysis, visualization, and collaboration, then they'll do things you never expected."

"And if those tools are easy to use and flexible," Bala said, "they will keep innovating. Plus they'll be likely to stay empowered and engaged, too."

"Here's a question," said Mulcahy. "How much can you predict in advance about the good things that will happen if you provide these tools?"

"To predict anything like that," Bonhoffer said, "you'd need a model of the value of the innovation you'd expect from each person who got the tools. Some of the people would innovate a lot, while others would use the innovations but not create them. I can't see how you would figure this out in advance."

"You would have to invest in this infrastructure on faith that there would be an ROI," Mulcahy said.

"That makes me uncomfortable," Moulton said. "My MBA training didn't include a course on faith. We had lots of courses on measuring financial value."

"Investing in infrastructure, as we have defined it," said Mulcahy, "does require some level of faith. But you can prove the value incrementally in small steps—you don't have to put infrastructure all over a plant in one fell swoop. You can put it in for one department. See how that works. Determine how people in your plant adapt to it. Find out what help they need to use the infrastructure. As you become comfortable that an investment in infrastructure makes sense, you can do more, where you need it. You may not need it everywhere."

"The infrastructure as you describe it doesn't seem focused on automation," said Bala.

"Right," Mulcahy said. "At first it's intended to break down the walls, feed the brains, close the loop, adapt the architecture, and support continuous improvement. Only after all that does automation really make sense because you then understand the problems you're dealing with and can crystallize the solution in an automated way."

"So that's when you use the big software applications for ERP, asset management, and so on," Bonhoffer said.

"No, no, no," Mulcahy said. "Every time I give this talk people think I'm bashing enterprise applications, but I'm not. The definition of infrastructure is systems that provide access to information, analysis and collaboration tools, and so on. Every enterprise application is a collaboration tool. Every enterprise application is a powerful source of infrastructure, if you use it that way. Nowadays, they almost all come with web services that allow you to get at the information quite easily. The automation of the enterprise applications must be approached more carefully based on the needs of your plant. A lot of what is in enterprise applications is automation of proven best practices. Other stuff is more cutting edge. You have to know your problems to know what applies.

"At first you want to have systems, networks, infrastructure, and enterprise applications that are a mile wide and an inch deep. The value of investment in infrastructure increases with the scope of information provided and the number of people who are involved. All sorts of good things happen then. The closest thing I have seen to what I really want in our plants is something like Facebook."

"Social networking software for college kids?" Moulton said.

"Think of it as an open, collaborative environment," said Mulcahy. "That's what I want in my plants, where it makes sense. In Facebook, you can create widgets, let other people know about them, get notified of what other people are doing, create communities of interest, share information."

"Google just created this standard called Open Social that has the same sort of layer defined across many sites," Bala said.

"Platforms like this," Mulcahy said, "with the right information and tools, are the essence of infrastructure."

Adapting the Architecture

"The next step is a willingness to adapt the architecture," said Mulcahy. "It's important to break the mindset that everything about the plant was set in stone when it was built."

"But plants are engineered with a purpose in mind," said Bonhoffer. "You can't just change things that cost tens or hundreds of millions to put in place."

"That doesn't mean you can't change anything," said Mulcahy. "This step is more of a reminder to have an open mind. You should be open to the possibility that the physical architecture of the plant, meaning the steel, can be changed. Sometimes just thinking in that way opens up people's minds so affordable changes occur to them. It is really hard to talk about how in general you might change the structure of a line or the cells in a plant. But there are other parts of the architecture of a plant that are easier to change. Adding infrastructure to extract and manage information from plant equipment or RFID tags and readers and sensors can have a dramatic effect on what becomes possible in a plant. Improved visibility allows for more optimization."

"So the architectural change is to add infrastructure for data collection, for turning the lights on," said Bonhoffer. "But that doesn't seem like an architectural change, perhaps an addition."

"Well, it depends on how you categorize things," continued Mulcahy. "The way networks are now converging in plants provides a great example of how architectures that were set up for different purposes can be incrementally adjusted into a new form. As I mentioned earlier, most plants have a siloed approach to networking. Each cell or workstation had equipment talking, frequently over non-standard network protocols, with PLCs that were controlling the equipment. This all was put in place before Ethernet and IP became the standard. And frankly, it is only recently that Industrial Ethernet and IP could handle the high speeds that some manufacturing applications needed.

"But now that that's true, you have Ethernet and IP at the company level, running the business operations of the plant, and you have the possibility of converging the network architecture of the plant onto that same standard. There are security issues to solve because the network in the cells or the workstations usually weren't built to be secure. You don't want your PLC controlling a high speed machine hacked into or taken offline by a virus. But if you get this convergence a lot of the things that we are seeking can happen."

"Why would convergence be of any benefit?" asked Bonhoffer. "What's the advantage of having everything on the same network standard?"

"Well, think of how it works without a network that connects the workstations to each other or to the business operations. You yell from one cell to another or go over there to see what's up. The plant manager doesn't see what's happening in the plant from his desk. But if you put the right kind of network in place, an architectural change, at a work station you can see out to the rest of the plant and into other workstations. From the rest of the plant you can see into the workstation. You can do a lot more optimization with this information because of convergence on a common standard."

"Can you give me an example of something you could do with a converged network?" asked Bonhoffer.

"Okay, imagine that you have one spot on the network where you can see all the traffic. Now imagine that at that spot you have a device that can look into the traffic and understand what is inside the packets being sent around. For example, if a PLC starts reporting that a device is slowing down or stopped or has indicated that it needs maintenance, you can identify that message and raise an alert. Or imagine that you can see larger patterns of what's going on that are revealed by network traffic sent by dozens of sources. Perhaps you notice that yield is unusually low in one of the early processes and that the effect of that will be that some important orders will be at risk. All of this is called network mining, where you look for certain patterns or special events and react to them."

"This sounds pretty advanced," said Bonhoffer.

"Well, it is not quite as hard as it sounds once you have the converged network in place," said Mulcahy. "And it is likely that this sort of capability will come as a product, and not be developed by the plant. But this is just one form of convergence. Imagine now that you overlay a communication system on the same network. You can do all sorts of tricks with sensors and RFID, keeping track of who is where, what equipment is where, where pallets are, with a generalized infrastructure. All of these changes can be made incrementally, but they are all enabled by changing the architecture by adopting a standard form of networking."

Continuous Incremental Improvement

"The last two steps," Mulcahy said, "continuous incremental improvement and creating a culture, are part of a stream of thought that begins with closing the loop. When you start to give people the ability to see the effects of their actions, it doesn't take long for them to start to make suggestions. If sensible suggestions are ignored, then people will stop making them.

"So, on one level, continuous improvement means listening to suggestions. But at the highest level, continuous improvement is about creating processes in the organization so that data is constantly being gathered and analyzed to determine the places in the organization that need to be changed. Some companies become drunk with continuous improvement and have lots of conflicting initiatives. It doesn't need to be that complicated. The novel *The Goal* puts forth a method invented by the author, Eliyahu Goldratt, called the

'Theory of Constraints.' The idea is to find the constraint in a system that limits productivity, then subordinate everything else to making that constraint as productive as possible. Eventually, you may find that the constraint has moved to a new part of the system, and you then start all over again. Six Sigma, a method we'll discuss in detail later, is a way to identify the causes of unwanted variation in a system and eliminate them. Total Quality Management is another method with different goals, and so is Lean. Before we move on, however, I want to give you an example of this last one, since many of its principles will be the basis for much of the work ahead of us.

"Throughout the '50s and '60s," Mulcahy said, "Toyota worked hard to develop their Toyota Production System, which was based on notions that had been in play ever since Eli Whitney invented the cotton gin. In particular, they elaborated on the work of W. Edwards Deming and Henry Ford. By the mid-'70s these guys had honed their system down to some basic principles that were aimed at ridding their processes of waste. Fifteen or so years went by before James Womack wrote a book in 1990 called, *The Machine That Changed The World*. He is the man who actually coined the term 'lean manufacturing.' The book made some real waves here in the States, enough to convince people in the plants that it was time to implement significant changes. The long and the short of Lean is this: until a plant can say with proven confidence that its processes aren't inconsistent, overburdened, or wasteful, its 'lean factor' has not yet reached critical mass."

"In theory, that sounds easy," Bala said. "Making it happen on the floor, every day, 365 days a year is an entirely different story, though."

"The first thing you've got to do when implementing Lean," Mulcahy said, "is identify your objectives. Any of you care to take a stab at what they might be?"

"The first one is a no-brainer," Bonhoffer said. "Value. What is the plant doing everyday? What is the enterprise trying to serve? It's trying to make a product that customers *value*."

"You hit on both of the plant's primary objectives in a single breath," Mulcahy said. "We want to focus on value, but we particularly want to focus on value from the perspectives of products and services. These, in turn, bring us to the customer, who, after all, is our ultimate target, whether it's a plant downstream or the people in the stores."

"It makes perfect sense," Moulton said. "Once you've zeroed in on your key values, you can design and create your activities around them."

"Value as a concept is an interesting, complicated affair," Mulcahy said. "Consider the way value is perceived by different customers, for instance. If you're selling a widget, your customer's first value criterion may be on-time delivery. When that's the case, you need to understand their demand patterns and plan your production to meet the delivery requirements that are a function of them. For another customer, value could be the price or quality of your product. Or it could be any of the above. On the other hand, your customer could be a part of your own organization, which would be true if you were producing subcomponents or subassemblies for your finished goods assembly plant. Whatever the case, it's imperative that you have crystal clarity into the value that you'd like to produce.

"Once you've determined your value, you can embark on an exercise called 'value stream mapping.' Basically, this entails mapping all of the different activities in a value stream process, identifying the source of your inventory, and determining the cycle and lead times for each of your process steps, both up- and downstream. Understanding these matters enables you to enhance the flow of product through your facilities. Theoretically, this is called 'consumption-based material pull.' In practice, this means that your product doesn't move unless your customer demand is pulling it."

"Isn't that," Bala said, "in direct contradiction to a push-based production, where you maximize the lot size or batch size of production to get the most out of your assets?"

"It is," Mulcahy said. "The reason 'pull-based' is better than 'push-based' is simple. When you run a push-based approach, sooner or later you're bound to lose track of the customer's needs—their demand pattern, their product mix requirements, and so forth."

"So how does Lean work on the floor itself?" Bonhoffer asked.

"The same way it does in the market," Mulcahy said. "Just as the market sends signals as to what is needed, and when, so too are signals sent up and down the production line, either to initiate a process or to stop one. This way of doing things can sometime force plants to reengineer the shop floor, often from scratch. The goal is to create 'cellular manufacturing units,' whereby you maximize the efficiency of your workers so that they can balance everything they do across the key steps in your processes. All of this gets happens by way of up- and downstream signals."

"All right," Bonhoffer said. "We've got the principles down. What about the waste you mentioned?"

"I'm glad to see you're all still with me," Mulcahy said, and began to write on the whiteboard. "In Lean, there are seven kinds of waste to be eliminated."

SEVEN TYPES OF WASTE IN A PLANT

- OVERPRODUCTION
- TRANSPORTATION
- WAITING
- INVENTORY
- MOTION
- OVER PROCESSING
- DEFECTS

"The first point here," Mulcahy said, "overproduction, is about honing the process so that you're not producing ahead of demand. In short, produce only what is needed, when it's needed. The second, transportation, concerns eliminating unnecessary product movement. If the process doesn't inherently require something to move, it ought not to move. And waiting. The last thing you want is workers sitting around on the line, waiting for product to show up. All processes must be engineered to ensure that when one step is complete the other is ready to go.

"As for inventory, having too little of it can generate obvious pain. But having too much of it can do the same, too. So you must pace your production such that inventories are kept on target. To do this requires that they be constantly monitored. You've got to anticipate any potential variability in your demand, as well as in the mix of products requested by your customer. All of your components, your work-in-progress, and your finished product are considered to be part of your inventory.

"Next on the list is motion. Whereas wasted transportation relates to moving *things* unnecessarily, wasted motion pertains to your people themselves. This means that each department must take precautions to improve local ergonomics, and to make sure that everyone has what they need on hand to do their job. You don't want people stopping what they're doing to run off to a tool shed.

"Now, over-processing. When you don't have the right tool, or the product design generates useless activity, you're working too hard. It's pretty darn simple—all processes must be winnowed down to their essential components. Last on the list are defects. This should be clear to anyone, though frequently it's not. When you create defective products, you've got to inspect and fix them, and that is lost time and money. One of the attractive features in the Japanese system is the way it empowers workers on the floor. Any time they see a bad batch or a quality defect, they can stop production of the entire production line. This is a core element of Lean. Waste no time addressing problems once they've been noted. When you analyze what's wrong and then fix it fast, it doesn't have the chance to become a systemic issue.

"That," Mulcahy said, "is Lean in a nutshell. Of course, there are entire books written on the subject, and we could spend weeks talking about it. I merely wanted to give you guys a good sense of where we're headed."

"All of these techniques can be effective," Bonhoffer said, "and all can be used ineptly. What I hear you saying is that everything starts by turning the lights on and understanding how well you are doing."

"Implementing a program of continuous improvement is healthy," said Mulcahy, "because it explicitly recognizes that the definition of perfection is always evolving. Organizations with continuous improvement programs aren't seduced by the idea of a big bang, some major change that will fix all their problems. Instead, they constantly categorize problems and challenges according to a Pareto analysis, asking themselves how to identify the 20% of the factors that cause 80% of their problems. Then they attack those factors, keep monitoring, and then do it again and again. In my experience this sort of rifle shot approach has a huge impact. Rather than implementing one project for $250,000 that returns $1 million, why not do five smaller improvement projects for $50,000 each that each returns $500,000?"

"So you do think about ROI sometimes," said Moulton.

"I do," Mulcahy said, "but I usually calculate it after the fact. I find the numbers are much bigger, and I know they're right."

Creating a Culture: Celebrate Wins

"At a higher level than continuous improvement is culture, which allows you to adapt your organization and move to new types of business models," Mulcahy said. "This is the soft and fuzzy part of running a plant. Culture is cultivated by communicating the values and expectations the company has for its employees, and is nurtured through shared rewards. In a company with a strong positive culture, everyone knows what they are supposed to do and, more importantly, why. People know this because when someone does something right it is pointed out and celebrated.

"The most vital aspect is a sense of trust. In a positive culture, the management wants to know what the staff is thinking, and the staff knows they want to know. In a positive culture, the efforts to improve things start by asking the operators or the technicians or whoever is close to the problem what they think is happening, and, just as importantly, what would help. Lots of analysis can follow, but in a positive culture the staff is valued and respected. It becomes their responsibility to make suggestions, point out problems, communicate, and raise their hands when they need help. In many ways, younger workers, the so-called digital natives, are more attuned to a positive culture. They expect it. They demand it. They were raised to work collaboratively and expect to be listened to."

"In a negative culture," Bonhoffer said, "people are afraid to speak up, ask questions, or make suggestions."

"Say you have a boiler that you never run above a certain temperature," Mulcahy said. "In a negative culture, nobody asks why. It may be because three plant managers ago there was a dangerous condition, or perhaps the plant manager who wrote that rule blew up a boiler at his previous plant. In a negative culture people know they're not valued. They simply follow orders and go through the motions. It's boring to work in such a culture. Everyone is just waiting for retirement."

"I'd much rather work at a perfect plant," Moulton said.

"Me, too," Mulcahy said. "But there are tremendous implications in a positive culture, especially when you have been steadily moving on all the dimensions that we have just described. Once information is available, walls are broken down, and people have the tools to see what's happening, it changes the way people work. It's like with Wikipedia. That project started with a traditional highly structured content management system and went nowhere. This sort of system was highly controlled and allowed very little freedom. When the wiki was introduced—a way of creating content that was flexible and easily adaptable, and especially easy to use—people used it to create a new set of rules about how to work together, rules that people at the time said would never work—for example, letting anyone change any page."

"It is amazing that Wikipedia really works that way," said Moulton.

"In a plant, the same sort of transformation can happen. Everybody isn't going to able to change anything, but if everybody can *know* everything or at least as much as possible, the culture will change. New forms of collaboration will emerge as needed. Putting in a new layer of technology and networks that make information more accessible is like putting a wiki in a plant. When you can see what's happening everywhere, when information is available and flows back and forth, then a new set of rules takes hold. This new culture can lead to organizational changes where new sorts of groups form. This can lead to new business models. For example, we have the same complex plant equipment in several of our plants at Wolverine. With the right infrastructure in place, we could have our best, most experienced people monitoring that equipment from a remote location to make sure it is running properly and being maintained as it should. If operators in cells can see the inventory levels in real time, farther upstream they can raise alarms earlier. The key to all of this is for the business significance of the information to be recognized as early as possible, possibly in real-time. Finding out that inventory is low is one thing. Understanding that it is low and going to stop a crucial order from going out is quite another."

"So technology and information lead to a culture of collaboration," said Moulton. "As opposed to one of top-down, hierarchical control."

"Exactly, and the more that the technology and information provide information in a business context the better this happens," said Mulcahy. "Let me draw for you what I see as the pattern."

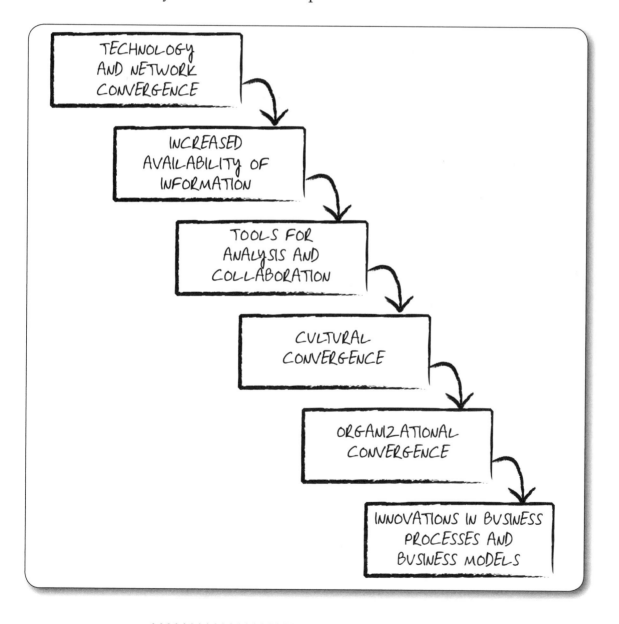

"The pattern I hope we can be a catalyst for at our plants is as follows: Technology and network improvements improve the flow and availability of information," said Mulcahy. "Then we add tools for analysis and collaboration so that people can understand what they are seeing. This should lead, Wikipedia style, to a new culture in which it is okay to ask others for help in solving problems. In some cases I have seen this lead to organizational changes like tighter alignment of maintenance and production. If all goes well, the whole company creates an understanding of the business and you can find new and better ways of working."

"I would love to be a part of that," said Bala.

"Now that you understand this vision at a high level," said Mulcahy, "I want you to go and research each of the areas assigned to you. Come back with specific ideas for how our plants can make progress using the steps I've just outlined to better meet Wolverine's goals."

"Well, guys," Bala said, turning to Moulton and Bonhoffer, "it sounds like we're off to boldly go where no MBA has gone before…"

Part II
Making Progress Toward Perfection

· ·

In Part II, the engineers who are being trained present results of their research on specific areas of manufacturing processes. The chapters in Part II walk through the most important processes in a plant, examining the goals of each process, the inherent challenges, and patterns of success and failure. In each chapter the big picture is covered but then the discussion dives into details and seeks to identify specific ways plants can improve their performance. The chapters start with strategy, planning and coordination, move to execution, asset management, energy management, and quality management. Then, at the end of Part II, broad topics are analyzed such as improving visibility and designing the architecture of a plant.

Chapter Six

Strategy, Coordination, and Planning

Contributing Authors:
C. Edward Bodington, Consultant, Retired
David Katona, SAP
Ian Ryan, SAP
Eric Streed, Bowater, Inc.

Peter Moulton, Joan Bonhoffer, and Krishna Balasubramaniam all sat around the conference room table, swapping travel horror stories over the last few crumbs of donuts. John Mulcahy stood by the whiteboard and cleared his throat for their attention.

"Welcome back, everyone. I know you've been busy traveling to plants, interviewing managers and executives, and reading everything you can get your hands on, in order to help us understand what constitutes the perfect plant," Mulcahy said. "We'll start by stepping back and looking at the big picture—beginning with strategy, coordination, and planning. After all, the plant is just one cog in the wheel of a bigger corporation—or at least it should be if it's going to be successful. Peter is going to fill us in on what he's learned."

Peter stepped up to the front of the room and took the pen from Mulcahy. "Strategy, coordination, and planning are primarily concerned with two big factors. First, the right things must happen at corporate to deliver instructions that the plant can execute. Second, the right information has to come from the plant floor so that long-term plans can be flexible and adaptable to abrupt changes in condition.

"Manufacturing companies tend to get bogged down when there is poor communication between the operating units and sales and operations. Bala and Joan, you'll probably bring up that same theme in your reports. Strategy has a lot to do with long-term goals being articulated in a boiled-down, Reader's Digest series of directives that the plant can use to clearly see those goals.

"Similarly, a plant often views itself as a singular entity. As a result, the plant becomes isolated from the company's overall goals, just as the strategic planners can be isolated from the factory's issues and constraints. This separation is the fundamental condition we have to break through in order to achieve the Perfect Plant at the Strategy and Planning level. To do this, we need to make sure there is a feedback loop throughout the hierarchy—a closed loop—through which up-to-date information is always flowing.

"It's important that we're clear about our terminology. 'Strategy' is the big picture being set at the corporate level—the budget, financial goals, levels of customer satisfaction, and thresholds for product quality. Strategic goals are articulated in terms of quarters and years. 'Planning,' on the other hand, is the scheduling of production runs. Its goals are expressed in months, weeks, days, and hours."

Sales and Operations Planning

"This next concept is the 'secret sauce' of strategy." Moulton turned to the whiteboard and wrote:

> ### S&OP: SALES AND OPERATIONS PLANNING

"At the simplest level, S&OP is about balancing supply and demand. In an ideal plant, which would produce the entirety of a single product, that's a fairly easy proposition. In the real world, however, that's not what we have. Multiple corporations support multiple business lines. Huge portions of manufacturing capability are 'virtualized,' outsourced, or spread across multiple plants and products. And your business units may even be competing for some of the same assets and resources." Moulton sketched a diagram on the whiteboard. "Here's how S&OP fits in with the whole production scheme."

"As you can see," Moulton continued, "there are three segments coming together. In one circle, you have sales and marketing. In another, you have manufacturing operations. In the last is your supply chain. S&OP sits at the point where they all intersect."

"Couldn't you say that the supply chain really drives S&OP, since it runs the network design optimization?" Bonhoffer asked.

"The supply chain," Moulton said, "should be getting feedback from sales and marketing that says, 'We want to explore either changing this product or customer mix, or we want to explore a new market. Run us some models that show the effect on distribution costs.' Manufacturing operations balances things out by providing a clear sense of what's happening at the factory level, and communicates plans to the people there that take all three parts into consideration."

"Maybe we could think of sales and operations planning as the link between strategy and execution," Bala said.

"Exactly," Moulton said. "The various units of the plant—picture them as 'mini-plants'—often compete for resources. S&OP determines the best way to allocate those resources. But it gets complicated, because although some of these plants are measured against the same metrics and KPIs, others use different measurements.

"When a plant is part of a business unit and reports up into that unit, S&OP is a straightforward proposition. If so, the plant is measured for its productivity, but not necessarily for its profit. It may be measured on throughput or operating efficiency."

"In which case," Mulcahy said, "you simply want to run the plant to the limit of its capacity and safety, and throw as much material through the line as possible."

"A 'Rough-Cut' view of S&OP says, 'Show me all the supply capacity that I have, and show me all the demand requirements,'" Moulton said. "When the answer arrives, the 'Rough Cut' asks, 'Do I have the capacity, in aggregate, to provide all this, and if not, where is the shortfall?' Your initial view, on the other hand, says, 'This is all the demand that sales is telling me for all of the products for all of the markets. Here is all the production I have available to produce all the products that are available.'

"In markets where you have multiple sites and scheduled maintenance windows to deal with, the sales and operations process has to be well organized. You project forward, looking very tightly at the next 90 days even as you try to provide a rolling forecast for the next 18 months that includes all of your planned maintenance, outages, or any other promotions that might come in."

"People are looking at the targets," Bonhoffer said. "They're saying, 'Yes, we're planning this promotion campaign from a sales standpoint, and we're predicting this sort of uptick.'"

"Or they're saying, 'Here's the seasonality of this market for this product in this particular sector,'" Bala said.

"Or, 'there will be a major outage, or we need to rebuild in this plant at this point in time,'" Mulcahy said.

"Exactly," Moulton said. "All of these points should be on that 18-month calendar. And if anything changes, it should be adjusted. Ideally, by the third week of every month, you have locked down your production schedule for the next month."

"Does the plan typically stay locked throughout the month?" Bonhoffer asked.

"It does," Moulton said. "However, since supply and demand never stays locked, S&OP's plan needs to reflect the locked-down targets, which consider all of their commitments and accountabilities. It also needs to reflect each target's activities. If the world never changed, you'd only need sales, marketing, and manufacturing. You'd simply balance them once and run the model forever. But that's not the reality in a competitive marketplace. To stay on top, you've got to engage a constant process of monitoring and adjusting. You have to watch distribution costs, market share, foreign exchange rates, and so forth. If the data says you should do something different in a week or a month, you have to be flexible enough to make the required changes."

"It sounds to me," Bala said, "as if a well-organized operation will have tight 90-day and 18-month cycles in which planned maintenance, outages, seasonal market changes, and other promotions are coming in. That way, targets can be set and goals met."

"Meanwhile," Moulton said, "sales and operations look at the balance of supply and demand each week and make the needed adjustments."

"Who makes sure this happens?" Bonhoffer asked. "How do meetings run? What's the hierarchy?"

"It's not the same everywhere," Moulton said. "But, generally, on the third week of each month, the chairman, CEO, and business unit leaders come together and set the plan for the next month. At the same time, they look forward three months. That meeting enables the planning department to execute against the sales and operations plan that is aligned to corporate strategy."

"Even if the biggest head honchos in the organization are not at the meeting each month," Mulcahy said, "they always want to know what happened and what was decided. That raises the bar of accountability and guarantees the information will be collected and shared."

"Who are the specific people that would attend this meeting?" Bala asked.

"The CEO, the CFO, the executive VP of manufacturing operations, and the head of sales," Moulton said. "If the company is divided by business units, the heads of each will be there as well.

"In addition, with the last meeting held two or three days ahead of the executive-level meeting, there is another meeting every week, where the S&OP director meets with the production planners and delegates from the business units or authoritative functions."

"These are the meetings," Mulcahy said, "where corporate sets out its financial goals for the plant. Depending on the goals, the managers might fight back to make them realistic and reachable."

"I imagine it can be a bit of a struggle," Bonhoffer said, "between corporate's idealistic dreams of profitability, and operations doling out heavy doses of reality regarding plant capacity."

"Somewhere between these two points of view," Moulton said, "live the real possibilities for what can be achieved. Once they figure it out, the production planners disperse the results to the plant managers. The individual plant production plans must then be aligned with the sales and operations plan so that the sum of the parts equals the whole, asset by asset. Usually, the plant manager reports up one level to an executive who has been part of the weekly sales and operations meeting.

"The S&OP planner's main concern is to balance operations so that the corporation makes the most profit. That means you don't plan more sales than you have production capability, unless there is inventory that must be sold."

"So the monthly executive meeting," Bonhoffer said, "is basically a 'management-by-exception' affair to get a synopsis of the prior month and ensure that everything is on track for the next three-month period, right? And the weekly meeting is where more fine-grain adjustments are made, brokering the relationship between the realities at the plant level and the long-range planning at the executive level."

"You've got it," Moulton said. "This mid-tier S&OP group is also responsible for making sure all customers are informed about changes in product flow. Remember, as well, that since the plan sets the expectation for production volume by product and asset, it also is a predictor of what raw materials will be required for each location. This is why S&OP is a valuable tool for the upstream supply chain partners, the vendors, and the suppliers, too."

"What if a decision can't wait until the executive meeting?" Bala asked.

"The director of the S&OP meeting may need to inform his superior of the events that have taken place, and the subsequent recommendations. The director will then request that a decision be made immediately with the promise that a report will be ready at the next meeting. That way, he won't lose any time. We call this the 'closed loop.' The S&OP meeting is the lynchpin that holds that loop together."

The Closed Loop

"The closed loop," Moulton said, "is about connecting the dots—and in this case, connecting them frequently. In its simplest form, the loop describes the relationship between supply and demand. You only need to add a few points to it—sales, strategy, planning, operations, and distribution—to see the interdependence of these elements."

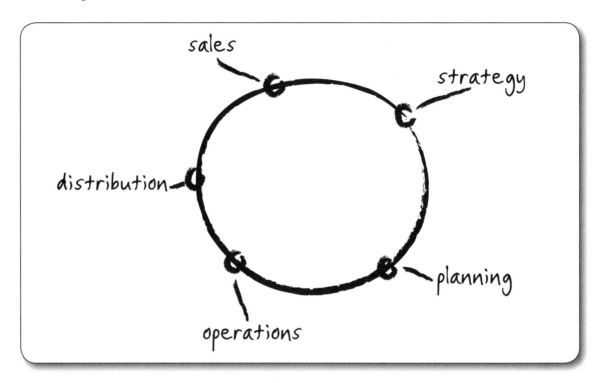

"When the loop is tracked weekly," Bonhoffer said, "people don't have to wait for financials at month's end to see whether their department or business unit is on track."

"And if they're not getting the information in real time," Moulton said, "they're getting a close approximation. This is important for several reasons. Speed and agility builds accountability. No one has an excuse for failing to stay on task. At the very least, they know they're missing goals. Plus, because the closed-loop assesses capacity at every level—upgrades, outages, and availability of raw materials—it also shortens the timeframe in which any shortfalls may be detected and rectified. The supply-demand loop is expected to be closed immediately. That way, no one can wait until the end of the quarter to say, 'I didn't realize we were missing the mark. I didn't have the data until last week.'"

"Based on some of the plants I've run," Mulcahy said, "that sounds borderline revolutionary."

"The closed loop model," Moulton said, "is a real culture-changer. It starts at the level of the CEO, who can see evidence that there is movement underway to meet expectations—whether that is efficiency, throughput, meeting demand, or utilizing supply. Moreover, managers across the enterprise can see how close they are to meeting goals.

"The closed loop seals previous holes in the planning, strategy, and execution processes, even as it takes care of those between the corporate, supply chain, and operations relationships. It's a very important and powerful step toward smoothly integrating disjointed departments and functions. For example, if production skews low, then sales will get on the phone and communicate with customers. Likewise, if production is skewing high, sales can adjust their efforts and promotions."

"Sounds ideal," Bonhoffer said. "Happens all the time, right?"

"Not really," Moulton said. "The S&OP concept has been around for more than 20 years. The statistics I've come across, however, say that despite this, only 65% of companies actually have a working S&OP process. Among those that do, virtually all of them have been doing it for less than five years."

The Fast Loop and the Slow Loop

"In addition to the closed loop," Moulton said, "there is a slow loop and a fast loop. The slow loop, which is separate and seemingly disconnected from the fast loop, entails corporate's long-term planning vision for revenue or cost projections. This loop typically forecasts events 6, 12, or 18 months out. The fast loop involves the day-to-day execution of those plans—the functions of operations, maintenance, supply sources, and labor issues, plus external factors like supply of raw materials and interference by government or community agencies. The big players here are the operations and maintenance managers."

"The slow loop," Bonhoffer said, "sounds like a vision of perfection, while the fast loop gives us a daily dose of reality—where you deal with the issues and problems that can develop as a result of your processes."

"Yes, and as you can imagine," Moulton said, "tension arises where they overlap. Plant operations are in a constant struggle to assess and meet the needs of the targets handed down from corporate. The struggle itself is a function of matters that affect capacity and output, such as maintenance issues, raw material supply changes, and unexpected emergencies."

"This presents a difficult situation," Mulcahy said. "The two loops are separate but not disconnected, as it seems at first. The space between them is at times quite blurry, more of a continuum of planning and execution."

"Is there a way, then," Bala asked, "to clear the air between these loops, between planning and execution?"

"Tools, such as software programs like those we discussed, do help both loops resolve their difficulties," Moulton said. "What they require in order to operate at peak performance, however, is a single, standardized platform. Each loop needs to see what the other is doing. Each needs to know what pressures and issues the other is responding to. And both need to know which goals are being met and why. Fast loop and slow loop, operations and corporate, as John just said, are not really discrete functions. In fact, a well-oiled plant, if you will, has the infrastructure to ensure that doesn't happen.

"For example, in a perfect plant, all operations in the fast loop will be recorded in a log that is sent to the slow loop for examination every three or six months. This accomplishes two purposes. The first concerns the annual planning process—information from the operational log is used by corporate to create forthcoming quarterly or annual schedules and goals. Secondly, data from the log also enables corporate to adjust the planning parameters—production rates or yields as capital projects, for example, can be activated. The same goes for production and maintenance scheduling. I would also point out that in this instance, operations— the fast loop—drives corporate—the slow loop.

"That must generate further tension in the fast loop," Bonhoffer said. "How is it negotiated?"

"Production is highly dependent on maintenance," Moulton said. "When production goals come down from corporate, operations must determine what capacity rate is needed to meet those goals. This involves collaborating with maintenance to guarantee the equipment is fit. To do this, planners and managers generate Microsoft Excel or Project spreadsheets to create the schedule of updates, repairs, and maintenance that is needed for production to meet its goals."

"Of course these are all merely preventative measures," Bonhoffer said. "An infinite number of maintenance issues are sure to arise."

"How is it possible to plan for unexpected breakdowns," Bala asked, "or, God forbid, a power outage?"

"Unfortunately," Moulton said, "there isn't a great answer. Ordinarily, there's a balance between the level of risk at which you operate and the average yearly production. Production doesn't want to turn their equipment over to maintenance because they've got targets to meet. And maintenance complains that they can't get access to perform the work to keep everything in order. Both sides have a somewhat myopic view of these concerns. Maintenance bases its decisions and schedules primarily on reliability levels. Production focuses strictly on output. Optimal solutions typically factor in both drivers simultaneously. The chief obstacle to success resides in the inability of each side to access the other's performance index on demand."

The Broken Loop

"Now I'd like to talk about a problem," Moulton said, "that is both the most common and the most unfortunate—the broken loop. In many companies, planners are off in a corner doing what they do best, planning. In some cases, they are so isolated that they don't even show the plan to the people running the plants."

"What?" said Bala.

"They're afraid it won't be accepted," Moulton said. "In this worst-case scenario, there isn't any real feedback from the plant itself to help the planners do a better job. In other cases, it's a little better—a third-party group analyzes the plant's performance and then reports to the planners. The problem here is that they do so a month later, when it's frequently too late to do anything with their data."

"That's absurd," Bonhoffer said. "How could anyone on the floor possibly understand what they're supposed to do?"

"Although operations is given specifications," Moulton said, "it's usually in a highly condensed form, a mere synopsis of the big-picture goals."

"In other words," Bala said, "operations doesn't understand because the information they're given is both incomplete and inaccurate."

"Yes," Moulton said, "and the people on the floor know it. Sometimes the plan's modeling is so bad that operations simply refuses to follow it."

"That's what happens," Mulcahy said, "when you're handed an order that says, 'We need a million widgets by Wednesday,' but have no idea why, or what is needed to make it happen."

"This is the broken loop," Moulton said. "Someone from strategy academically calculates how much raw material is needed to manufacture a given quantity of product. They send it to operations, expecting them to find a way to make it happen."

"At that point, operations is shooting in the dark, using tribal knowledge," Bonhoffer said.

"This is terrible," Bala said. "Tell me there is a software solution buried in there somewhere!"

Process Control and Planning Software

"Not to worry, Bala," Moulton said. "There is a solution. But it's not an instant fix, nor is it limited to software. Two core pieces of the latter are needed to create the ideal closed loop—the process information and planning systems— and each must be tightly integrated with the other.

"Immediate issues on the plant floor make it tough to change the planning system unless the two are linked in real-time. When something breaks on the floor, you must be able to quickly recalibrate the plan to accommodate the new level of production capacity. Problems like this can't wait until the next weekly or monthly meeting. Without immediate attention, serious money will be lost. The way to create this real-time link is to connect the planning system to a process information system such as Pi."

"Once you do that, how do you reach a stage where your process control information and responsive planning tool are optimally integrated?" Bonhoffer asked.

"It isn't easy," Moulton said. "A lot of advanced process control software requires more real-time data inputs than most plants can muster. A lot, too, depends on the quality of your models. To build them, you've got to see the patterns that your instruments produce and then make sense of them historically. Success often depends on trial and error. Over time, you'll find the right level of instrumentation you need to tune your model."

"What about the payoff?" Mulcahy asked. "Is it worth all that work?"

"Here's an example," Moulton said. "Chevron runs a system that is so responsive and reliable that within a matter of hours after its crude oil has been delivered, all of the recipes to refine it have been adjusted. About 40% of the time these adjustments are immediate and automatic."

"The whole corporation must have signed on without much fuss," Bala said, "if the system helps to generate major profits."

"In the future," Moulton said, "we'll see data collected in real time, with goals and targets adjusted automatically. This is called 'responsive planning.' On a larger scale, responsive planning links the financial output of the plant with expectations for prices and profits against costs. These metrics are then measured against strategy."

"That closes the loop in a very meaningful way," Mulcahy said.

"Just remember," said Moulton, "that all of this is very unlikely to be effective without strong S&OP. It's the go-between that responds to and understands the plant's realities and needs as much as it understands the strategy and vision of corporate."

Strategy and Execution in Process Industries

"It's worth spending some time discussing how strategy and planning are executed in process industries," Moulton said. "They tend to be much more unpredictable than discrete industries, whose raw materials are essentially components made by other manufacturers. In discrete industries, your primary concern lies in making sure that your supply chain provides you with the material you need at the rate you need it. Your variability changes with the supply. In process industries, on the other hand, uncertainty arises in both the quantity and quality of your supply, since you usually need it in several varieties.

"Take the example of a large refiner. Typically, it works with 15 to 20 different crudes per month, none of whose supply levels are consistent. You can't just say, 'We'll do what we did last month,' because each month is different. Success depends upon the individual process operation. With a refinery, you can ramp production down so that it won't exceed any maximums on furnace temperatures or run too close to safety limits. Doing this, though, lowers profitability. That's why the most profitable plants run their equipment to the limits."

"They have to drive everything like a sports car in commercials," Bala said. "You know, with a professional driver on a closed course. To negotiate traffic like most people, wasting fuel switching lanes, accelerating, and braking, is to lose the race."

"And to run at peak performance," said Moulton, "all your instrumentation has to be very accurate. The feedback loop has to be tight, too, otherwise, you're always in danger of an accident or seriously underperforming. But sophisticated technology isn't the only factor for success. You need an expert driver, as well. In our case, that driver is the collective group consciousness that acts in a prudently aggressive way based on information derived from its technology.

"For instance, Chevron closed the loop for their gasoline refineries by examining the octane levels of each batch's finished product. They controlled the levels throughout the batch with a real-time process control system that feeds into their planning model and allows them to calculate 'biases,' or the deviation from the model, very quickly. The model is flexible enough to adjust for each successive batch.

"Planning in a process-type plant requires a model that consumes raw data. It must also understand transformations at the chemical or mixture level well enough to predict and evaluate what emerges from the process. On top of that, you need a way to close the loop so that the economic models are reconciled with it."

"This is very different," Mulcahy said, "from the discrete industries. They reconcile a bunch of separate parts with the final product through the funnel of an economic model that says, 'If I reduce the number of times I bolt the wheel on this car from eight to six, I can save X amount of dollars.'"

"It's not as simple to use the supply-chain model for an industry that relies on commodities," said Moulton. "Their typical economics are expressed by the corporate management as, 'Our optimum is to run this raw material and produce these products. And with that we're going to make a certain gross margin, and, after expenses, a certain cash margin.' Maybe the supply guys on the raw materials side say, 'We can't do that. It'll cost us $0.50 a barrel or a penny a gallon.' Oftentimes, corporate looks at those two optimums and says, 'Which is the sum of the two? If you're going to lose $0.50, but I'm going to make a buck, then let manufacturing do it. The supply or distribution guys will just have to suck it up.'

"This scenario occurs at many oil companies in a centralized planning and economics group, with relatively senior people, who are often called supply chain pilots. They look at those economics continuously to ensure that the different parts of the chain are using the same information."

Strategy KPIs and Responsible Parties
"So how does all of this play out in terms of the KPIs?" Mulcahy asked.

"I look at it from the perspective of the EVP of manufacturing," Moulton said, "His first responsibility is to operational safety. Environmentally safe storage is second. Reliability is third. Then comes profitability, and then product quality.

"As for KPIs," Moulton said, and began to write on the whiteboard, "the most important one in the context of coordinating strategy in the plant is return on capital employed, or ROCE. It's calculated like this."

$$ROCE = \frac{\text{Pretax operating profit}}{\text{Capital employed}} = \frac{EBIT}{\text{Total assets} - \text{Current liabilities}}$$

"Other than ROCE, there's your gross margin—that's revenues minus raw materials. Gross margin is a big one in refineries. Because of the way crude oils vary, there is a 10:1 ratio between the impact of cutting raw material costs versus other cost-cutting moves. This is why raw material inputs are analyzed by whole teams of people. Watching the commodities markets, for instance, is huge in this area. Analysts will reach conclusions like, 'We'll buy the crude at $1.00 a barrel less than we paid last quarter, and although we can produce $0.25 less of a certain quality gasoline, which will incur $0.25 more operating cost, we should still do so—at the end of the day, we save $0.50 per barrel.'"

"And how frequently does that happen?" Bonhoffer asked.

"Depending on the supply chain," Moulton said, "and how your raw material is delivered, it can happen as frequently as every two to four weeks. If the refinery's information is up-to-the-minute, and it has multiple manufacturing and distribution channels through which to redirect the raw materials, it can optimize hour by hour. The very best companies are constantly evaluating gross versus net margin. Most, however, don't have the ability to access real-time data."

"Are there any other KPIs we need to know about?" Mulcahy asked.

"Beyond gross margin and ROCE," Moulton said, "it's tough to generalize across all process industries. There is, however, one more capability to consider regarding general profitability, and that's 'percent of optimum captured.' It describes the variance between your real numbers and idealized goals."

"And your ideal," Bonhoffer said, "is to have all raw materials on hand while running at full capacity with no outages or safety concerns. That way, you can know the exact amount and quality of product you will produce."

"Once you've established that ideal," Moulton said, "you can weigh it against your actual constraints, such as a major supplier's lack of a certain variety of crude or the cost of maintaining or replacing a piece of aging equipment."

"A minute ago," Bala said, "you noted that the EVP of manufacturing's first concern was to operational safety. What are the KPIs there?"

"There are both leading and lagging safety KPIs," Moulton said. "The lagging statistics concern the frequency and severity of accidents. Frequency is measured by number of incidences of each cut or bruise, for instance, and severity covers whether someone got a bandage or an amputation. These are reported to OSHA at the end of each month.

"A leading KPI is behavioral safety, which pertains to monitoring processes as a means of identifying unsafe practices. The goal is greater accident prevention. It takes a bit more manpower, but it beats a poor safety record and OSHA citations. The plant assigns people to report the number of safe and unsafe acts they find. When they locate breaches in protocol, the details are entered in a safety log and the offenders are brought in for training."

"What about the manufacturing EVPs themselves?" Bonhoffer asked. "They give all the orders, but how are they evaluated?"

"Over the year," Moulton said, "they are judged mainly on deltas, which are changes in statistics or ratios. These include improvement of profitability, accident rates, environmental footprint, and the like."

'Rolling Down' and 'Rolling Up': The Tug-of-War between Corporate and Operations

"KPIs," Moulton said, "create serious tension between corporate and operations. Obviously, a lot rides on the two finding peaceful solutions to their differences. For example, each side has its own idea of planned versus unplanned maintenance. If a top manager says something like, 'You can expect some shutdowns, but the rest is totally unpredictable,' there is a problem. He should tell you that the plant tracks the usage, historic maintenance schedules, and breakdowns and slowdowns of each piece of equipment. More, he should know how those histories dictate what the plant as a whole expects from its equipment. There should be precise, data-based predictions about the overall health of operations for the coming months, and everyone from the plant to the top of corporate should clearly understand them."

"No doubt the goal is to keep production steady," Bonhoffer said, "in spite of any planned or unplanned maintenance activities."

"Many factors determine whether that happens," Moulton said. "Other important KPIs include financials, human resources, and transportation. Do you have enough maintenance technicians to sufficiently handle a breakdown? If not, do you have sufficient financial resources to hire more people? If maintenance interrupts production, can you adjust transportation or inventory to accommodate the ensuing production changes? Maintenance issues influence every level of the company. The relevant negotiations are far from trivial."

"What kind of information does the plant manager need to provide the EVP?" asked Mulcahy.

"The EVP," Moulton said, "requests information from the plant manager through a 'roll-down.' The plant manager 'rolls up' by writing a monthly report that covers each of the company's major KPIs.

"Roll-downs also go from the plant manager to his employees on the floor," Moulton said. "The technical, operations, maintenance, and health and environmental safety managers all send him roll-ups that include the relevant KPIs."

"Am I correct to assume," Bonhoffer asked, "that both absolute and trend numbers are used in these reports?"

"You are," Moulton said. "After all, one month does not make a year."

"What about future directions?" Bala asked. "With all of the instrumentation and integration that we're encouraging, the EVP of manufacturing could be sitting in his office and watching KPIs without having to wait for the roll-up. Is it possible that this becomes a daily or real-time event?"

"No one has been able to make an economic justification for real-time KPI reporting yet," Moulton said. "But that time will probably come, because there are situations where a quick decision can save costly waste. These situations can often test a plant's organizational mettle by showing how significant the human factor really is."

When the Rubber Hits the Road: Decision-Making Based on Strategic Models

"Suppose you have to decide to shut down a line or defer maintenance 30 days," Moulton continued. "The less time it takes for corporate to make a decision, the better off the person making the call in the plant will be. Often, these are seat-of-the-pants, intuitive decisions. For instance, say a pump goes down on New Year's Eve. The plant foreman calls a maintenance guy, who looks at the spare pump's record. If it looks good, he makes an instant decision not to call out a crew that he knows will cost triple time. If he can't make that decision, it rolls up one level, and it keeps on rolling up until someone finds the economics that will enable a good decision. Absent the data, the plant manager will go to the floor and say, 'Damn it, you keep this place running, whatever it costs.' He knows what his risk-reward is. He's going to get an 'Atta boy' if he gets the thing fixed that night, regardless if it costs him $10,000 to call out guys from the party. He also knows that if it stays broken, he's going to get canned."

"But there's got to be an alternate approach, one that's a bit more sane," Bala said.

"The alternative is arming yourself with more facts and figures," Moulton said. "The shift foreman needs to know, for instance, that every time he loses capacity because of an ailing pump, it's going to cost $10.00 a barrel. Therefore, he always needs to know the condition of his spare pump. If he's not willing to risk that $10-a-barrel shutdown, he also needs to know it's only going to cost $3,000 to call out the repair crew to make things right. In a more sophisticated plant, better data enables you to reach the same decision with greater confidence. You know that your mean-time-between-failure for this kind of pump is three years. This pump is only a year old, so there's no reason to panic."

Best Questions

"Let's now take a look at our best questions," Moulton said. "Assuming you have an hour to walk into a plant and fire away at anyone, here's a list of questions to ask to get a good sense of how well their strategy and planning are coordinated with the realities of the plant. The answers provided by managers and executives at a plant should indicate how well the strategy, coordination, and planning are working together."

Moulton wrote on the board:

> ## BEST QUESTIONS:
>
> **1** Is this plant run as part of an overall supply chain?

"Do you make what you sell," Moulton said, "or do you sell what you make? Are you the original manufacturer, like an auto-maker, or are you reconstituting a commodity, with a market on either side of the plant? Refining would be a good example of the latter. Generally, this would be a question to ask senior management before you went down to the floor. It helps determine whether you're looking at a discrete factory or a process factory."

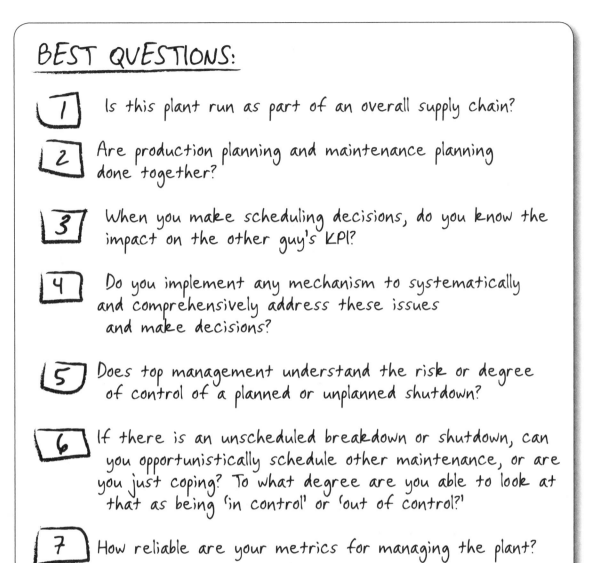

BEST QUESTIONS:

1. Is this plant run as part of an overall supply chain?

2. Are production planning and maintenance planning done together?

3. When you make scheduling decisions, do you know the impact on the other guy's KPI?

4. Do you implement any mechanism to systematically and comprehensively address these issues and make decisions?

5. Does top management understand the risk or degree of control of a planned or unplanned shutdown?

6. If there is an unscheduled breakdown or shutdown, can you opportunistically schedule other maintenance, or are you just coping? To what degree are you able to look at that as being 'in control' or 'out of control?'

7. How reliable are your metrics for managing the plant?

"I have a question about number six," Mulcahy said. "What sort of answer might suggest that you need to contend with certain risks in the way you run the plant?"

"The worst answer is a blank stare," Moulton said. "The best answer would be that they'd established an acceptable level of risk and know exactly what the plant can tolerate—say, an 8% risk of breakdown. For example, they might have spreadsheets and hard data and some concrete information on which they can base an estimate. That's definitely better than nothing. If they've been running a production environment and gathering data about how long things will run for before they need to be shut down and repaired— a.k.a. preventative maintenance—they'll be able to provide an estimate of the failure-free interval and an assessment of a guaranteed failure point. Somewhere between the guaranteed failure point and the failure-free interval there's a curve that starts to change. As you cruise through the failure-free interval, your risk starts to increase.

"In other words, if you had 24 hours between the failure-free interval and the guaranteed failure point, then when you're at 12 hours over the failure-free interval is your risk of a breakdown now at 50%? Maybe, maybe not. It depends on the piece of equipment. But if you can assess the amount of risk in that little interval, and then add up the risk over all the pieces of equipment, you can get an assessment of the overall risk in the plant."

"OK, so the overall risk is the average risk of all the equipment in the whole plant. That is easy," Bala said. "In sum: the more data you have, the better decisions you can make."

"I have more best questions," Moulton said, returning to the board.

> ## MORE BEST QUESTIONS:
>
> **8** Does the plant compare its planning program prediction with what's actually happening in the plant?
>
> **9** Do you know what S&OP is?

"I want to tell you a story about question number nine," Moulton said. "As you know, I am an advocate of S&OP, which is why I went to a seminar on strategy and vision as preparation for giving this presentation. The presenter asked the room, 'How many of you have heard of S&OP?' Amazingly, only 50% of the participants raised their hands. Then the presenter asked, 'How many of you have a defined S&OP process?' Guess how many people raised their hands then? Just one! These were sophisticated companies in attendance, too."

 Do you have a visible leader of your supply chain?

"This question was one of many from an article I read," Moulton said. "It asked a number of best questions. Its basic proposition was this: if you can't answer these questions as 'yes,' then you probably are the problem. I suggest you all read it."

 Is there visible support from the executive level?

"How would you know whether the support was visible?" Mulcahy asked.

"You would ask the question more specifically," Moulton said. "'Do my CFO and CEO have visible knowledge and interest in the outcome of that meeting?' This spawns further questions, such as…"

 How well does the meeting reflect reality?

 Can you use the meeting to adjust to either market or operational situations?

 Are the results understood and incorporated into the perfect plant?

"One way to know that the results are not being used productively," Moulton said, "is to ask the manager if he is continuously juggling calls from multiple sales people, production management, and senior management asking whether they need to change grades or insert a given order. If so, there are people who don't understand what the manager is being measured against. There isn't a clear distinction of roles."

 How many of your maintenance decisions are made with good data, tested data, or quality information, and in how many of them do you let the economics do the talking?

"I think we all know the most likely response to this question," Moulton said.

Perfect Plant Playbook

"To close this afternoon," Moulton said, "I'll take you through some quick pointers on how to get started with optimizing strategy, planning, and coordination at the perfect plant. You can make a real dent in a strategically challenged organization armed with little more than a pencil and spiral notebook.

"Let's start with simple supply-demand balancing. It's amazing how much it can enhance your overall understanding of how to improve things. It just gets people thinking in a more collaborative manner and forces the issue.

"And before you worry too much about software, it's critical to account for your plant's S&OP. If nobody seems to know what it is, then either you don't need it, because operations are so simple, or you need it badly. If your planners are creating 90-day targets but you only get a feedback loop from the plant once a month, you need an intermediary enforcer, or group of enforcers and mediators, to ensure that the information flows between the two camps. Without the intermediary, valuable information is just leaking away.

"Suppose you do want to create a responsive, tactical planning system with real-time updates to the process representations in the model. It may involve the scary but necessary step of ditching your current planning tool. A familiar system that's inadequate now will only limit the performance of the integrated system.

"You also need to examine the structure of your process. Before installing any software, you may need to reorganize your people. In fact, if you don't do this first, the stage may be set for a big software failure. Many plants are run from the top-down, where the plan is imposed on schedule and processes. If processes deviate from the plan, the process supervisors or plant managers have to explain why. This results in poorly defined targets for advanced process control systems when it comes time to automate. If you look at strategy from a bottom-up approach, where the plan is tuned to the process, the processes are still subject to targets and specifications. But you can update and re-run the plan as many times as necessary to balance it with the processes. Once you figure out if that works, then you can think about the software you need.

"I'll leave you with 11 critical success factors," Moulton said, and wrote more on the board, "that I cribbed from a lovely book called *Planning, Scheduling and Control Integration in the Process Industries*, by C. Edward Bodington.

"In order to implement a successful integration of planning, scheduling, and control, you need…"

THE CRITICAL SUCCESS FACTORS

✳ A realistic and well-documented business process model and material flow diagram of what you want and expect to achieve, the timing, and the activities and ownership identified

✳ A Process Information System for real time data collection and analysis of process operations that is blueprinted and configured to support the expected business process model.

✳ Data communications networks for easy, standardized transfer of information between elements.

✳ A central, rationalized database for storage and dissemination of all input and results.

✳ Model-based data reconciliation both for the overall plant, and for the individual processes.

✳ Advanced Process Control, including process optimization.
A formal computerized scheduling system to manage process interactions and inventories, to capture and report production and shipments against plan into a form useful to the advanced process control systems.

✳ A responsive tactical planning system with real time updates to the process representations. A plan redeveloped as often as necessary to maintain coordination between customer requirements and the processes.

✳ Expert System applications imbedded in all the other elements to interpret data and results and improve the efficiency of data analysis.

✳ Process models tuned in real time so that planning predictions for current operation agree with actual performance.

✳ An organizational structure that rewards cooperation and teamwork.

"While this advice was gained from experience in the process industries, it's not hard to generalize these lessons," said Moulton.

"It is clear these points come from experience," said Mulcahy. "This was a fascinating session, Peter. Thanks for your effort."

Chapter Seven

Execution in the Perfect Plant

. . . .

Contributing Authors:
Charlie Gifford, 21st Century Manufacturing Solutions, LLC
Stuart Robinson, Cisco Systems, Inc.
Carlos Rojas, Cisco Systems, Inc.
Phanibhushan Sistu, Tata Consultancy Services

"*O*kay, gang," Mulcahy said, "Peter's already filled us in on strategy, and today he will present the second half of his research, how to put some of that strategy into action—he's going to talk about execution in the perfect plant."

Joan and Bala applauded politely as Peter Moulton carried a large stack of notes to the front table and stepped up to the whiteboard. "Thanks, guys. Execution is a big subject, and a poorly defined one, even though it constitutes the chief processes in any manufacturing plant, involving almost everyone in it and one heck of a lot of tasks."

"Bring it on," Bala said.

What Is Execution?

"The line between execution and planning," Moulton said, "is somewhat blurry. The best way to think of the relationship between the two is as a continuum. The more unified they are, the better equipped you'll be to resolve problems when they occur and subsequently execute to plan.

"In the past, planning and execution have been divided. Planning dealt with all of the plants, and sometimes with trading, as well. Execution, on the other hand, simply entailed the plant's implementation strategy. Even though the historical operating approach persists at many plants today, new methods and technology have been developed to help streamline the interaction between these two seemingly exclusive facets.

"The big picture of manufacturing execution is reflected by the model contained in enterprise resource planning software, or ERP. It involves a constant flow of incoming orders, raw materials, energy and information, and people. It also includes the management of inventories and the distribution of products once they leave the plant.

"Conversely," continued Moulton, "overall planning to meet market demand comes from the corporate level to planners at the plants, and then to the shop floor. The trick lies in understanding how to manage the supply chain and provide feedback to ensure that those instructions are feasible.

"It's not easy, but I'll try to define execution such that it applies to both process industries—which convert raw materials into something we can use, such as gasoline or food—and discrete industries—which assemble products like cars and electronics out of individual parts. As John has already illustrated, the pressures are different. Process industries are concerned with preserving optimal circumstances, managing energy, and maintaining equipment, while discrete industries focus largely on managing the supply chain and staying attuned to customer demand.

"Once I explain the difference between execution in the process and discrete industries, I'll talk about the software industry's efforts to make sense of execution. Next, I'll align the automated processes on the plant floor with those in the headquarters office, so that financial goals and planning are coordinated with those of production."

The People and Organization of Execution

"To start the discussion," Moulton said, "I have to give something of a cartoon version of execution, because there are so many exceptions once we delve into the specifics of plant-floor operations in different industries. We'll begin by looking at the relationship between management and production. I want you to imagine two loops: the slow loop and the fast loop."

The Slow Loop and the Fast Loop

"The slow loop relates to the planning side," explained Moulton. "It has a very broad scope, a long time frame, and is made up of the people who establish the desired production output for the company for a year. From that output, they derive a revenue target and a cost target. This is usually a lengthy process that goes through a lot of reviews—every three to six months, at least."

"I assume," Bonhoffer said, "that this group of people would include the vice president of operations at the corporate level, the VP of finance, the chief financial officer, and maybe even the VP of supply chain when this responsibility doesn't fall under the VP of operations."

"The CEO may even be brought in to ensure the targets are appropriate, given expectations in the marketplace," said Moulton. "The CEO might ask, 'What did we produce last year, and what are our shareholders expecting?' or might say, 'Let's take last year's output and boost it by 10 percent.' Of course, production-limited plant operation is only one of many modes—sometimes they may want to increase margin or open up new markets.

"Either way, these people are slow and deliberate. Even though they're setting targets in the fall that won't be put into effect until the succeeding calendar year, those targets can make or break the company.

"Contrast that with the fast loop, the operational execution phase. This is where you run equipment and turn out products. The people here are under a lot of time pressure. Local events can cause sudden transience that must be managed because there are labor disputes, supply chain variations, equipment failures, unexpected maintenance, and so on. The guys in the trenches deal with things on a day-to-day basis, often 24 x 365. Things are constantly changing and they have to manage the response to meet production targets passed to them from the slow loop. For example, production scheduling in the slow loop can translate to inventory management problems—leaving little time or space for optimization—at the fast loop."

"Let me guess," Bala said. "The fast loop people are saying things like, 'You don't know what I go through every day.'"

"There can be a significant gap between the corporate requirements and the plant's ability to meet those targets," Moulton said, "but all high-speed flexibility is at the plant level. It's not so much a one-way street where the plant-operations people don't have any input into corporate targets, but more that a means of continuous feedback is missing between the loops. It's difficult for information from the plant to work its way back up to corporate in the middle of production cycles."

"I can picture," Mulcahy said, "a plant manager telling corporate, 'I know we planned on this target, but equipment problems are going to force us to take a three-week outage as soon as possible. We'll do what we can at the plant, but you should check your orders at the other plants, logistics, and customer support, and perhaps even let the trading desk know that they need to purchase product during that time.'"

"And the question that comes back is, 'What is the new capacity?'" Moulton said. "If you lose one line or 30 percent of the capacity of a unit, does that necessarily mean you will produce 30 percent less product? Maybe, maybe not. This is why the models used for planning in corporate must agree with the models used to make this decision at the plant. But…"

Information Gaps

"I know exactly what you're going to say," Bala said. "The models used for corporate are totally different from the models used for production, and communications barriers prevent the two from updating each other."

"We have a winner!" Moulton said. "The plans coming down from corporate are commonly reviewed by people with a lot of experience and who can quickly determine whether they're realistic. But experienced people eventually retire or leave the company, and when they do, their experience—their 'tribal knowledge'—leaves with them. If your model for the operational capacity of the plant is kept in someone's head, it's not codified, isn't as accessible to others as it should be, and definitely isn't connected to the corporate models.

"So the artifact of manually run autonomous plants manifests as two things: the slow feedback loop between the plant floor and the head office, and the tendency to let the operations people do a lot of the steering and decision-making on their own, which concentrates power in the hands of experienced people, to the exclusion of many other people. This explains some of the reluctance to change."

"Can this go the other way, too?" Bonhoffer asked. "Aren't there market forces at the corporate level that may or may not get communicated to the floor in time to react?"

"Absolutely," Moulton said. "You could get a surge in demand before your plan gets adopted, or an important supplier has trouble meeting targets, and that ripples through to you. Or perhaps there is a new reporting or regulation law. There are both internal and external factors that cause chafing between the slow and fast loops.

"The result is a plan that is wide in scope, but not timely, so it must be renewed with new information on a routine basis, because it will never be based on the actual operating capacity at the time the instructions are transmitted. Generally, there is no common operating model, and often not even a common nomenclature."

Irregular Implementation

"Let me give you an example of how a plan is typically implemented on the floor today," Moulton said. "As a plant manager who oversees production and maintenance people, you're given a target for a specific quantity of product to make over a year. You'll turn to your production people and say, 'Go figure out how to do this. What equipment do you need, and at what capacity will you run that equipment? Will we run at 60% or at 90%?'

"And you will say to your maintenance people, 'Listen to what these guys tell you, because you need ensure the equipment can meet those operating constraints.' If we run at 60% capacity, a piece of equipment may require maintenance every three months, but at 90% capacity it might need maintenance every two months, with an increased level of monitoring.

"Given the constraints on how the plant is going to run, people will typically scurry away to their desks and manually work out how to put a maintenance and production schedule together.

"The maintenance people will look at what equipment they have," Moulton said. "In many plants, this information is available in a maintenance management system or an asset management system, but that system has limited capability to manipulate, run cases, and to test ideas. The data is all over the place. It's in people's heads and on scraps of paper, and often ends up in Excel spreadsheets. Preventative maintenance and operating history are captured in Excel, too, and a schedule for doing future preventative maintenance will be devised. Because of the ease of use and 'ownership' of Excel—which is truly loved at the plant level because users don't have to get IT's permission to use it—this will never cease and may get even more prevalent with the newer version of Excel that handles basic problems. The key is to ensure that the information brought into Excel from other systems gets there automatically and reliably and that you can extract information from Excel and run analytics off it just as easily.

"The production people, meanwhile, are trying to ensure their targets can be met. Though maintenance and production don't collaborate at the management level to produce the coming year's operating schedule, in the plant, they collaborate on a daily basis. Though these two groups have their own schedules, with a fair degree of isolation, they must work together to create the real operating schedule.

"The various spreadsheets, however, are often not well-maintained and are like little artifacts of the people who made them. It's almost impossible to have a shared model organized this way, which is why good communication between the desktop and central systems is essential. How do they ensure there is one version of the truth?

"The scenario I just described, which accounts for the majority of the plants, is not even the worst case. In the worst case there are no electronic records or plans at all."

"In the real world," Mulcahy said, "you're setting yourself up for problems if you only do reactive, fix-it-when-it-breaks maintenance. If the spreadsheets are disconnected, or worse, on paper, it would take a long time to recover, right?"

"I talked to many people who've seen it happen," said Moulton. "You can't get a global view of the operations as a connection of units. Because you can't determine the effects of shutting down only a portion of the line, you can't answer questions such as, 'What is the effect of shutting down the whole line?' or, 'What are the cascade effects, and what customer orders are not met?'"

"That sounds like looking for solutions in the dark with a solar-powered flashlight," Bala said.

The Culture of the Floor

"Now it's time for some tales from the trenches," Moulton said. "As John indicated earlier, the guys on the floor are under a lot of demands for their time, but the sum total of their actions represent most of the adjustments that are done on a daily or hourly basis. Plants cannot run for a day, or even an hour, without intelligent adjustment for disturbances. In this complex dance, the effects of their changes are immediate and obvious.

"Basically, a diverse group on the floor performs all the tasks that have to get done in a day, only one of which is 'meet the requirements of the business plan.' They do this every day, every shift. For everyone to stay motivated, the work has to be challenging and satisfying even for the accomplished operators. This is also a good training ground for new engineers in the plant.

"When you look at all the requirements for an operator, you find an incredible amount of tasks to be executed by a bunch of people with varying skill levels. The operations manager must keep them moving in a direction to meet the goals of the plant safely and efficiently while coping with vacations, sick days, and training.

"As you can imagine," continued Moulton, "headquarters can generate a lot of frustration on the floor, especially when that means learning new software, running surveys, and changing procedures—let alone when a merger or an acquisition occurs. There's a saying that I like: 'The worker works the way the worker wants to work.' When corporate comes in with manufacturing execution system—which I'll get to in detail in a minute—it forces the process to be done a certain way. Well, the operator doesn't want to go through 10 or 15 different screens to do what they already know how to do—they know that a slow response could create a hazardous situation. The operator's standpoint is, 'Don't interfere with my work. Go ahead and collect this data, and enforce the process, but don't make me do anything extra to make it happen.'

"The good systems are built by people that work with the operators and understand their needs. These systems contain manageable information that is vital to the operation and offer tools to make the operators' lives easier. Less helpful systems require operators to input data for the edification and enjoyment of others—these have much higher incidences of missing information and errors. Here's an example of making their lives easier; the operators loved the addition of email to maintenance software; until then, they didn't have a system to help operators and mechanics communicate. The software designers have to keep the needs of the operators in mind and not insult their intelligence."

"All of this brings up the question of organization," Bonhoffer said. "What typically happens in the plant? What's the organizational structure?"

"Picture a pyramid that tapers up to one guy, the CEO, at the top," Moulton said. "As you proceed down each level, there are a few more people, each of whom oversees a team of people below him. The first honcho at the upper reaches of this structure is the plant manager, beneath whom you'll typically find a production manager, an environmental health & safety manager, a maintenance manager, a supply manager, an engineering manager, and the head of HR. Each day, as we learned when John talked about the cast of characters in a plant, they meet first thing at the morning meeting to discuss actions and make decisions about the day ahead."

A Typical Day Executing at the Plant

"So what happens once the morning meeting is over?" Bonhoffer asked. "Does everyone just turn into a robot and do his tasks?"

"There is a lot of repetition for operators on the floor—many tasks have to be done the same way, every day," Moulton said. "But the rest of the staff and management focus more on projects than on routine tasks. Even on the floor, however, there needs to be an organized way to deal with problems. I'll spend more time on that when we get to the playbook at the end of the presentation. For now, I want to take you through a day at the plant.

"We'll start with the production manager, who oversees the shift supervisors. Depending on the plant, there could be from two to four shifts, with one supervisor for each shift per area, and some duties that differ between day and night shifts. The night shift crews run pretty steadily as the temperatures cool and routine activities such as engineering and maintenance cease. The day crew generally has to deal with those issues. The plan is simply one of the many guidelines that the operator sees, but it has a lower priority than alarms that could lead to problems."

"Does the planner figure into the day-to-day planning?" Bonhoffer asked.

"The planner goes back to the office after the meeting," Moulton said. "The plan is communicated and tracked by the shift supervisor, and targets are given to the operators as one of their daily orders. The shift supervisors are often engineers with lots of experience, and one of them might say something like: 'We have to change the reformer from 96 octane to 102 research octane, to provide a high-octane reformate for the premium gasoline.' Or, 'We have to shift our reformer to aromatics production,' or, 'We have to increase charge of the alky plant to use our available olefins from the FCC.' There are always changes created by a change in plan or faults in the equipment. The shift supervisor must also be aware of inventories and other limits external to their area that could affect them.

"Under the operations shift supervisor are the operators, normally union workers. These are the people who actually push the buttons and turn the knobs on the machinery. They actually ensure execution happens and in many industries they've found that tools that provide information or offer flexibility at this level are very valuable. When I was on the floor of one plant, they shared that, in the past, during oil-grade changes, they simply let the additives drain, without turning them off for 15 minutes. But once they were shown what this cost, they changed the procedure to shut off the additives during this time—saving $50,000 per year. That gets back to this whole idea of closing the loop between fast and slow and improving communications."

"So, as he's sitting in the morning meeting, the shift supervisor is thinking about all the things that have to get done," said Mulcahy. "This guy ranks high on the list of People Under the Most Pressure."

"Yep, he's always thinking about the game of Whack-a-Mole he's going to have to play out there," said Moulton.

"So what do the rest of these guys do all day after the morning meeting?" asked Bala.

"The plant manager does a lot of the public relations work for the plant," said Mulcahy, "meeting with local politicians, the EPA, and other external groups. The rest of the time, he fends off headquarters' questions and intrusions as he prepares for his routine meeting with upper management.

"The engineering manager performs long-term engineering upgrades, writes proposals for the same, deals with the justification for the budget proposal—which usually means citing ROI—reports on past projects, and assigns the staff to the requested tasks.

"The maintenance supervisor works with operations to schedule routine maintenance. He also assigns work orders to available mechanics, schedules training for his people, and spends way too much time filling out forms for the ERP maintenance system.

"The quality manager checks customer support requests," continued Mulcahy, "looks for ways to improve quality, reviews customer complaints and, if he works in pharmaceuticals or other industries that follow Good Manufacturing Practice protocols, he conducts audits."

Plant Manager's Execution Worries

"So, while the floor people scramble around with the screens, knobs, and machines, the plant manager sweats bullets upstairs," said Moulton. "Here's what he is sweating about.

"First and foremost, plant managers are concerned about collaboration between the production, quality, environmental, and maintenance groups.

They worry that their plants might be running with a higher than acceptable level of risk, or make a bad product, or that they might get shut down. They worry about a critical piece of equipment breaking and causing a major accident, putting people in jeopardy.

"Plant managers are also concerned, but not necessarily worried, about the opposite situation—running with a much *lower* level of risk, so that the risk of having a breakdown is very small. This happens if the maintenance people are doing too much maintenance. In this sense, all plant operations suffer from this paradox—the love of stability versus the need for efficiency.

"If the maintenance people produce a schedule that satisfies their requirements and gets all the equipment under preventative maintenance in a timely fashion," continued Moulton, "they may actually be performing maintenance too often. Unless they employ a dynamic equipment sensor diagnostics system to monitor and predict mean-times-to-failures from failure modes analysis systems, they have no way of knowing whether they have a good maintenance schedule, in terms of its ability to satisfy the requirements of risk at the plant management level. Since no maintenance person sets foot in an operating plant without permission of the operators, it behooves everyone to make sure this is carefully coordinated. Spreadsheets are good analytical tools but lousy databases.

"Plant managers also worry about resource availability and want to take into account the time of the year for maintenance and preparing for the annual turnaround. Maintenance cannot pick the date, but once it is set, they have to ensure that the maintenance workers with the right skill level are available, that parts are on hand, and that outside resources—such as cranes—are ordered, permitted, and available.

"So, the things that keep a plant manager awake at night are generally concerns about his ability to meet HQ's production targets and cost goals, while running a safe, reliable, and efficient operation, and the likelihood of some event taking place that will cause him to fail. This could be a maintenance-related breakdown, a lack of raw materials, storage or other facilities, or upper management demanding changes to keep the plant economical."

Standards and the MES

"When it comes to shop floor automation, there is a conceptual framework for pervasive computing called MES," Moulton said.

"M-E-S-S?" asked Bala.

"Yes and no," Moulton said. "We call it the MES mess. The original acronym MES stood for Manufacturing Execution Systems. Today, the term itself means different things to different people. To some, an MES is a way of solving a simple problem—for example, an operator instruction or process workflow issue. To others, MES is a comprehensive offering that includes everything from automated work instructions across the production line to real-time information capture supporting highly automated genealogy and tracking. In some cases, MES means a combination of preconfigured packaged applications and customized workflows or composite applications that are specific to a particular type of manufacturing operation or relevant to a particular industry.

"Many of the people I talked to felt that although the term MES has tremendous name recognition, there's an illusion it's some sort of magic bullet—a standardized solution that fits perfectly between ERP and plant floor systems and closes the plant-to-enterprise gap. The reality is that there is no single solution, and the perception of what constitutes an MES varies from industry to industry, from plant to plant, and even from person to person within the same plant.

"The best way to think about MES is from an outside-in point of view," continued Moulton. "Generally speaking, MES is an umbrella term used to describe a host of solutions to execution-related functional problems. These solutions include home grown implementations, custom process and information integrations, and packaged software deployments designed to solve anything from issues related to product genealogy and equipment and labor tracking to inventory and asset management, defect and resolution monitoring, and KPI monitoring and alarming. The industry has worked hard to understand problems related to all these concerns from the inside-out, and have managed to achieve a certain level of mastery between levels of systems in plants, including a variety of standards for communications between those levels. What I'd like to do is look at execution from both angles, starting with

MES as a whole, and then proceeding to each layer of systems in a plant. I will warn you, though, that this discussion will unleash a whole host of acronyms, representing systems that are either a part of MES, presented as MES, or as competition for MES, depending on who you talk to."

"A little acronym soup is the perfect appetizer for lunch," Bala said.

History of MES and ERP

"It's helpful to look at the rise of ERP and MES together, because MES seeks to resolve a lot of the issues on the factory floor that ERP attacks in the office," said Moulton.

"Before ERP systems were introduced, managers went and bought a general ledger, an accounts payable system, a billing system, etcetera, and then stitched all that stuff together. If you were running 50 factories or had 50 different business units, each one had 50 different kinds of systems stitched together. There was 'no push-button close' at the end of the month. Everything was manual. Everything was reentered. That led to lots of errors and was generally unmanageable.

"And then came ERP, whose vendors said, 'We're going to give you a single financial model that can run your entire business.' And for the last 15 years, that's where companies have gravitated. ERP systems provided a way to create master databases and avoid multiple data entry, as well as present a standardized definition of transactions, such as an 'order.'

"Given the heterogeneity of the manufacturing landscape, the more successful MES systems tend to develop in specific industries and encapsulate a lot of domain knowledge and perform specific functions. Since many MES implementations started off as small-scale projects attempting to solve problems specific to a single plant within a specific industry, there still isn't an MES that is truly comparable to an ERP across multiple factories, performing different kinds of processes. Attempts to create a standardized packaged MES solution, basically systems that are a database and a set of configuration tools, have not been very successful. In a way, this is similar to ERP. In the early ERP systems, 90% of the process was custom coding and configuration, but as we learned how to make business processes consistent across facilities, according to accepted practice, this custom work has gone down.

"As ERP systems were developed and implemented," Moulton went on, "the manufacturing portion of the enterprise was really overlooked. Companies spent time implementing ERP and getting a financial model they could manage. Now that this is pretty much done, MES is experiencing a renaissance. Plant managers are looking at the factory and saying, 'In one plant, I have 35 different systems doing traceability, genealogy, quality control and labor management. Across my entire organization, I've got several hundred systems.' These managers lack a single manufacturing model that enforces best practices consistently across product lines, and they're plagued by the plethora of systems. Answering a simple question like 'How are we doing?' requires a project to get all the information, including availability, cost per unit of product, traceability of components, and comparison with targets and industry benchmarks. Now companies are saying, 'It's time to standardize in our plants.'"

"So, is it just a case of people organically realizing they need better tools for the factory floor, by way of comparison?" asked Mulcahy. "What about regulatory pressure?"

"Regulations are the second major reason for acquiring MES (after the bottom line), whether the plant is making toys, tires, or medical devices," said Moulton. "I won't spend too much time on this, because Joan will cover it when she talks about quality management, but I want to touch on the reasons traceability is so important.

"Does everybody remember a few years ago, when we had a severe shortage of flu vaccine? A lot of that had to do with the Chiron plant in the UK being shut down by the British Medicines and Healthcare Products Regulatory Agency because of some non-conforming product in their batch. The regulators said, 'Show me how it got in there.' But they couldn't—there was no record of traceability. The plant was shut down.

"Often in regulated industries, the FDA or its equivalent will look for something called a Device History Record, or DHR, that shows all the materials going into the product as well as how people were trained, and what tools they used. The regulators want to see how they are certifying their own operations. It's a lot easier to keep track if you have an MES.

"This is starting to affect other industries as well—especially those that might face a recall. When you hear that an entire plant output has been recalled, this usually means that they did not have the traceability necessary to find the problem or isolate it to specific lots."

ERP Applied to Manufacturing

"I won't dwell too long on ERP, but it's important to understand its role on the manufacturing floor," Moulton said. "ERP is often used for planning manufacturing at an aggregated level. It manages the list of supplies and keeps track of production needs. In some cases, the manufacturing execution capability that is part of standard ERP offerings is sufficient to run production operations at the line level, without the need for a specialized MES offering. In other cases, a specialized or industry-specific MES is necessary to augment ERP in order to execute on production plans and to provide detailed instructions for how to accomplish them.

"There is an intimate connection between these layers of systems—ERP, MES and the system that houses the real-time data, normally called a Historian.

"Consider the case of a polyethylene supplier," he continued, "who produced their product in five plants in three countries. The product was made in batch reactors—typically three to five running in parallel—and then went to parallel blenders, and then off to a number of silos. Batch cycles are typically 45 minutes, so when a customer order was filled from a silo, there would be material from many different batches and blenders. Associated with each process order was a COA, or certificate of analysis, that showed some composite quality from the material collected for the shipment to the customer. If a customer called with a complaint, this was the prime data that was available to customer service, but if the COA was not enough, the ERP system would not have any information on individual batches. That information was stored in the plant MES computer. Thus, there was a 'drill down' needed to find out if the problem was a single misbehaving reactor or something else. This often would require additional 'drill downs' to the Historian to try and determine what was wrong—maybe a new operator was not following the correct ramp rate for the reactor temperature. All this now has to be reversed. Once the problem is found, they have to investigate which batches were made with this problem and which silo they were sent to and at what time, and then customer service needs to determine who else received material from that faulty reactor or procedure.

"This may sound like space-age stuff, but it's an example from a real installation five years ago."

MES: The ERP of the Plant Floor

"MES was born out of the semiconductor industry. The creation of a semiconductor is an incredibly complex operation, involving communication between 'cells' in the material. Gases and compounds have to be mixed with the proper balance to ultimately create a physical product with many characteristics that have to be tracked and monitored.

"MES became popular in electronics because there are so many components to manage at such a high rate of speed. Because large contract manufacturers create microchips used in everything from radios to pacemakers, it's helpful to know where and when those chips were manufactured and what devices they were placed in, in case anything goes wrong."

"Which never happens," commented Bala, wryly.

"Well, research has shown that these problems are a lot easier to solve if there is an MES providing some kind of traceability," Moulton said. "*Industry Week* did a survey called 'Best Plants.' They found that companies that use MES are more profitable, use less energy, have greater cycle-time reductions, and make better use of assets than those that don't. And ROI is on the order of seven times greater."

Benefits of MES

"I know you skeptical MBAs might need a little more convincing," Moulton said. "Here are a few of the other benefits of MES. First, an MES can help create an audit trail. I've shown why that's important in the medical industry—there is incredible pressure for manufacturers to create them. However, since the MES organizes information from the plants, it makes no sense to add an MES without first upgrading the basic infrastructure that supplies the information. That means upgrading the sensors—which requires new transmitters as needed—modern control equipment—like programmable logic controllers and distributed control systems—and basic real-time data management, through Historians. But you can't stop at the electronics. In other words, don't leave out the tank farm, pipeline stations, blenders, rail loaders, utility divisions, and other parts normally called the 'Balance of Plant' that are often not included in the data management.

"That's an example from process industries. MES applies to other industries, too. I recently heard about a helicopter manufacturer where for every helicopter being assembled there was a 1,000-page book containing the work instructions of how it was to be built. That book started filling up with change orders because there were tooling orders or changes in the requirements. Whole teams of people were assigned to create these books, doing nothing but managing paperwork to make sure they didn't make any mistakes. Eventually that becomes a drag on resources, rendering the plant uncompetitive. This is an area where MES can really help."

Moulton continued, "Then there's data accuracy. The fewer opportunities to reenter information and commit errors, the better. An MES error-proofs your operation by supporting the process information and through its automated links to the Historian, the asset management, quality management, and other systems. The goal of an MES is to limit variability by documenting workflow.

"Another MES capability is that it increases the automation of procedures, which reduces errors and makes your whole operation more efficient. The MES often also provides an integrated visualization, so that you can have increased machine utilization by knowing what's in-process and what can be used on what machines. You can make near real-time decisions as a result.

"MES also does route enforcement, which essentially means ensuring the process is followed the way that it was designed, which helps with throughput—meaning you're manufacturing the most product, the right way, as quickly as possible."

Basic MES types

"I don't want to give the impression that MES is just an application that only has one flavor," said Moulton. "There are at least two major types, and each tends to have sub-types in a given industry.

"The first type I'll call a toolkit. These solutions offer the most flexibility and offer both a quick time-to-value and low cost. Since these toolkits also include manufacturing services, and use a service-oriented architecture (SOA) approach, corporate and plant IT groups can work together with plant personnel to rapidly create composite applications that deliver the precise features and functionality that the organization's production facilities need to run their unique execution environment. These composite applications can be quickly scaled across multiple plants to enable standardization. This approach generally avoids the 'MES as a big bang project' quandary and doesn't require extensive proof cycles or significant budget outlays.

"The second is more of a packaged application. These systems tend to be offered based on the industry type and are designed for a specific purpose, such as traceability or energy management. The packaged apps tend to have customization or enhancement areas where you can design them to run in a specific environment, with an object-based programming interface. They also tend to be industry-specific; you will see MES for food and beverages and for automotive but rarely would you see a packaged MES application that could be used in both.

"We're starting to see organizations using both types of MES applications to get the benefits of industry expertise delivered through packaged applications as well as the rich flexibility offered through manufacturing services and a composition environment."

Structure of MES
"Now, I'll take you through the various functional parts that comprise an MES," said Moulton. "MESA, a trade group that promotes the use of MES systems and seeks to encourage standardization has created the second version of a model explaining the high level structure of MES. Let me draw it up for you."

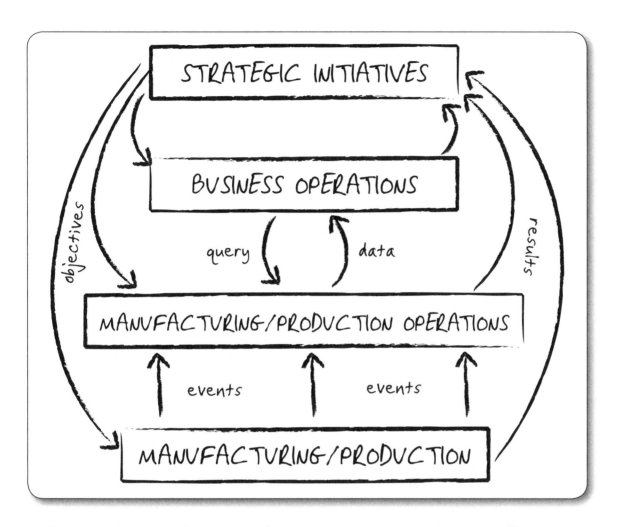

"At the top level are the strategic initiatives of a company, these are efforts to promote Lean, Product Lifecycle Management, the Real Time Enterprise, big picture stuff. This is the level from which the objectives for the rest of the company flow. Then you have business operations, which is the layer at which ERP systems run the company. CRM, supply chain, compliance, all these enterprise-wide sort of initiatives happen at this level. Then you have what we've been writing about in this book, manufacturing and production operations. This is the systems like MES, quality management, asset management, product tracking, process management, and so forth. At the bottom is the actual manufacturing floor. But this is a high level view that is useful to sort out the big picture.

"But when you get down to the architecture of an MES system, here are the moving parts. Usually, at the core, there's a flat, high-speed proprietary database that does all the data collection and then pushes that information into another database that's indexed and made for reporting purposes. The information sources for this database are other systems such as maintenance for work orders, LIMS (Laboratory Information Management Systems) for quality issues, Historian for real-time analytics, and others.

"The MES then presents this information to both a data and a service interface for use by other applications, or to a visualization layer. The data interface could have no human interface or it could be used to drive a Programmable Logic Controller (PLC), which in turn drives a big panel above all the machines. The visualization layer might do the same thing with a web display. These tell you what's going on. The MES might pull information from ERP. For example, the expected equipment, recipe, and bill of materials could come from ERP as a general recipe and be converted by the MES or other systems into the control recipe.

"For all this to work together," Moulton continued, "the MES will give you a plan by creating instructions with a sequence of logical steps. It details what equipment to use and at which points data needs to be collected. If the data is entered into the MES, it should be written back into the Historian to ensure you have a complete record. The MES can do something proactive, such as looking at the viscosity of a substance and telling you that down the line, this material may have to be processed differently than if the viscosity were within its normal limits. At each point, the MES validates that the previous step was performed correctly, while thinking about the next thing on the to-do list. Time is not a factor—even if the first steps happened months ago, the MES will remember: 'For required tests, we know that we can't send this thing out of the door until it's done.' It then enforces the process step that otherwise somebody would have to remember."

"Okay, so how does the MES know all this stuff? How does it enforce the process?" asked Mulcahy.

"The secret sauce that's in the MES is the data model that can associate the plant record, the product record, and the serialization record of all the different components," Moulton said. "Ideally, that data model would be so flexible it could be sliced apart in dozens of different ways and brought back together again, while still maintaining its integrity."

"What are some of the things the data model represents?" asked Bala.

"Well, there's compliance data, the model of the manufacturing process, including the bill of materials, and the work instructions for implementing the process, for starters," said Moulton. "Then you need an industry-specific interface to make it all happen. And as I said, that can range from direct switching controls for machines to interactive 3-D models."

Manufacturing execution

"Can you illustrate a little more about how the MES fits into the overall concept of execution in manufacturing?" Mulcahy asked.

"I can break it into three categories," Moulton said. "There's resource allocation, work instructions, and reporting.

"Resource allocation is the practice of assigning different portions of a workflow to different resources, which could be specific plants, lines, or machines.

"When it comes to work instructions, there are two types: either the work comes to the unit or the unit comes to the work.

"In a 'work comes to the unit' scenario, such as a line, the instructions guide the process, often without much human intervention, from unit to unit. A 'unit comes to the work' scenario is for situations that require manual operation, like manual blending or parts installation in an assembly process. In this case, workers perform dozens of tasks that might be on a work list. Some tasks can be performed in any order while others must be performed in a specific sequence. Some have to be signed and dated. The MES enforces that."

"Okay, let me summarize MES functionality as I understand it," said Bonhoffer. "Part of it is just collecting information about the specific products and sending that information to the Historian. It provides tools to create and maintain work instructions for a particular process step or steps. It then can track the material, in a process industry, or the work-in-progress and end product, in a discrete industry, through these steps and give you traceability. The last part is reporting its information back to other applications, including the ERP system."

"You pretty much nailed it, Joan," said Moulton.

When MES is Overkill

"So an MES solves all the problems in a plant and nobody ever complains about it, right?" said Bala.

"I knew I could count on you to ask the tough questions," said Moulton. "In fact, there are many examples of situations where an MES is a solution looking for a problem and causes angst to those that have to use it—a good example is when the primary function is for data entry and aggregation for the use of others. If you cannot create a collaborative situation in those cases, in which the plant workers benefit from the MES, too, don't expect MES to be well supported in the plant.

"Some processes don't have a model complex enough to require a separate system. In other cases you can get by with a Historian on top of the SCADA—Supervisory Control and Data Acquisition—or DCS systems. All that might be needed is some kind of visualization, a much simpler piece of software that includes some plant dashboards.

"Take something like metal stamping or injection molding. You have a machine stamping out pieces of metal or plastic. The quality of the product can be easily managed by the feed speed of the machine, some certification of raw materials, and those kinds of things. But you don't really need high traceability when you have one ingredient going into a mold and getting shoved out. So you have control equipment that manages and controls the conditions, such as the temperature of the extruder. If it's getting out of whack, you know it's going to screw up the plastic and you'll have to throw it away. It's pretty much a two-step process, so an MES is not required.

"The characteristics that *do* merit an MES include a highly regulated environment, very expensive materials, a complex bill with lots of parts, or a product that requires high levels of configuration, like a pharmaceutical batch plant or bottling plant, where it can be configured so many different ways."

Levels of Plant Automation

"In order to understand how to better optimize the relationships between the people and technology on the shop floor and the people and technology on the top floor, I'll take you through the hierarchy of automation at a plant, starting at the bottom and moving up," said Moulton. "Remember that while these levels are valid as a general description, there may be wide variance in what a company has on its floor, based on whether it is process or discrete, how many levels of details it has to handle, and how distributed its factories are. There are many generations of automation installed in some factories, and all were built to do certain tasks and operate on proprietary standards. The idea of all this stuff working together is still pretty much a dream for most companies—but we'll get to that."

Level 1: Shop-Floor Process Control

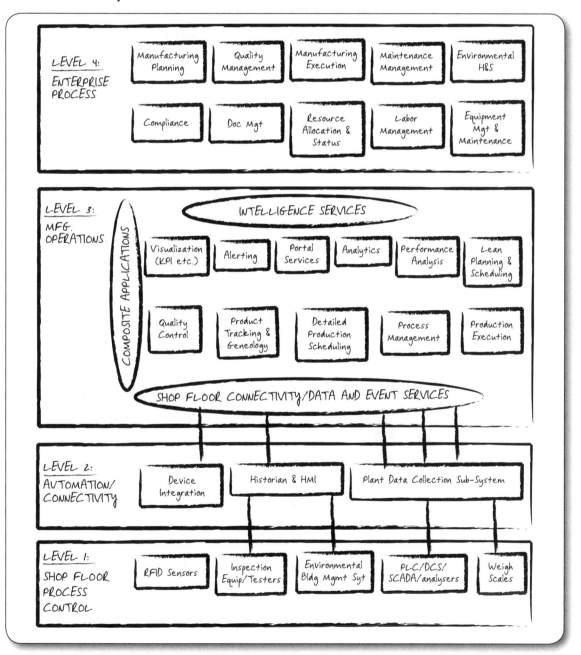

"Think of level one on the shop floor as the rubber hitting the road—where the execution truly has to happen," said Moulton. "This is where machines are doing the work, and the gauges, dials, and other technology provide instructions to the machines and report back the status of those machines.

"Level One includes the software that directly guides machines, including the Programmable Logic Controller (PLC). The PLC has its roots in discrete industries, although the lines between PLC and other process control devices have blurred somewhat. It's a control system that executes instructions and moves things physically. PLCs are fairly simplistic, hardened computer devices that perform simple tasks, like opening and closing valves or regulating temperature, amid extreme temperatures, dust, electrical noise, and other conditions on the factory floor that would damage more sophisticated devices. PLCs measure the number of revolutions, temperature, and pressure, but they aren't terribly sophisticated.

"Also on level one you would find Radio Frequency Identification, or RFID, sensors, which keep track of products and pieces of products moving down the line that are tagged with microchips or micro-antennae. This allows plants to keep track of where material was shipped, or what product it was installed in, or where the product is located in-process.

"Here you also find the Distributed Control Systems (DCS), which tend to appear in continuous or batch-oriented processes such as oil refining, power generation, and steelmaking. They're similar to PLCs, opening and closing valves and turning machines on and off, sometimes based on information collected locally at the source, sometimes in response to information broadcast from elsewhere in the enterprise. They are basically proprietary computers that make sure stuff doesn't blow up.

"Also on level one, you have environmental building management systems, which in an ordinary house or office would be as simple as a thermostat. When you get to big factories, they include things like radiation detectors, temperature gauges, blower fans, fire suppression—the stuff you want to work in case something blows up or is about to blow up."

"I could have used that in my high-school chemistry class," said Bala.

"You're never actually going to allow him near the floor, are you, John?" teased Bonhoffer.

Level 2: Automation/Connectivity

"Level Two is a layer of abstraction above Level One," Moulton continued. "This is the automation and connectivity layer, which abstracts the actual physical plant floor and provides sophisticated ways of dealing with information about the operation of the plant.

"Level two is where data integration devices come in, such as Supervisory Control and Data Acquisition, SCADA, devices. These devices have components that allow them to perform tasks according to a schedule. They don't necessarily operate in real time, whereas the lower grade technology usually functions in real time. Much of the time, a SCADA device does not 'control,' but only reports. A SCADA would typically keep track of a DCS or a system of PLCs.

"Here's a rundown of some of the other terms you will encounter in Level Two: Historians interface with all the controlling and reporting devices on the factory floor and elsewhere in the plant—such as LIMS, quality management systems, utility systems, and the Internet—and gather and sequence-sort information in real time. The Historian is kind of a super-fast, focused database that collects and categorizes information about events on the factory floor in real time and supports high-speed event-based analytics on that data.

"Then there is the Human Machine Interface, or HMI. So once you actually collect this information, you are now able to display it to a human being, typically an operator on the floor. The operator might have a screen, which presents him with a real-time view of what's happening in the plant. He uses the HMI to react to information coming from the Historians and set the Level One equipment to work."

"So, the Historian mostly interfaces with sensors and equipment," said Bonhoffer. "Although it has user interfaces and performs data collection, calculations, aggregations, and visualization, it gets its information unsolicited from its scanner modules and directly from the process control system. The MES layer aggregates and combines the information into forms that are useful for the plant, particularly operations and maintenance."

"The key difference here is that the Historian is physically connected to plant machinery and to sensors and is considered part of the plant's infrastructure while the MES defines how information is best aggregated and organized from the application viewpoint," said Moulton.

Level 3: Manufacturing Operations

"Okay, we're halfway to the top," said Moulton. "Now, in level three, manufacturing operations, the systems have to serve two masters; their users include people HQ tasked with the planning and scheduling of the enterprise as well as workers in the plants, who are trying to work around practical problems to meet those guidelines. The MES is sort of a bridge between them.

"The MES is a means of aggregating the information coming up from all the devices on level one and two. Basically, it batches, organizes, and saves information so that it's intelligible to humans, as opposed to burying the operator under an avalanche of real-time information.

"It won't surprise you to learn that ERP vendors, who have been selling what is essentially financial planning software to the corporate side of manufacturers for a dozen or so years, are seeing demand for better and more information from the plants, as plants try to cope with the demands of faster change and better transparency. Meanwhile, the automation and MES vendors want to increase the value of automation, and thus they need to be more cognizant of the financial value for manufacturing. The result is the need for communication between these systems.

"In the olden days," he continued, "ERP took daily, weekly, or monthly batches of information from level two, making some monthly reports, and perhaps driving some execution and providing transactions back and forth. That means that there have to be communication standards between the corporate and plant-level systems. I'll get to those in a minute.

"One of the things that happens on level three is manufacturing planning. That's essentially the process of deciding which products to manufacture where, at the aggregate level. In some cases you could even come up with a detailed plan, saying, 'Here's my production schedule for the day,' in each plant."

"So this is not just a corporate-level function?" asked Bonhoffer. "It can be very detailed in terms of the plant floor."

"Definitely," said Moulton. "Many of the actions cannot be done at the HQ level because of the time factor, but some of the decisions transcend the plant, such as the allocation of production to the plants for logistic or capability reasons. This will require that the planning function in the plant use the ERP software's Manufacturing Planning capabilities as their starting point. Usually they will use ERP to do global aggregate planning, but they might use other types of software, even spreadsheets, to do detailed scheduling. Once the targets are sent to the plants, much of the flexibility is removed and planning and scheduling at the plant is more about inventory and equipment management than optimization.

"This is also true of other level three functions, such as quality management, as a broad category, which includes quality control and compliance management—which includes documentation. This area would provide the guidance and apparatus for dealing with a recall or a customer complaint, and so fine granularity is needed for drilling down to find the root cause and remediate the problem with minimal time and operational impact. The plant also manages the continuous quality monitoring to support strategies like lean manufacturing.

"And now, once again," Moulton went on, "I'm returning to where the MES fits in all this. A manufacturing execution system might have components for planning, quality management, compliance, resource allocation, labor management, asset management, and maintenance management. But in its purest form, manufacturing execution is really more related to providing information necessary to support work instructions, such as, 'Tell me what I need to do next and who needs to do it.'

"The second part of execution is, 'Now that I've told you what you need to do, or what the machine needs to do, notify me once it's done, and tell me what it's doing now.'

"Resource allocation is on level three and can be considered a component of manufacturing execution, because it's basically helping create the manufacturing plan. And then it allocates and distributes that plan among the resources, which could be plants or machines, and then provides those resources with information, such as schedules and recipes. "

Level 4: Enterprise Process

"Okay, now we're on level four," said Moulton, "The air is thinner up here, where we find the conference room with the big executive chairs and the catered lunch. What happens on level four is enterprise process—typically the domain of the ERP system, but the quality of the decisions here have a wide effect and are only as good as the information that fuels them. That's why people in corporate want greater visibility into, and control over, what happens in the plants. There is an ever-greater realization that much of the 'flexibility' to respond comes after the plan is created and sent to the plants. How you respond can affect the bottom line."

"The distance and time between the slow and fast loops is shrinking," Mulcahy said. "If you're too conservative, you will build inventory; too fast and you'll fail to meet customer demands."

"That's right," said Moulton. "Historically, in an ERP system you looked at things at an aggregated level and seldom on more than a monthly or quarterly basis, with a drill down presenting daily information at best. You used it to create a materials requirements planning, or MRP run, which was then communicated down to the MES for scheduling and implementation. At the end of the day, you'd upload the results from the MES to ERP for number-crunching overnight. Today it might be necessary to see much more information to implement a corporate-level response. When you see a recall that takes back the entire plant output, that's a reflection of low data fidelity, as we will see during the visibility discussion from Bala.

"But the world has changed and now you don't want to have that information purely on a transactional basis. You need current information on demand. You also want to be able to distribute that information to anybody in the company who needs it. You want to be able to support mobility inside and outside of the plant—using PDA devices or laptops equipped with secure Internet access to the applications and let those closer to the action shift resource allocations on the fly. You want to enable communications across all forms of technologies and devices such that they are seamless to the user and don't become the constraint to adjusting manufacturing execution on a real-time basis. That's today's environment—the last decade we worked on enabling the operators and automating processes, and this decade we have to do the same for the rest of the manufacturing operations. For example, a quality control manager should be able to stop the shipment of a defective product to affected customers from the rail yard.

"Communications and digital transmission are collapsing these 'layers,' and the need is arising for MES portals to aggregate process-control information and actions with those from the ERP level.

"If I were a plant manager, and I wanted to see information specifically related to the overall production and the essential elements that affected production, I would want to create a dashboard very easily in order to do that."

"So, today's MES is about connecting ERP and process control, trying to close the loops and open up portals," said Bala.

Standards

"I've taken you through all the levels of automation, and now we need to talk about how to integrate them," said Moulton. "Software has improved our lives in the plant in so many ways. Dangerous jobs have been automated, financial planning is easier than it used to be, and orders arrive electronically. Unfortunately, there are still major gaps.

"For example, we just talked about how incredibly useful the MES is. But if you have multiple factories, or a combination of discrete and process facilities, you may have MES from different software companies. This is particularly likely if you recently acquired other companies or have roped new partners into your supply chain.

"Without standards, each time you bring on a new MES, you have to undertake a separate integration project with your ERP platform, which is more likely to be scalable across multiple business lines. Sometimes there are aspects that don't integrate well, and that means manual reentry of information is required."

"Holy fat fingers, Batman!" said Bala.

"Exactly," said Moulton. "You have the cost of implementation and integration plus a likelihood that you are introducing errors. But if you have standards, you greatly improve your chances of carrying off the operations successfully, both within and outside the plant.

"Okay, so here comes the march of the standards."

OPC: OLE for Process Control

"One of the most useful protocols to come up is OPC, or Object-Linking and Embedding for Process Control," said Moulton. "It was developed to link field devices in process industries to software and hardware controlling those processes. Since 2006, the standard has simply been rebranded OPC and is no longer considered an acronym, to reflect all the additions and improvements that have been added, so that it now facilitates interoperability across levels one, two, and three in a plant in both discrete and process industries."

"So, you would use OPC to connect your ERP system to several different MES as well as to create drill-downs to specific pieces of equipment running on a PLC or DCS?" asked Bonhoffer.

"That's OPC in a nutshell," said Moulton. "It's also important to mention that it's web-services based and thus supports the real-time interactions that plant operators and the head office now require."

MIMOSA

Moulton continued: "Now, OPC is basically the lowest level of data exchange at the plant. It can store and record and transfer information, but it's not really designed to interpret it. That's where more purpose-specific standards come in. One of these is MIMOSA, which stands for Machinery Information Management Open Systems Alliance. MIMOSA provides a layer of intelligence for interpreting that data. The OPC standard will communicate the information 'this machine has now hit 100,000 revolutions' from the PLC, but it does not know what to do with that information. MIMOSA allows you to construct a model of the maintenance characteristics of a piece of equipment, which tells you that this is a maintenance event."

ISA Standards 88 and 95

"We're climbing the stack of standards just like we climbed the automation levels before," quipped Moulton. "We are now getting to the level three and four standards. Next is ISA-88, which was developed to define procedures in the batch and process industries. It dictates how data should be modeled and stored in a system and describes how a recipe should be executed. For example, if you are making paint, and there are four steps, ISA-88 will define those steps and tell you whether it has any sub-steps.

"At a level above that is ISA-95, which is used in both discrete and process industries. It provides an event-driven roadmap for coordinating execution across machines, people, and materials. ISA-95 is set up to characterize the capabilities of a plant and the capacity of a plant to fulfill orders. It breaks manufacturing operations and functions into four activity models. Those models cover maintenance, production, quality, and inventory operations. A maintenance application might have to talk to two or three production applications as well as quality and inventory systems. It sets in motion, coordinates, and communicates between those processes described by ISA-88, OPC, and MIMOSA. ISA-95 lets those conversations happen without custom interfaces, in real time. As we move toward a 'pull' manufacturing model, where customer demand drives delivery and very little is held in inventory, this becomes a critical standard. ISA-95 allows you to perform capacity scheduling, which has been sort of a black art until recently."

OAG

"You will also hear about a standard called OAG, which refers to its originators, the Open Application Group," said Moulton. "I would put this standard at level four, because what it does is allow for semantically consistent modeling of business processes through XML schema. In some areas it overlaps with ISA-95, which is really focused only on manufacturing, but it will help greatly with coordinating multiple business lines that have business processes that ultimately affect manufacturing. For example, connecting a model for auto design with sales, and connecting sales with the assembly line. I think of OAG as primarily existing in the corporate realm and as interlocking and overlapping with ISA-95, but not really competing with it. It's definitely at the highest level and is still under development.

"Ultimately, these standards are working toward an end state where you can model a business process, integrate objects and services together, and execute that model using execution systems that operate on standards-based toolkits, rather than on isolated, vertical enterprise applications that are frozen and non-configurable."

Networking

"Now that I've talked about the machines, applications, and standards for operating those machines and applications, I want to take you on a short walk through networking, the physical configuration of wires and operating systems underneath all of these wonderful standards," said Moulton.

"First, here's an example of the dream state of execution and visibility built on the perfect network: there is a steel production line in France that has two operators and is 40 kilometers long. It's a multibillion-dollar automated plant, and most of the time the controllers have their feet up on the console. That kind of operation is only possible because of integrated, IP-based Ethernet networking.

"But in most plants there is a great deal of human activity, despite all the automation. And the information still has to flow, whether you are attempting end-to-end automation or simply improving safety. Historically, plants have been automated on a piece-by-piece basis, using proprietary systems and high-speed cabling, which in some cases exceeded the speed of the enterprise computing technology that was available at the time. It was purpose-built, and it served its purpose.

"But," continued Moulton, "now that factories are critical pieces of an ever-widening supply chain, those high-speed, closed-loop systems are no longer optimal for running a superior operation. Particularly in the process industries, some places really have machine automation nicked. But the communication with the next level of the enterprise is often missing. If the bottling plant has a batch that goes wrong, they need to be able to notify and propagate that fact up through the organization and out to the entire chain of suppliers and distributors, as quickly as possible. All the functional areas of the company and its supply chain need to talk to each other, as much as you need machines to talk to each other and to their operators. The best way for that to happen is to get a unified IP network coming up from the floor to the enterprise level. Now, Ethernet technology has improved in speed to a point where it is appropriate to deploy on the factory floor as well as across the enterprise."

"So we just rip out and replace all these systems that have been working fine for years?" asked Bala. "The plant manager is not going to want to hear that."

"Ripping out the old systems isn't necessary," said Moulton. "Using the standards I described, IP can be the overlaid transport network on top of these specialized systems. IP packet technology is the carrier for XML, which carries OAG, ISA-95, and all the others. Gateways that speak these standards can link up to the IP network, which supports the enterprise ERP and other business systems, so you can effectively connect a PLC to the CEO. As we've seen previously, the more visibility you have the better. People can make better decisions faster, and because the overlaid IP network is there supporting all of those applications, from ERP to PLC, there is a lot less of logging into five separate applications to report a problem or ask a question. That sort of delay is a big productivity killer and can be minimized.

"The IP implementation doesn't have to be all-encompassing to improve safety and productivity. At the Maher Terminal in Newark, New Jersey, IP telephony allows someone on a telephone in an office to directly connect to a two-way radio on the docks. They didn't have to reinvest in their two-way radios, PBX phone systems, or wireless handheld devices. They merged these capabilities on IP so that a high-level executive could contact a dockhand directly for up-to-the-minute information about a shipment. It's not end-to-end automation— but it *is* end-to-end *in*formation.

"Here's another example," Moulton said. "At Inco Mines in Canada, there is a system for managing airflow to keep the miners breathing. It is a high-cost operation that's obviously critical. But Inco found a way to integrate this system, which uses proprietary controllers, with RFID tags on all of its miners' helmets, so that the system knows when a tunnel is occupied and when it isn't. The system reduces power and airflow when tunnels are unoccupied, which saves a lot of money. Additionally, the supervisors now know where all the miners are all the time, which could be a lifesaver in an emergency. Without IP networking, this would not be possible.

"Once you have functionally linked machines and existing technologies in this way, you can then use IP to develop the next wave of communication, such as video links, mashups, and web conferencing. That would provide new ways for high-level executives and partners along the supply chain to collaborate with people on the floor with deep manufacturing knowledge, as automation continues to improve the day-to-day operations and allows people from all levels and points along the chain to add value to the entire system and to their own jobs."

"This may seem like an obvious question, but what about security?" asked Mulcahy.

"Good point, John," said Moulton. "As you mentioned when you talked to us about processes, if systems running on the floor are IP-based, but are running Windows 95, NT, or even IBM OS/2 as their operating system, they're likely to lack firewalls or virus protection, because they didn't have to when they were installed. But emerging IP security standards now allow you to construct enterprise and factory firewalls, and there are standards, ISA S99, for bridging those firewalls securely.

"Once security is established, you can set up dedicated virtual connections—over the Web, even wirelessly—so that a PLC in one city could run a machine in another. Currently the software needs to be in relatively close proximity to the machine, but the main reason for that is, on the first order, a lack of integration with the IP network, but second, because of security concerns. But those are being overcome, and the benefits are already becoming clear."

KPIs for Execution

"There isn't much of a point in talking about all the capabilities in the world of manufacturing automation software if we don't know the goals, so now's a good time to talk about the key performance indicators (KPIs) for execution," said Moulton.

"Ultimately, at the highest level, you're always comparing the plant's current mode of operation with alternative ways of operating, including shutting down.

"At times, this means that you look at throughput, which is basically the measure of how much stuff you can push across the transom in a given timeframe. This is also known as production output. At other times, such as during a glut, you might want to look at the total cost of delivering to the customer, including logistics, on a plant-by-plant basis, to help with the scheduling for the next month. And in the process industry, you want to measure the utilization of equipment, and the common metric here is OEE, Overall Equipment Effectiveness. Note that plants also continue to operate when there is a glut of product, so that means you need a way of dealing with inventory.

"Much of this is viewed according to its effect on operating income, or the difference between revenues and expenses. There are many applications that must run at the plant level to analyze the operation and create a knowledge base of information. It is not just the aggregation of measured data."

Moulton continued, "One of the factors that influences these decisions is the reliability level of the equipment in a plant, which could be related to the age of the facility or the quality of the maintenance. HQ will consider plant reliability in both production allocation and capital expenditures, and in doing so, will tend to favor the more reliable plants. It falls on the maintenance department to keep the facility at an acceptable level of operation; this will be the driver for their decisions. Good solutions usually are somewhere in the middle. To maintain their focus, these two groups create their own indices, but their goals are common—low cost, high-reliability operation that adheres to the plan produced by HQ.

"It's important to have consistent definitions of reliability between facilities. Because each plant competes for resources, this is an area where error can creep in. For example, if major equipment breaks, but the plant manages to run partial operation with what's left, does that count as downtime? That needs to be defined.

"Plants consist of more than just equipment—a lot of a plant's costs are labor-related, both for operations and maintenance. In order to assess how to produce an order, HQ needs good information on its human resource usage, which includes all costs associated with labor. These costs are most effectively understood if they are compared to industry benchmarks, if available, or between internal plants if there are no industry benchmarks. Regardless, it must be done in a consistent manner.

"One of the KPIs you see often in the fast loop, but which doesn't get fed back into the slow Loop very much, is OEE—Overall Equipment Effectiveness. OEE compares how well your manufacturing equipment is running, versus the conception of how they would run in an ideal plant. This KPI might be used by HQ to make purchasing decisions, or by the plants to look for areas of improvement. The resulting measurement is expressed as the ratio of the actual output of the equipment divided by the maximum possible output of the equipment under ideal conditions.

"OEE takes a holistic view of all the losses that impact equipment performance. That includes the equipment not being available when it's needed, not running at the ideal rate, or not producing first-pass A-1 quality output."

"So, how do you measure it?" asked Bonhoffer.

"The components of OEE are availability, reliability, and speed," said Moulton. "'Availability' means: is equipment up or down, running or not running? It could be idle, running with product, or down because of mechanical problems or because the products that require this equipment are not scheduled for a particular run.

"As to reliability, you don't want the machine to be down for unplanned maintenance, but you do want it shut off if it is not needed, in order to save energy.

"Ideally you are optimizing those three things. If you run it too fast, you could end up scrapping a bunch of product or break the machine, or you just use too much energy. For Wolverine trucks, we found that a 10% overload increases maintenance 50%."

"OEE sounds like an important KPI," said Mulcahy.

"If it's consistent across plants, it is," said Moulton. "It bridges asset management and operations, but it is an analytical method—the results still have to be viewed in a business context in order to support decisions. At the local level, it's been viewed as sort of a 'silver bullet,' because it can quickly identify a lot of different problems, from equipment breakdowns to sloppy quality practices.

"I'll give you an example from oil refining. In refining, you're looking at two big areas—percentage asset and resource utilization and mass and energy balance.

"Asset and resource utilization is critical in refining. Today, refiners run these plants to the hilt all day, every day, with a really narrow margin. You have to know that you're using all your equipment as effectively as possible. Mass and energy balance is basically looking at your raw materials and the finished product—if the gasoline that's going out does not reflect the fullest utilization of what's coming in, you have a problem to fix.

"In the auto industry, the big two KPIs are DMPO and Six Sigma. DPMO is defects per million opportunities. In a highly transactional environment, that's a very common term. In automotive, the requirement is zero DPMO.

"Of course," he continued, "you all know Six Sigma, which is a big part of quality management. I won't steal Joan's thunder, but basically, it's a set of practices developed by Motorola in the 1980s that are intended to eliminate defects, comprising all the quality improvement techniques of the prior decades. Six Sigma sets a standard of 3.4 DPMO, that is 3.4 defects out of every million opportunities. It's a broadly used KPI across industrial as well as office and commercial environments.

"In the electronics industry, you're most interested in achieving the lowest cost of production. Therefore, you are interested in finished-product first-pass yield, and a high rate of on-time delivery, a high rate of changeover, and a very low customization time, because that allows you to build more products faster. NPI, your time from new product introduction to mass production, is important, because your product mix and changeover rate is very, very high.

"The key is that KPIs have to support the decision processes pertinent to specific industries. Most of the costs in process industries, such as refining, are energy-related, but most of the costs in auto manufacturing, and most discrete industries, are labor-related. But it's fair to say, across all industries, that if you are not fully making use of all your assets, including your people, you are probably missing an opportunity to optimize."

Best Questions

"Now that we have a deeper understanding of what it takes to execute in a plant, let me try to infuse you with some questions you'd ask when you hit the plant floor," said Moulton. "I'll give you the general questions first, then some questions you'd ask the plant manager and the quality department.

"First, I'd ask whether the plant folks are calculating OEE, first-pass yield, NPI or some other metric, such as turnaround time. Do you compare that metric to those of your peers in your industry? There is benchmark data available for you to do that. How do you compare your operation with that of your peers in the company and in the industry? Start with public financial data. This won't provide first pass details but will give you some idea when you compare the COGS, or Cost of Goods Sold, ratio to the revenues as compared to yours.

"Then, I'd ask, 'What do the trends look like?' They'll probably come back to you with a figure. They'll say they are at a certain industry-wide level, and they'll think they're doing fine. But don't let them be satisfied with that, because of the probable answer to the next question, which is, 'What is your overall margin out of this factory?'

"Chances are pretty good that they don't have their data collected properly. They think they're running first-pass yield at 97%, and it's actually more like 75%.

"Next, you'd want to ask, 'What do you base your decisions on? What is your decision-support tool? What kind of tools do you use? Are you using a whiteboard? Are you using Excel? What tool do you use when you make decisions?'"

"And is there a right answer to that question?" asked Bonhoffer.

"That depends on the operations," said Moulton. "In some operations, it is okay to have a whiteboard and go in and spend a minute on that. But in most operations today, the complexity is high enough that a whiteboard won't cover it. Many manufacturers use Excel. That works most of the time for decision making on the plant floor, but not so well if used in isolation. It does not, by itself, provide a comprehensive view for management to get a grasp on what's going on.

"Next, I'd want to know whether they were implementing lean manufacturing or Six Sigma, and how they go about doing that. Of course, depending on the answer, there would be more questions to ask on those topics.

"Another thing I'd want to know is, 'Do you get audited by your customers?' or, 'Do you get audited by any regulatory agency?' The answer is usually yes. And if it is, you ask, 'Well, what are the results of those audits? Do you have any compliance issues?' You'll usually get an answer like, 'We have an operator certification issue. We can't prove as a part of the product record that the operator that performed the operation was certified to do the job.' And you ask, 'Why can't you do that? You've got training records, right?'

"'Yeah, we've got training records.'

"'And you've got a time that the operator clocked in and out, right?'

"'Well, yeah,' they answer."

Moulton looked around the room.

"Can anyone think of what the missing factor is?" asked Moulton.

"Maybe it wasn't the same operator the whole time," said Mulcahy.

"Spoken like a true veteran of the factory floor!" said Moulton. "People interchange jobs, and they're not necessarily assigned to a specific position. So there's a gap in the labor record. That's a problem. And even if you have broken an operator's job into defined tasks and identified the training needed to perform those tasks, you can't guarantee that the operator who is performing that task is properly trained. That is, the information is not available in real time. If a head operator is sick, it's not uncommon to bump up the board operator for a shift, and that can happen without any notice at all. Often that's not communicated to management until after the fact, if at all. Complicating this issue is the fact that, at the end of the day, the factory needs to keep running.

"Sometimes there are great opportunities hidden behind the problems you uncover. So a really good question to ask is, 'If there is an unscheduled breakdown, or unscheduled shutdown, can you opportunistically schedule other maintenance tasks? Or are you just coping?'

"And then you follow the answer to that with, 'To what degree are you able to look at that as being in control or being out of control?' Find out from them where they think they should be in terms of variance from the schedule. There is much to be gained from being proactive rather than reactive.

"The next question addresses a common problem, which is a lack of coordination between corporate planning and plant operations: 'Do you make your production plans and your operations plans together or are they separate? Are there two groups sitting in separate offices and making these plans separately and then trying to communicate them with each other?' That would be good to know."

Moulton went on, "When it comes to the plant manager or materials manager, I'd have a few specific questions whose answers would tell me a lot about whether they are doing a good job with traceability.

"I'd say to whoever is in charge of finished goods, 'Can you provide me with a detailed, serialized traceability record of what went into this product?' A lot of times they can. They say, 'Yes, here's the bill of materials, and here's all the products that were tracked.' And then I'd put the question in a different way. I'd pick a component off that product and I'd say, 'Can you show me where this was used? Can you show me every other item this component went into?' Generally that's a little bit more difficult if they don't have an automated system. And that shows gaps in traceability.

"The question that will give you the best indication of a traceability gap is, 'Can you identify the root causes of all your quality defects?' Here's an example that I came across recently. There's a factory that assembles custom cabs for 18-wheeler trucks, the epitome of a discrete process. There's a work instruction that says, 'Here are all the specifics. The customer's ordered specific colors, a certain bed, this particular engine, this seat, and so on.' It's very worker-intensive.

"Now the example breaks in two. So, the fuel tank needs to be attached to the frame with a torque of 95 foot-pounds per square inch. The torque wrench was broken. But they wanted to keep the line moving. So they created a quality-exception note that said, 'This wrench is not torqued to 95 pounds,' and they stuck that note physically on the product.

"At the end of the line, the cab went off to this fix-staging area where all of these issues are identified and people go and fix them all. But the root cause was totally lost. They didn't know the torque wrench was broken. All they knew was, 'it wasn't torqued, so we're going to torque it.'

"This happened for a few weeks, and then somebody got smart and sat down in the QA center and said, 'Why do I keep having to torque these?' And they walked down there and they asked the operator, 'Why do I keep having to do this?' 'Well, the torque wrench is broken.' But no one knew it. Why? Because there was little or no collaboration between operations and quality control! So they were creating a bad product without really getting to the root cause. That's another area that you should look for: gaps in identifying quality issues.

"I'm sure Joan will have some great suggestions for us in the quality department, but when it comes to execution I'd want to know a few things from the quality managers: 'What is your defect rate? What's your scrap rate? And what is your yield percentage on products?' And they'll be able to give it to me, and it might be high. And I'll say, 'Well, how are you collecting it?' They'll answer, and I'll say, 'Do you have any identified gaps in the process?' In other words, 'Do you find a product that's nonconforming at the time that it's nonconforming, or later in the process?' This common gap happens because plants often do not integrate the quality function with the manufacturing function at the same time."

Common Mistakes in Execution

"All right, we're almost at the finish line," said Moulton. "I'm going to show you examples of common mistakes in execution, some of which may be counterintuitive. Then I'll take you through the Perfect Plant Playbook for Improving Execution, which should provide the tools you need to leave the room feeling like you have a grip on what Execution is and how you can make it better.

"Okay, problem number one—too much data."

"I never thought I'd hear you say that," said Bala.

"It's true," said Moulton. "You can actually have too much data to make a good decision. We've all seen the scenario where a plant is promised some kind of technology, like a manufacturing system, which is supposed to resolve the decision-making problem. But that system turns out to be just a big encyclopedia, and the onus for decision-making is still on the people. You don't need a preponderance of information to make the right decision—you need the right information.

"The key to converting this data is twofold—analytics and context—and it is done at all levels. The Historian performs its computations directly on the input stream of data as it happens and its context is the physical model. The MES performs computations either as a result of a request or on a routine, batch basis—such as 'compute the OLAP cube for the month'—and the context is the process or product model. The physical model is much more scalable, it has millions of points, but the process model, such as material balance, and product model, such as bill of materials or traceability, are much more intuitive.

"Number two—you don't really know the operating risk, whether it's too high, low, or at optimum."

Moulton continued, "Number three—and this is a big one—is the tension between production and maintenance. I've alluded to this before, but I want to reinforce it again. The production people don't want to turn the equipment over to the maintenance people, because they've got these targets to meet. This is entirely understandable. If the red light on your dashboard hasn't lit up and said, 'Check your engine,' why would you take your car to the mechanic? You're simply going to continue driving until the light comes on. The maintenance people, on the other hand, complain that they can't get access to perform essential maintenance to keep everything running in perfect working order. It all comes down to not coordinating schedules.

"Last big one—decisions are made without considering the right KPIs, such as looking at overall profit vs. production, when the goal is margins or costs; or looking at the KPIs at the wrong scale, such as those of the individual divisions or units, rather than a comparison across plants of a consistent KPI. You make decisions and see the measures change, but you don't know the impact on the company."

"Okay, Peter, that was great," said Mulcahy. "Now—can you lead us out of the dark? Let's hear that playbook."

Perfect Plant Playbook: How to Improve Execution

"All right, kids, time for the grand conclusion," said Moulton. "I'll give you the Playbook for Execution—a few tips on how you can improve execution in your facility. I'll start with a project-specific example and then make some general statements, since the likelihood is that you guys will be called in when there's already an acknowledgement that the project has to happen.

"It's critical that you understand the business performance metrics you're using," said Moulton. "Suppose you determine you need a detailed traceability record because you're an electronics contract manufacturer. You have 100 lines in your factory with 50 machines on each line, and you're making 340,000 different configurations a day, collecting more than two million transactions in a day. If you don't have any kind of automated traceability, that's going to be kind of difficult. Well, assuming you're going to try to build this automated traceability system, and you want to make the project successful. You have to understand what the traceability requirements are because the requirements themselves indicate the design of the whole data collection mechanism and determine how you configure the data model to collect information in order to provide that traceability record.

"Another thing we'd ask for is your corporate performance metrics. If you're looking at first pass yield, you're looking at OEE. You need to have a clear definition of OEE in your factory. Remember that when it comes to metrics, a lot of people collect them, but it turns out that they're turning up incorrect data. Or they're calculating them incorrectly, or they're not collecting the right data in the first place. So make sure there's a definition of how you intend to calculate performance.

"You'll get into trouble if you install an MES and expect to push 'go' and cause magic to happen. An MES is very granular and event-driven. You can't just say, 'One of the things we want to do is increase first-pass yield.' Well, how are you calculating it, on what products, in what kind of environment, at what level of granularity? The definition of all those things is really important in order to be successful.

"In a lot of cases, companies have the information they need, they just don't necessarily have a good way of collecting and making sense of it," Moulton continued. "So I'd recommend investing in a platform that can automate the access and maintenance of data. That could be a centralized database or central repository for the assets, or it could be a system of 'smart connectors' that link distributed databases that hold the appropriate master data for each division or functional area. This is very important, especially for asset maintenance. So whether you implement a CMMS, computerized maintenance management system—also known as an enterprise asset management system—and you populate that database with information from across the organization, or whether you make that part of your ERP implementation, you implement an asset management application, and the workflow and business processes need to support that. It's very important to do this because you can't begin to make any sense of a comprehensive maintenance strategy unless you have the data. And some organizations don't have the data. Assembling the data for this system is one way to find out what's missing.

"Speaking of data capture—you want to make sure you're formalizing the collection of data that's in people's heads. You don't want to run your company based on information that could disappear when people retire or, even worse, succumb to health problems without warning. Web 2.0 technologies such as wikis and other straightforward, social-networking tools could be put to use in capturing this knowledge.

"Lastly, ensure there's a collaborative approach to production and maintenance scheduling so that a process in place that brings the groups together to work in harmony and aligns their goals at the level of the overall plant, and therefore sets their sights on strategic goals, rather than just their individual departmental goals."

"Peter, that was excellent," said Mulcahy. "Thanks for tackling a tough subject area and making it easier for all of us to understand."

"My pleasure, John," said Moulton. "Class dismissed. Time for recess and lunch."

"You're buying," said Bala, as they all grabbed their gear and filed out of the conference room.

Chapter Eight

Asset Management

Contributing Authors:
HaJo Lockermann, SAP
Terry Wireman, Vesta Partners, LLC

Joan Bonhoffer sat at the head of the conference table, going over her notes and handouts for her upcoming presentation, while Peter Moulton and Krishna Bala drank coffee and quietly compared their progress on the project so far. After a moment, John Mulcahy emerged from his adjoining office, carrying a box of markers and a note pad.

"Last session," Mulcahy said, "Peter gave us an important look at execution. Today Joan will talk us through the ins and outs of asset management." He ceremoniously handed Bonhoffer the box of whiteboard markers, which she accepted with a playfully regal nod of her head.

"My goal, as John defined it," she said, "was to figure out what the experts say about successful asset management in plants and to hear what our own plants have to tell us. After meeting with a multitude of experts and visiting each of the plants, my conclusion is that if we did nothing but focus on asset management this year, we will have done quite well for ourselves. Getting asset management right means that many other things must also be going well."

"So what type of people did you talk to?" asked Mulcahy.

"I started with some top IT analysts, because I felt they could give me a good view of the processes and the big picture. Terry Wireman from Vesta Partners has written several books on asset management and related topics. He provided the big picture. Kristian Steenstrup from Gartner created a hierarchy of maintenance strategies that provides a clear way of seeing and implementing with them. The people I spoke with have talked to hundreds, if not thousands, of companies, so meeting with them was like attending a graduate seminar. At first I couldn't keep up, but I picked up the lingo pretty quickly and then, like any true nerd, I found all of this stuff intriguing."

"I've discovered," Bala said, "that not everyone fully appreciates the IT universe. Wouldn't starting with IT make some people in the plant suspicious?"

"I'm sure we can assume she balanced out that perspective," Moulton said. "Who else was on the list?"

"The asset management vendors were also illuminating," Bonhoffer said. "They've talked to as many or more companies as the analysts, and have had to struggle to make their solutions actually work. I got a fantastic overview of all of the different kinds of data involved in asset management, as well as the way companies are starting to standardize their approaches. This is important. Not only do we need to acquire the right data, but also we must learn how to make sense of it such that it works for us. And once we have used the data to make decisions about what we want to do, we need to consider how we intend to implement it. One of the managers took the idea of asset management in the plant and connected it to this larger concept of enterprise asset management, which changed my perspective slightly.

"After I had spent so much time focusing on software," Bonhoffer said, "it occurred to me that IT can only help us once we understand our processes. To do this, we needed to get inside the heads of people in the plants. We were were able to come up with a list of mistakes to avoid that we can circulate to our plants. My trip through our plants added even more items to this list. For example, implementing centrally mandated systems without enough local input is a common way to overspend. I also found that implementing systems in isolation can be just as much of a problem."

"That doesn't surprise me," Mulcahy said. "Taking a top-down or bottom-up approach is no guarantee of success in an environment as complex as a plant."

What is Asset Management?

"The first thing that confused me about this topic," Bonhoffer said, "is that the term 'asset management' doesn't seem to emphasize one of the main activities of the area, which is maintenance. In the most abstract sense of the word, asset management in a plant is about increasing the return on the money invested in all assets. The definition of assets is basically everything you can physically see when you walk through a plant. Three types of money are involved with this: money used to buy the assets, money spent fixing and maintaining the assets, and money spent running the assets to make products. Tracking all of this in a transaction-based system is corporate's responsibility."

"That's the kind of system," Bala said, "that John would use as EVP of Manufacturing. What about inside the plants?"

"People there," Bonhoffer said, "are more interested in a system that helps them keep everything going and communicates the needs to all five shifts. It's not about ROI, but about scheduling, efficiencies, capturing maintenance histories, and reporting period results. People in the plant need a way to implement advanced strategies that reduce unscheduled downtime. Engineering at corporate needs a way to help ensure that long-term problems are solved. Originally software to support maintenance of equipment was called Computerized Maintenance Management Systems, or CMMS. Later, that name got dropped, and, along with every other asset-related matter, was placed beneath the umbrella of the vague term we use now, 'asset management.'"

"I'm sure there must be an analyst firm to blame," Bala said.

"It's just like the terms 'enterprise' and 'open source,'" Moulton said. "They're used so often, in so many ways, it's hard to know what they mean."

"They reduce language to a level of generality," Bala said, "that borders on meaninglessness."

"True as that may be," Mulcahy said, "we just have to live with the term. Fortunately, everyone knows what it means."

"So if you talk about increasing return on assets as being the goal of asset management," Bonhoffer said, "then the original purchase price is sunk cost. You can increase return, however, by decreasing the money spent to maintain the assets and increasing the money made from using them." Bonhoffer wrote an equation on the whiteboard. "You can draw a map of almost everything to do with asset management starting from this ratio."

$$\frac{\text{Money earned from using the assets} - \text{money spent maintaining the assets}}{\text{Money invested to buy the assets}}$$

RETURN ON ASSETS

"There is a huge amount of play in all these numbers. By making different assumptions, you can distort your ROA. Most companies would have a tough time making this calculation in a defensible way, especially in the plant where some of the data is missing. Another real challenge in this area lies is benchmarking. Take a like-for-like pump exchange, for instance. Whereas one plant may capitalize the entire project, another might capitalize the equipment, but expense the labor. Accurately benchmarking your ROA at different sites requires that a standard be selected. We'll delve into the details of this later."

Cast of Characters

"Everyone at the plant reports to the plant manager," Bonhoffer said, "so ultimately, when something big happens, the plant manager gets involved. But the day-to-day action in asset management centers around the maintenance supervisor. It can also involve the production supervisor, the quality manager, the head of engineering, and whoever is in charge of planning, usually the planning coordinator. One way to look at asset management is as a constant stream of deal making between these five roles."

"If asset management is really about maintenance," Bala said, "what's the conflict?"

"It's primarily about scheduling, and lies between the maintenance supervisor and the production supervisor," Bonhoffer said. "The maintenance supervisor focuses on the equipment. His goals are to perform scheduled maintenance and to avoid unplanned outages due to equipment breakdowns. From time to time he wants to shut down the equipment to maintain or repair it. The maintenance supervisor, as we will learn, uses any number of strategies to figure out when equipment needs maintenance. And, like everyone else, he's also interested in keeping costs as low as possible."

"So the maintenance manager is Mr. Fix It," Moulton said.

"Which would make the production supervisor," Bala said, "Mr. Pedal to the Metal."

"Exactly," Bonhoffer said. "The production supervisor is rewarded for keeping the plant running and getting as much production done as needed to meet the orders. Downtime for maintenance gets in the way of this, and unplanned downtime can be a disaster. That's why it's so important that Mr. Fix It be given information that is timely and accurate enough for him to drive actionable results."

"How do the quality, planning, and engineering roles fit into this?" Bala asked.

"The quality manager," Bonhoffer said, "attempts to make sure the products are created to specifications, since product that is off spec decreases production. Planning is all about figuring out how to create the products needed to fill the orders from corporate. Plans at the plant level have to accommodate windows for maintenance and respond to unplanned downtime. Engineering strives to improve the long-term performance of the plant. This means helping maintenance decide between like-for-like replacements and upgrades. Also, there may be significant engineering required to set up production of new products, especially while working around current production. Engineering is also often tasked with improvement of financial return or quality. I have a good diagram to illustrate the roles, responsibilities, and different values."

"How do these roles end up meshing together?" Bala said.

"This example came up a couple times," Bonhoffer said. "Let's say the planner is told by corporate about a new time-sensitive order. The planner and the production supervisor work out a deal to get the order done, but there's a catch. They have to run the equipment at higher than normal speeds, plus skip a maintenance window. The maintenance manager, of course, could get quite upset by this. Can the equipment make it to the next maintenance window? To find out, he needs to ask the engineering manager about the effect of running the equipment at higher than normal speeds."

"That doesn't sound so bad," Bala said.

"This is absurdly oversimplified," Bonhoffer said. "In the typical plant there are 5,000 to 10,000 assets. Some are in the critical path, like the equipment on the line or cooling pumps. Others, like a light bulb or the air conditioner in the break room, are not as critical. Just being aware of all of this is the first challenge. Then you need to understand how to take care of it all and make sure that your plan allows you to produce what you need. It makes no sense to have beautifully maintained equipment if you aren't making money. You can have perfect equipment, and still get the plant shut down. Depending on the strategy from corporate, and the expected life of the plant, it might make sense to delay maintenance and reduce the working life of some kinds of equipment."

History
"Twenty years ago," Mulcahy said, "we never engaged in the sort of conversation you just described. Either production would skip the maintenance window without checking, or the maintenance manager would shut down the line without asking."

"That still happens sometimes," Bonhoffer said. "But in the best run places, there is good collaboration. Decisions are made transparently, with complete information. In the worst run plants, the maintenance people are prima donnas. They have nothing to lose by taking all the time they want to fix things. After all, they have a great excuse—imminent danger to personnel. The more common problem lies in a misunderstanding of the critical path. A machine breaks. It turns out to be more critical than realized, but parts to fix it aren't available. Before you know it, the downtime lasts much longer than you had estimated."

"We once handled such matters using a system of work orders," Mulcahy said. "The operators would fill out forms requesting work—either inspections or scheduled maintenance. Clipboards would be passed to maintenance supervisors, and then to the maintenance technicians, who would look at the orders, grab any parts, and do the work. This system was first automated with the implementation of the CMMS you just mentioned, Joan. It started out as software on mainframes that processed work orders based on a simple model of the equipment in a plant. It was more of a job scheduling system than a real model of the assets."

"I'm told that the real model of the assets," Bonhoffer said, "was in the mind of the maintenance supervisor."

"In every plant there were one or two guys who knew the equipment like their families," Mulcahy said. "They were like the Barney character on Mission Impossible, who could fix anything."

"Or Scotty on Star Trek," Moulton said.

"Or Geordi La Forge," Bala said. "Remember, we're moving into the next generation of plant management."

"These were the guys who knew when the dilithium crystals were going to blow," said Mulcahy. "And they knew how to prevent it. When any of them retired, the plant suffered massive shock."

"Capturing tribal knowledge is a big focus of the modern asset management systems," said Bonhoffer. "Since most of the modern generation of asset management software aims to create a complete model of the assets along with bills of materials for parts, maintenance histories, inspection reports, performance data, and so forth, the management of assets becomes more systematic and less a matter of relying on a key person's special skills and knowledge. However, before we talk about systems, we need to examine how people keep score of, and balance, the conflicting values."

KPIs

"As I explained," Mulcahy said, "in my day, it was the plant manager who did the balancing. After hearing everyone out, Thomas Mattern, the plant manager who trained me, would make the call about whether to do the work the maintenance supervisor had requested, or to keep production going."

"Plants," Bonhoffer said, "have become too big and complex for the key-person approach to work very well most of the time. Plant managers do call the shots at the morning meeting. Throughout the day, however, they are busy meeting with local groups, performing safety reviews, analyzing financials, and dealing with the nice people from corporate. It's a much more outward facing job than it used to be. Now the work is often left to the people who report to the plant manager, so it's crucial that they have the right incentives to work together."

"Otherwise," Mulcahy said, "whoever is the most politically powerful pushes to make their KPIs work for them. In plants, operations are the top dog because they're responsible for putting people and equipment in jeopardy. A worst-case scenario would involve a production manager who runs things full tilt until the machinery breaks, and then blames maintenance for not keeping it running. Even in best-case scenarios, it's rare that the maintenance manager shuts the line down whenever he wants. The trick is to get people to work together for the good of the plant. KPIs should be designed to keep things in balance. Everyone across the organization needs a shared set of KPIs and a singular vision for how to achieve established goals. Remember, too, the difference between metrics and measures. Most KPIs are just measures—they are easy to compute. Metrics, on the other hand, are a measure of what is important *from the viewpoint of the customer*. Production rates are a measure. How close you meet your promised date is a metric. In the end, metrics are the only things that should influence behavior. As for asset management programs, they can be as diverse as those that simply track inventory to those that build a multi-dimensional history of multiple assets. The goals and the vision for achieving them must be closely aligned and understood."

"My research has shown there is no easy way to do this," Bonhoffer said. "Each of the five roles involved has its own KPIs to measure functional processes. These are measurements of how well you're meeting your planned maintenance, availability, mean-time between failure, and, my favorite, wrench time—the amount of time maintenance technicians actually spend fixing equipment. These measurements are at the lowest level of the KPI pyramid. At the top of the pyramid are the highest level financial and business related KPIs. Return on assets is the king for this area, but return on capital employed, and just plain old operating profits are all crucial. The key to this balancing act is the aggregated KPIs that combine the measures for each of the roles. The goal is to motivate each of the roles to achieve the optimal performance overall, as opposed to a narrow measure that might punish other areas if optimized in isolation."

"So what KPIs are at this level?" Bala asked.

"The KPI that gets the most attention is OEE, or overall equipment effectiveness," Bonhoffer said, and wrote the OEE formula on the whiteboard.

$$OEE = EQUIPMENT\ AVAILABILITY \times PERFORMANCE\ EFFICIENCY \times QUALITY\ RATE$$

"The goal is to see whether your use of equipment is balanced. OEE is the product of three numbers: equipment availability, performance efficiency, and quality rate. You want to see a number that encompasses all these factors. Equipment availability indicates that you can run when you need to. Performance efficiency shows whether you're getting the most out of your resources. Quality rate lets you see that you aren't making defective products."

"In the long run," Moulton said, "these KPIs also prevent people from thinking they can rob Peter to pay Paul."

"I was impressed at first, as well," Bonhoffer said. "Then it was explained to me how easily it is to game this number. Equipment availability is straightforward. All the metrics that flow into it tell you how well you're keeping the equipment ready to work. You've got wrench time, mean time to failure and repair, and planned to unplanned maintenance. Together, they reflect the health of your planned maintenance program."

"Are these more granular metrics direct input in the equipment availability?" Bala asked.

"They're simply the metrics for activities that are related to availability," Bonhoffer said. "The other two metrics are where most of the distortion or, in the worst case, manipulation of this metric happens. Efficiency, for example— against what does it measure your performance? Many places compare current performance to historical averages. This is fine, though it won't reflect the equipment's actual capabilities any more than John's dream Ferrari will provide an accurate benchmark for its true capabilities if he only drives it 40 miles per hour. You can do the same thing with quality rate by selectively including or excluding various kinds of defects."

"All you're saying," Moulton said, "is that this number, like any other, has to be used properly and sincerely."

"Some of the distortions are unconscious, though," Bonhoffer said. "It's not enough to use OEE. You've got to dig into it to make sure it means something. In some plants, I'm told, this metric is seen as more of a solution than it actually is. One of the reasons is that doing a better job requires people to perform work that they may not have the time or skills to perform. At bottom, we need to use the right diagnostics to drive maintenance activities, and then measure PM and CM, or preventive maintenance and condition maintenance, ratios to determine if we're doing the right amount of each."

Process and Architecture

"This really catches my interest," Mulcahy said, "because it seems that the whole floor for asset management has been raised. It's no longer about people putting out fires. Before I get too excited, though, I want to see whether you got all of this from the maintenance people, since they could have inflated the importance of the maintenance role in the plant. "

"Fortunately," Bonhoffer said, "there's a growing body of literature to help us keep this all in perspective. Wireman has written numerous books on this topic, for instance. The one he wrote on KPIs is especially instructive. John Moubray has written some excellent stuff on Reliability Centered Maintenance, which provides the most comprehensive theoretical framework. Although it won't apply directly to specific equipment in a plant, it's vastly improved my thinking about the plant as a whole. The Smart Signal guys, too, have a fascinating system that uses real-time statistics to get an operating signature for an individual piece of equipment. If used correctly, it can provide an early warning about when equipment will fail, or even a model to predict failure. Remote monitoring is becoming more popular because it can drive down costs and increase standardization of the way assets are managed. But the key for plants, as I learned, is to understand their asset management problem and apply the parts of all of this that make sense. You don't need a heart surgeon to cut your steak, and you don't need reliability-centered maintenance to change a light bulb.

"One thing I discovered is that attention to asset management is now starting much earlier in the process. There's a whole class of companies called EPCs, which stands for Engineering, Procurement, and Construction. These are the Bechtels and Fluors of the world, who build power plants, nuclear reactors, refineries, and other large manufacturing facilities. The asset management process starts with them. They use products for asset management during the design and construction phases so that part of the deliverable is a fully populated database of assets. The best explanation for what people want from EPCs came from an owner-operator who said, 'I want you to deliver two plants—one made of steel, the other made of information—and I want them to be the same.'"

"So the challenge of asset management in an existing plant," Bala said, "is to build the plant made of information to the level you need to maintain the plant made of steel."

"It's now practical to capture and maintain all of the information about all of the equipment," Bonhoffer said. "But you want to maintain the context, as well. It doesn't make sense to have thousands of data points about every piece of equipment without the tools to search and analyze the mined data. You want to leverage your efforts, and to do that, you must be able to analyze and react. For many plants, the inability to do this is a major barrier. The people in charge of maintenance don't have the wherewithal to execute the analysis they need to better understand their data. Not only is it imperative to establish a data architecture, but also, once you've done that, everyone working with it must abide by a set of rules and definitions that describe how to use that data."

"Are you saying they know how to maintain the equipment on a tactical level," Moulton said, "without giving equal consideration to their strategy?"

"It's different at each plant," Bonhoffer said. "Even so, the range of analysis required to do the right work is vast. Naively implemented asset management systems are often reactive, as opposed to proactive. People track work without having planned it beforehand. I read a recent book called *Lost in Translation* that describes how to implement effective IT by thinking of each part of a company as an information system with five dimensions—values, policies, events, content, and trust. The authors call it the 'VPEC-T framework.' The concept provides a powerful lens through which to more clearly see asset management from a high level, especially as it relates to value.

"Now, we've already discussed value in term of KPIs," Bonhoffer said, and began to create a new list on the whiteboard, "but I'd like look at it another way, too. Both the operations department and the plant manager, for instance, are rewarded based on throughput, quality, and responsiveness. When the plant operates smoothly, they're happy. The maintenance manager wants the same thing, in the form of smoothly running equipment and no unscheduled outages. So do the engineers. They want their equipment to perform at peak efficiency while meeting their long-term goals. Corporate, on the other hand, may value different things. If the plant is near the end of life, it may make sense to cut back on capital but to improve maintenance and let engineering worry about the equipment. If the plant is key for the long term, it may make better sense to spend more capital."

VALUES

PLANT MANAGER, OPERATIONS
More throughput

ENGINEERING
Increased performance

MAINTENANCE
Avoid unplanned outages, protect equipment

QUALITY
Maximize product quality

CORPORATE
Establish goals and set expectations for useful life of the equipment

"Here's a way this might all play out in practice," Bonhoffer said. "Imagine a plant in a sold-out market, whose energy costs are hurting productivity. To remedy these concerns, corporate might expand the plant and replace, rather than repair, any equipment that is on the blink."

"They could also inventory all of their old equipment," Bala said, "and separate those they'll repair from those they'll run until failure. As for those that waste energy, they could be preemptively replaced."

"All good ideas," said Mulcahy. "But remember—the point here is to ensure that your asset management program never runs on automatic. It must undergo constant assessment with an eye toward serving the larger corporate goals."

Maintenance strategies

"Once you get into it," Bonhoffer said, and began to create yet another diagram on the whiteboard, "you find that there are many choices to make, none of which are obvious. To cite just one example, for each piece of equipment in the plant there are at least half a dozen maintenance strategies that may be appropriate, of which one is the best. The goal is to find out which one that is.

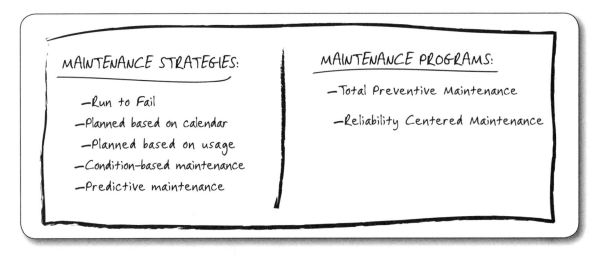

MAINTENANCE STRATEGIES:

—Run to Fail
—Planned based on calendar
—Planned based on usage
—Condition-based maintenance
—Predictive maintenance

MAINTENANCE PROGRAMS:

—Total Preventive Maintenance
—Reliability Centered Maintenance

"Kristian Steenstrup from Gartner was extremely helpful in explaining all this. He provided some simple graphics, to help you get the idea.

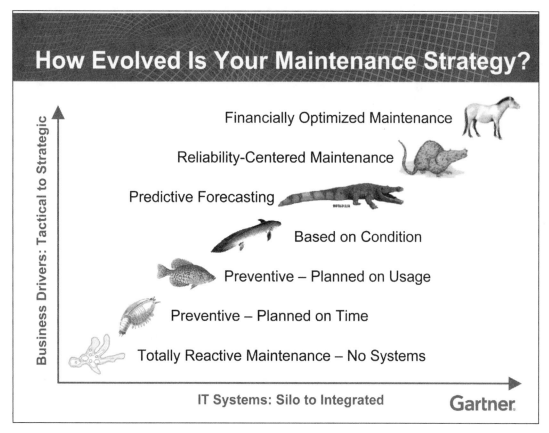

Source: Gartner Inc 2006

He has much prettier graphics, but you get the idea. 'Run to Fail' is the oldest strategy in the book—don't fix anything until it breaks. It's a fine way of working with equipment that isn't critical or that costs the same to let it fail. Light bulbs, laptops, paper towel dispensers in the bathroom, and the like fall into this category."

"The plant manager would not say his burnt out light bulbs weren't critical," Moulton said.

"It's always complicated, of course," Bonhoffer said, "but you get the idea. Some things can run to failure and be fixed when you can get to it. When the cost of failure rises, you can execute planned maintenance based on time or usage, the way, for instance, that some people maintain their cars. Changing your oil every 3,000 miles would fall under the usage model. Getting a safety inspection once a year falls under the time, or calendar, model. These strategies are basic and can be applied at any plant. To pick the one that matches the usage, you can simply ask, 'Is this something that deteriorates over time, or does it depend on how much you use it?'

"The next group of strategies requires you to invest in some sort of technology. Condition-based maintenance involves checking for circumstances that merit attention. The gist is the idea is to collect and analyze data whose results you use to drive actionable results. One example that Streenstrup found at a company in Asia was the 'grey cards' that technicians used to dip in the grease lubricating railroad cars. When the grease was darker than the card, you changed the grease."

"I love things so simple that you can't mess them up," Mulcahy said.

"Of course that's a very low-tech form of condition monitoring," Bonhoffer said. "Nowadays, real-time spectrometers test oil for impurities, and sensors detect vibrations. Companies like Smart Signal offer technology that monitors the behavior of devices based on the historical norms. Patterns emerge. When a piece of equipment's behavior deviates from the pattern, you inspect the equipment. The more data you want to collect and monitor, the more technology you'll require."

"What distinguishes condition-based maintenance from predictive?" Bala asked. "The condition is just a way to predict that a failure is near."

"That's true," Bonhoffer said. "But the best predictive maintenance specifies the exact time of failure. It relies on an accurate model of some aspect of the machine to show when it will fail. Such models don't grow on trees, either. They take time and money to develop."

"The more complex the maintenance strategy," Moulton said, "the more expensive it is, right?"

"And as you just noted, Joan," Bala said, "there are so many to choose from. How do you figure out when and where to apply one or the other?"

The critical path

"In theory," Bonhoffer said, "it's possible to develop a model that predicts when your light bulbs will fail. In practice, however, we simply maintain an enormous stock of light bulbs. This reduces the impact of failure and widens the window for maintenance. The downside is how it increases inventory cost."

"But say I have just one light bulb," Moulton said. "Why should I still care if it fails?"

"This is not a question about light bulbs per se," Bonhoffer said, and pointed to the whiteboard. "We have a variety of maintenance programs, each of whose goal is to narrow your focus to the most important equipment in the plant so that you can determine the critical path. The real question is, 'Where is the impact of failure most costly?'"

"Are there formal approaches to determining the critical path?" Bala said.

"Reliability Centered Maintenance is one of the most advanced," Bonhoffer said. "RCM comes from the aerospace and aviation industries, where the cost of failure is extremely serious. People die. At first, airplanes were maintained with maintenance based on time or usage. But the parts didn't fail as often as the predictions said they would. And replacing parts can lead to errors. This created the unpleasant situation where maintenance led to decreased reliability and inaccurate schedules. With jet engines, the time between overhauls is dictated by the quality of the monitoring and historical information maintained. The shortest time between overhauls is reserved for engines that have manual readings on a routine basis, and the longest time for engines with real-time data monitoring, analysis, and recording."

"Not super efficient," Mulcahy said. "Even so, since these are airplanes we're talking about, I think the conservative approach is best."

"The RCM framework starts with what is called a failure modes and effects analysis," Bonhoffer said. "Instead of taking the manufacturer's recommendation about the life of parts, you look at the machine as a system. If it's an airplane, you look at all the ways it could fail and what the effects would be. Then you construct your maintenance strategy to prevent catastrophic failure. Feeding this analysis back also leads to improvements in design."

"After you perform this failure mode analysis and find a vulnerability," Bala said, "you figure out a way to introduce redundancy, which lowers your maintenance requirements, right?"

"But in a plant that has critical equipment such as turbines or feed conveyor systems," Bonhoffer said, "RCM works best without redundancy. If you model a plant as a system, and then perform your failure mode analysis, the relationship between critical pieces of equipment becomes clear. This can lead to the introduction of redundancy or advanced strategies to reduce downtime."

"Just like the failing equipment we discussed earlier," Moulton said. "You could calculate the expected value of increased uptime less the expected cost of downtime, and then compare the cost of implementing the advanced strategy with the benefit."

"But the biggest benefit from doing an RCM analysis on the plant as a system," Bonhoffer said, "is that it identifies which equipment is critical. Of the 5,000 to 10,000 assets in a plant, you want to spend your time on the ones that matter most. RCM is just one way to find the dependencies. While you could have learned most of this by using common sense and paying attention, a more systematic approach enables you to capture and disperse big chunks of tribal knowledge about key equipment."

Asset management software

"It sounds like the real task," Mulcahy said, "is to understand the critical equipment, assign the right maintenance strategy to it, and do what it takes to keep everything running. Can existing asset management software help you do all this?"

"There's no short answer to that question," Bonhoffer said, and began to draw another diagram. "Asset management software has evolved in the following stages."

EVOLUTION OF ASSET MANAGEMENT SOFTWARE

Mainframe-based CMMS

Personal Computer-based CMMS

Best of breed Asset Management Software

Asset management software extended from ERP software

"Everything started with CMMS on mainframes or personal computers," said Bonhoffer. "These systems turned paper work orders into an electronic record and provided communication between maintenance personnel. This made it much easier to enter maintenance schedules and manage the work orders as a team. The work order is the key document. It's used for planning, and all parts and labor are charged to it. It can be used to create an asset or maintenance history, too. Having the work orders in a database turned the lights on in a big way.

"Then came best of breed asset management software, which offered more data and more automation. These systems have a rich data model, bills of materials for each piece of equipment, asset and maintenance histories, inspection reports, photographs, links to manufacturer specifications, notes captured by technicians, and lots of reporting. Some functions, however, such as communication, have been replaced by other solutions, including Exchange, portals, and blogs. Asset management systems allow you to assign various maintenance strategies to a piece of equipment so that work orders are automatically generated based on the calendar or inspection data. These systems can also accept measurement values. If a condition indicates the need for maintenance, a work order for an inspection or repair is automatically generated. The more advanced functionality includes extending the system to mobile devices. With these, you can take pictures and draw. You can also capture the dependencies between parts to determine the impact of a failure."

"How is best of breed different from the asset management software sold by the ERP vendors?" Bala said.

"Here's where the vendors argue quite a bit," Bonhoffer said. "They usually call their software enterprise asset management, or EAM, software. Asset management is an extension of the core model of a business that is kept on ERP. While the best of breed software has an intense focus on the equipment, the EAM software connects the descriptions of the equipment to the financial, budgetary, and process models in the ERP software. In other words, asset management becomes an integrated extension of ERP. People don't need a separate identity to log in to the system, the costs are tracked and rolled up, and established workflow processes, email notifications, and user interfaces are used."

"So which is better?" Moulton said.

"There's no general purpose answer," Bonhoffer said. "EAM vendors say their comprehensive standardized solutions are integrated with other important applications, such as warehouse, and do everything important. Non-ERP vendors would say that the integration with other applications, while important, is not as valuable as the concentration on the job of the mechanic. From the partnerships that have formed, it's clear that both categories of companies have respect for each other. The companies that sell business suites also sell plant level maintenance applications. The non-ERP vendors are improving integration. In some instances, the EAM solution may be enough. In others, the point solution or both are needed. Either way, these are advanced condition assessment systems that represent an evolution from plain tribal knowledge. Before you can choose the right one, you must first understand the assets you want to manage. Remember, you don't need to know everything about everything, just everything about choice concerns. It costs money to gather information, and more to store it. Anything extra is waste."

"What have our plants done?" Mulcahy said.

"We seem to have one of each sort of mistake," Bonhoffer said. "At one plant they bought a best of breed system they didn't really need. Your predecessor as EVP of Manufacturing Operations then forced the ERP asset module on one of the plants that actually needed the best of breed EAM solution. At some point, we have to decide how to balance the need for a standard approach, which we could get if we picked an EAM solution, with the fact that some of our plants require specialized asset management and would prefer to use the best of breed."

"That's why we get paid the big bucks," Mulcahy said.

Enduring Challenges

"There are a range of other issues we need to address at the corporate level if we're going to do a good job," Bonhoffer said as she wrote on the whiteboard, "and none of them are easy."

ASSET MANAGEMENT CHALLENGES

TRIBAL KNOWLEDGE
—How can we capture the knowledge that is locked in people's brains?

ORGANIZATION
—How can we align maintenance and operations so they are not in conflict?

CHANGING CULTURE
—How can we shift the focus toward new asset management strategies when needed?

COMMUNICATION BETWEEN ASSET MANAGEMENT AND C-LEVEL
—How can the key problems facing asset management be put into business terms?

KEEPING ASSET MANAGEMENT EXECUTION SYNCHRONIZED WITH CORPORATE STRATEGY
—How can we continue checking asset management assumptions against new strategy?

ASSET MANAGEMENT SOFTWARE
—Should we have a policy or recommendation about acquiring asset management software?

"There is no way to solve any of these problems from our cubes in corporate," said Bonhoffer. "But the plants don't have the budget to support the research you're asking for, either, so we can only help show the way. All of these problems are interrelated. For example, with many workers retiring in the next 5 to 10 years, loss of tribal knowledge is a worry across almost every aspect of the plant. It's especially acute in asset management. But if you systematically capture tribal knowledge, where do you put it, and how do you find it when you need it? Unless you're going to use a wiki or something like that, you need asset management software set up with the right data model. You also need to provide incentives to capture knowledge.

"Another area of concern is organizational alignment. You want operations cranking out the product, and you want the equipment maintained, and yet often the two departments don't use a common scheduler. At one of our plants, they put the operations and maintenance people right next to each other in the same set of offices. This informally encouraged knowledge transfer and awareness of each other's problems. Another approach was to have the operators perform simple maintenance tasks that they could handle. One plant put maintenance and operations in the same department with a set of common KPIs. None of this stops the tension, but it increases the incentive to communicate.

"To capture tribal knowledge, or to align maintenance and operations requires a change in culture, and that's never easy. Steenstrup also told me a great story about how a mining company achieved a culture change that better aligned operations and maintenance by making a simple policy change. They had lots of heavy equipment run by operators who were rewarded for more volume. They used massive bulldozers and trucks to move mountains of dirt and ore. Maintenance was an afterthought. The operators simply ran the equipment until it broke.

"They changed the culture by reprioritizing how maintenance was done. Unscheduled repairs were put to the back of the line and planned maintenance had top priority. This meant that operators who ran their equipment until it broke now paid a stiff penalty in terms of downtime. It didn't take long for operators to make showing up for planned maintenance a priority."

"But we can't make specific cultural change recommendations," Mulcahy said. "Those have to come from the plants."

"That's right," Bonhoffer said. "But the people in a facility want to succeed, so we can provide the tools and information needed to drive collaboration. We can also help shine the light on the sort of change that's needed by improving communication. The reason the mining company knew it needed to change their culture was that the maintenance issue was clearly communicated in business terms to a high enough level. Whoever ran maintenance was able to articulate that emergency repairs were more harmful to the equipment and had potential to lengthen downtime, so better maintenance planning could increase output."

"Teaching the nerds who run maintenance to speak in terms that will grab the attention of the policy makers won't be easy," Moulton said.

"But by providing examples and educating both sides," Bonhoffer said, "we can make an impact. If we get this right, then we should be able to better synchronize the asset management practices with corporate goals. For example, when a plant that has been in a sold-out market finds that this is no longer the case, then the asset management strategy should change from one focused on uptime to one focused on reducing costs. Or if a plant is going to be sold, then perhaps an investment in asset management can increase the price by giving potential buyers more confidence in the quality of the plant."

"In my experience," Mulcahy said, "I've never heard someone at corporate, or even a plant manager, say, 'Well, part of this strategy change means we'll have to change our maintenance practices.'"

"Any recommendations we make or training we do in this area has to address how the software will support it," Bonhoffer said. "This was the biggest complaint I got when I visited the plants and asked about asset management. They often felt that since technology had been inflicted on them without proper consultation or analysis, it never worked."

Asset Management from the Plant's Perspective

"Here's a problem," Bonhoffer said. "Apparently, the former EVP of Manufacturing, along with many other top-level people, mandated an EAM solution without first having learned to make the system work. IT, not the maintenance managers in the plants, was in charge of the project. Most IT departments don't fully understand the business process unless you work closely with them. When you do this, they can see that since the system is evolutionary, it's never complete or done. New equipment is constantly added or changed. Algorithms are constantly being improved through more data or better use of existing data. In our case, sometimes IT set the system up to collect too little data, sometimes too much. Sometimes the data was irrelevant. Collecting it didn't help run maintenance any better, and yet it required a lot of data entry. Too often, they said, the system just tracked work orders without doing the needed work of learning how to improve maintenance."

"That sounds typical of corporate executives who aren't listening," Mulcahy said.

"Nevertheless," Bonhoffer said, "in the end, even if you create a network of systems that makes good use of the work order to build asset and maintenance histories, you'll need to spend time analyzing whether the work you have planned is the right work. This requires a nuanced relationship between data-collection systems, diagnostic data-collection systems, manual-inspection data systems, lab analysis, and so forth, followed up by decision support and then, in turn, by work management."

Best Questions about Asset Management

"We're now ready to see the results of my analysis," Bonhoffer said, and began to write on the whiteboard, "in the form of best questions. Let's start with those you could use to assess the level of maturity a plant has for asset management if you only had an hour or so to do it."

TOP QUESTIONS FOR A QUICK EVALUATION OF ASSET MANAGEMENT MATURITY:

(?) What is your CRITICAL EQUIPMENT that if it failed could halt production?

(?) What is your MAINTENANCE STRATEGY for each category of equipment?

(?) How are INCENTIVES and KPIs balanced to encourage COOPERATION between maintenance and operations?

(?) How is COLLABORATION between maintenance and operations around planning and problem resolution supported?

(?) How did you determine the AMOUNT of data to capture in your asset management system?

(?) How is the WORK ORDER used to capture data for asset and maintenance histories?

"The first question about critical equipment establishes the level of analysis that has been done," Bonhoffer said. "Many plants have an informal sense of what's critical but have never thought everything out, written it down, and scrutinized it. The best answer here is that the company has a document used for training that shows all of the equipment related to the critical path."

"So if a company can't answer that quickly," Moulton said, "then they probably haven't done the analysis."

"You can tell when someone is making something up on the fly," Bonhoffer said. "If they don't have any documentation, that's another clue to how seriously they have considered something. When asking these questions, it's important to make sure you're addressing the person who should know the answer. This first question would be best asked to the director or VP of maintenance. It would, of course, be ideal if all the maintenance techs had the answer, as well."

"So you get additional information from how widely propagated the key knowledge is," Bala said.

"Another key point," Bonhoffer said, "is that not everyone has to have all this knowledge. The best answer to the question about the maintenance strategy for each category of equipment might come from a search through the asset management system or training documentation. The questions about KPIs and support for collaboration tell us whether they have their eyes on the business results and are aware that there are tensions to balance. It is the operators and maintenance techs that will start the conversations about how to make trade-offs. They need to be aware that it's their job to raise issues for everyone to discuss. Support for collaboration means that there must be a way to get the attention of the right people and record the results of any decisions."

"Otherwise," Mulcahy said, "they just do what's on the schedule without considering the consequences."

"The last two questions," Bonhoffer said, "get at the quality of the data being captured and how well the standard maintenance processes are used to keep up the database that describes the assets. If the IT department decided what fields would be used, that tells you a lot. If the work order captures useful data that is not harvested, that could be a problem."

"One way we could quickly get a handle on our plants," Moulton said, "would be to send them these questions and have them respond with answers in a day. They won't be able to paper over anything in that little time, and it will get across what we think is important."

"That could be construed as a bit hostile," Bonhoffer said. "It would be better to ask these in a more friendly way, as part of the process of building a stronger asset management program. Here is a longer list of questions that can be used if we have more time to spend, or if the people in the plant feel that answering these would be useful." Bonhoffer wrote several more questions on the board.

(?) HOW IS THAT INFORMATION CORRELATED, ANALYZED, AND PUT INTO A BUSINESS CONTEXT?

- What KPIs are collected to measure maintenance activities?
- How visible are asset management KPIs at all levels?
- Who is involved in changing maintenance and production schedules on the fly?

(?) WHAT ARE THE MOST EFFECTIVE PATTERNS OF EXECUTION?

- Are mobile devices appropriate for use by maintenance technicians?
- Can condition monitoring be automated and performed in real time with spectrometers or other sensors?

(?) HOW IS THE ACTIVITY IN THIS AREA MONITORED, ANALYZED, AND CORRECTED?

- Do planners from production and maintenance meet and review how well the plans they made were executed?
- Are planning methods improved based on an analysis of how well the plans were executed?

(?) WHAT ARE THE OPPORTUNITIES TO APPLY AUTOMATION?

- Does the asset management system automatically generate work orders based on schedules, inspection reports, or other input?
- Is any equipment so critical and so productive that an investment in advanced condition monitoring and predictive maintenance would be justified?
- Would RFID tagging of devices help improve maintenance processes enough to justify the investment?

(?) HOW CAN YOU ENCOURAGE A SUCCESSFUL CULTURE IN THIS AREA?

- Have any organizational strategies to encourage cooperation been considered such as putting maintenance and operations staff in adjacent offices?

Asset Management Opportunities

After looking at the list, Mulcahy had a question. "Joan," he said, "what's your general advice as to how we should start to improve asset management?"

"Like everything else we're dealing with," Bonhoffer said, "we can't just do it in one fell swoop. There are levels of maturity and sophistication in asset management. It's important to understand our processes so that we can determine what data we need to support them. We've got to understand the data, too. We've also got to have a firm grasp on our existing tribal knowledge. Once we have all these in hand, we need to consider how best to leverage them to establish a condition score for all of our critical equipment. It's at this point that we'll pinpoint the exact locations of our data, and then centralize it for management and decision-support activities. In short, we want to know where we're starting, where we want to go, how the ideal asset management processes support corporate strategy, and how that strategy may change."

"Some of the biggest mistakes I've seen," Mulcahy said, "have been around misapplying technology, hoping it would solve the problem instead of having it provide a deeper understanding of exactly what you want to do and how to change the business processes to do it. So I'm on board with an incremental approach. But what would you have our departments do?"

"Answering the questions in the handout is a great first step," Bonhoffer said. "Next, we need to collect more data or make better use of data to help identify opportunities. After that, we need to identify the critical equipment and increase the sophistication with which we manage it, especially if doing so will bring big gains."

"Much easier to think about than to do," Mulcahy said. "Thanks for getting us off to a great start."

Chapter Nine
Energy Management

Contributing Authors:
Charlier Miller, Praxair, Inc.
Eric Streed, Bowater, Inc.

"All right, you guys," Bonhoffer said to Mulcahy, Bala, and Moulton as she plopped down a pile of notes and books on the conference table. "I have a ton of fantastic ideas to share from experts about the best methods to change how we work with our energy resources. Today, energy management is more important than ever. The cost of using—and abusing—energy has risen exponentially and will continue to do so. These costs are financial, environmental, social, the whole deal. You can run a plant the old way with a measure of success, but until you've done a minute-by-minute analysis of the types and amounts of energy your plant consumes, the bottom line will still be a long way off, which means your competition has an opportunity to jump ahead."

"Who did you talk to during your research?" Mulcahy said.

"I started with James Breeze," said Bonhoffer, "who was on the revolutionary Kodak utilities team that implemented their energy management project on PI. When it was all said and done, Kodak was able to completely shut down one of their two power plants and save over 20 million dollars a year. Later I met with Eric Streed, a specialist in the supply-demand balancing of overall operations management. Some of his views surprised me. He has quite a different perspective from the other folks we've talked to. By the time I was through with these people, I had a good education."

What is Energy Management?

"The main thing that struck me when talking to all of these people was their emphasis on the need to change two things: how we think about energy and how we use it. I mean, what is energy, anyway?" said Bonhoffer.

"Maybe energy management is a misnomer," Bala said. "What's really in play is the large use of resources. I like to think about it as 'The Force' in *Star Wars*."

"Actually," Bonhoffer said, "'The Force' is a great way to look at the aggregate total of every kind of energy a plant uses in its operations. 'The Force' in a plant is the energy that runs into and out of every single asset. It doesn't merely include a plant's electricity, but also its oil, water, steam, clean dry air, nitrogen, oxygen, and solvents—and anything else that can be termed a 'shared utility.'"

"Most people understand this intuitively," said Mulcahy, "but when it comes to manifesting that understanding in the real world, we generally drop the ball."

"That's what all the people I spoke with tried to drive home," Bonhoffer said. "Energy management is the discipline of conserving resources to lower costs to the greatest possible degree. The goal of every smart business is to get the best throughput at the lowest cost, right? The last thing you want is to make your lowest contribution products during the highest peak hours. What you do want is to make your most profitable products on the assets that are at once the most productive and least costly."

"With energy costs going through the ceiling," Moulton said, "the fewer resources you use, and the more you save using them, the bigger your ROI at the end of the day."

"And there's more," Bonhoffer said. "Creating an effective energy management program is no longer simply a matter of dealing with your energy sources.

Information, as you know, is a major component in every aspect of today's business world. Breeze and Streed both stressed how important it is to examine the relationship between the amount of energy and the amount of information required to make a product.

"Consider two hypothetical lumber yards. At one yard, contractors call with a list of needed materials and the dates and places the materials are needed. This yard simply puts everything onto a big pallet and drops it off at the specified site, as agreed, and the business is concluded. The second lumber yard, on the other hand, works with a new generation of contractors who send them detailed CAD drawings of their projects, along with their project schedules. As a result, the yard can prepare exact takeoffs of materials for every day or week of work on a contractor's schedule, and then deliver *only the materials that are needed at the time they are needed.*

"Both yards deliver the same product to the same point and the interaction is the same between customer and yard. But the second yard's products have far greater information content than the first yard's. Consequently, the contractor who deals with this yard saves an enormous amount of money and resources. Since he has more information about his project, he can exercise greater control over the processes required to complete it and thus use only what he needs, when he needs it. In today's manufacturing plants, energy management, or utility management, needs to work just like this. In fact, you can say a well-managed energy program is the result of a happy marriage between information and energy."

"It seems so obvious," Bala said. "Why haven't people thought about energy and resources this way sooner?"

"It's not that they haven't thought about it," Mulcahy said, "but that they haven't thought about it in a way that best serves their interests."

"What do you mean?" asked Moulton.

"Survival," Bala said. "Plain and simple. Costs are rising alarmingly high and statutory norms are the tightest ever. Get a couple of fires like that under you and you are going to move."

"Now that you've got us hooked, Joan," Mulcahy said, "tell us more."

Cast of Characters

"Before we go any further," Bonhoffer said, "I want to give you an idea of the kinds of people who will fill the roster of the energy management team. It involves a surprisingly diverse group."

"You could feasibly use someone from every department for a project of this scope," Moulton said. "I mean, everything now is enterprise—resource planning, project management, asset management. The entire plant uses energy, so why not energy management, too? Shouldn't the energy costs that the board sees be a roll-up from each process owner?"

"I wouldn't go so far as to say that the team runs enterprise-wide," Bonhoffer said, "but you're close. Establishing a worthwhile program requires resources, sometimes quite a bit of them, and to get them, you need to go all the way to the top."

"Ah, yes," Mulcahy said. "Our good old friends in corporate."

"Without one of the honchos as a sponsor, your project is dead in the water," said Bonhoffer. "The team at Kodak needed to integrate hundreds of meters with their new energy information system, which required many to be upgraded or replaced—anything but a trivial expense. The person you'll need on your side sits at the Operations VP level. IT has the bucks to spend on computers, but they don't have the pull to pay for meters, call in labor, schedule overtime, all the things you need to successfully overhaul your energy program. The VP won't just want to hear that you've got a good idea to bring down energy costs, either. She'll want a comprehensive plan: who will do the work, when will it be done, how long will it take, and how much will it cost. Most importantly, what's the payoff?"

"I would imagine you'll also need someone on your side from technical, too," Bala said.

"A process engineer?" asked Mulcahy.

"Or a facilities engineer," Bonhoffer said. "It could be either or both, depending on the extent of the changes you want to make. Once corporate is on board, you'll need at least two full-time people and several part-timers to do the actual work. Together they will establish goals, do tracking, and facilitate energy kaizens."

"Hold on there a second," Moulton said. "I've heard of kaizens before, but I could use a quick refresher."

"Ditto," Bala said.

"An energy kaizen," Bonhoffer said, "is a concentrated, focused energy assessment that typically takes three to five days. Big operations take longer. You assemble an initial team with cross-functional skill sets, somebody from operations, someone from instrumentation or electrical, maybe someone who is straight mechanical.

"The goal is to assess the problem, keeping a constant eye out for non-capital solutions that use what you already have. For example, maybe you run a distributed controller or a billing automation system that hasn't been properly commissioned or isn't fully utilized. You can make a lot of improvements just through executing program changes or time-of-day schedule changes. All of these things are uncovered when performing kaizens."

"A list of titles at this juncture might be helpful," Mulcahy said. "What do you think?"

Bonhoffer grabbed her pen and began to write (see graphic, below). "Corporate and technical are at the top of the list," she said, "followed by your executions team. Technical includes either a process or a facilities engineer. If you're dealing with heavy industrial or manufacturing, it will be a process engineer. If you've got an office building on your hands, it will be a facilities engineer. You'll have both if you're dealing with a business campus that includes plants and offices.

"Next you'll need an instrumentation or electrical person. A lot of the work involves dealing with programming changes to the HVAC or lighting controls. Finally, you'll want somebody from operations, to provide 'outside eyes.'

"This part of the squad doesn't need any particular background in energy or even in science. You give them a list, or an idea of what you're looking for, and let them give the place a good going over. They may be office staff or admin people. I've heard of teams including folks from safety, as well. They could be from an EH&S-type organization, too, or they could be from HR. What's important is the fresh perspective."

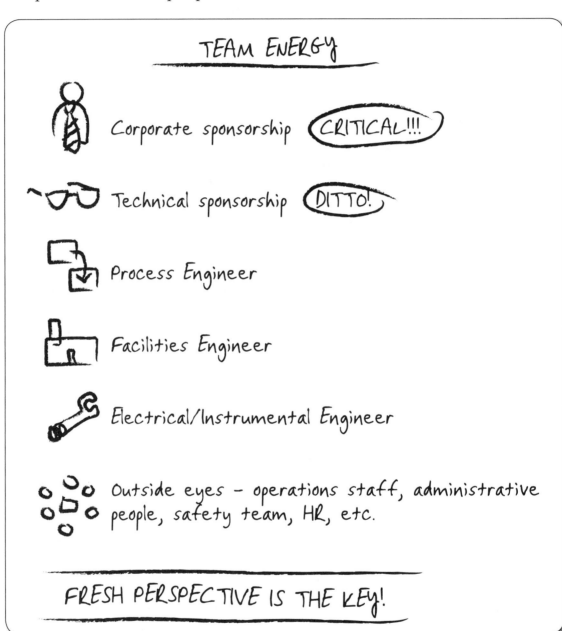

History

"With all this kaizen stuff," Bala said, "it sounds like you're going to lay out an entirely new way of doing things."

"First," Bonhoffer said, "I'm going to give you a brief history lesson on how things used to get done."

"I remember the old way," Mulcahy said. "It was all muscle and no brain."

"If you ask most utilities to define their main function," said Bonhoffer, "they won't say it is to deliver the utility. They feel their job is strictly to provide reliability. What you had in the old days—and what we still have too much of—is a guy who installed a massive boiler rated at 50,000 pounds per hour at 550 psig, which is double the required capacity. His logic for doing this was founded on the notion of security. So long as he had surplus, he knew he would always be able to deliver steam without fear of failure.

"Operations were not in line with utility. No one was concerned with information, which is absolutely critical today. No one was asking the right questions about process. 'Do you actually need to run this way? Or can we do it better by doing it differently?' Moreover, each process in the supply chain was being optimized at the expense of the adjoining process. No one was looking at the big picture."

"That's it?" Moulton asked. "That's the whole history of the way plants used to work with and use energy?"

"Almost," Bonhoffer said. "The other thing I want to talk about is how plants used to measure their output. The old way of 'managing' energy was to wait until the books were closed at the end of the month and then examine the bills, trying to put a cost to the usage by comparing one to the other. You'd be shocked at how many businesses still do it this way. It's almost criminal."

"What's the problem with doing it that way?" asked Moulton.

"It's like trying to match 10 names to 10 people in a room, none of whom you've ever met. All you have are the names and the people. Every once in a while you may get lucky and call Joe, Joe. But mostly you'll be in the scary land of trial and error. The same goes with trying to match your energy costs to your energy usage."

"Is there a quote unquote classic scenario for what you're describing?" Bala asked.

"Until recently," Bonhoffer said, "companies have been dealing with instruments equipped with their own analog gauges. So a meter reader enters the numbers from the gauges into a spreadsheet. Later, a keypuncher enters those numbers into a system that performs a calculation against a list of bills. Now, if you get a bill and then allocate your usage back across all of your costs, it's impossible to achieve a truly accurate assessment. Why? In all likelihood, that bill includes multiple periods of time in a given month, each of which includes various rates for the constituent energy components—like off-peak hours for electricity. If you don't know exactly when and where the energy is going, you can't control it with any accuracy."

"You have to remove archaic allocation out of the equation," Mulcahy said, "especially when those allocations are one-time events."

"You need to go from a purely utility oriented, cost-saving operation," Bonhoffer said, "to one that uses timely, accurate data to achieve a balance between energy flow and resource management. You need to shift from a one-time assessment—at the end of the month or quarter—to real-time assessments at various points in a day."

"That all sounds good in theory," Bala said, "but the trick is how to do it."

"There is a trick, all right," said Bonhoffer. "Actually, between Streed and Breeze, there were so many I could hardly keep up."

Changing the Company Culture

"My father used to recite an old saw," Bonhoffer said. "'If you keep doing what you've done, you'll keep getting what you've got.'

"Most of us can see that our old view of the world's resources no longer serves us. But this knowledge makes little difference if no actions are taken to create change. Before a business can expect new and different results, its people must think and act in new and innovative ways.

"My experts, however, stressed a significant catch here. This sea change of attitude and behavior cannot simply manifest at the top, among the muckety-mucks of the corporate elite. It has to resonate throughout the entire business, from top to bottom and side-to-side. The entire corporate culture must undergo a paradigm shift in the way it sees, thinks, feels, and acts about where resources come from and how much of them there are. Just as importantly, it needs to know what can and can't be achieved by consuming its resources, as well as how much it costs to consume them."

"I would imagine," Mulcahy said, "that improving a corporation's use of its energy resources depends upon its ability to show people the consequences of their actions."

"Yes," Bala said, "in addition to the manufacturing processes that motivate those actions."

"People," Bonhoffer said, "must be able to concretely visualize how their actions correspond to the energy resources they consume, on a minute-by-minute basis. To do this, two things must happen: first, you have to give your people the means to affect their working lives. Second, you have to teach them to respect those means."

"It's imperative," Moulton said, "that every employee understands 'The Force' in a plant, as you said. They've got to know how energy flows through a business campus or building site, and how that flow can be made as efficient as possible."

"Efficient in terms of cost, that is," Mulcahy said.

"Optimally through a combination of increasing efficient usage while reducing waste," Bonhoffer said.

"But how can you persuade your workforce to become aware of the way their actions affect resource and energy usage?" Bala asked.

"James Breeze gave me a fantastic example," Bonhoffer said, "Essentially, he and his team didn't so much figure out how to boil water with less energy, but instead educated their corporate citizens into appreciating the value of boiling water with less energy *only when that water is needed.*

"Innovation, he reminded me, is always limited by the scope of the innovator's knowledge. The management team at Kodak understood that people usually don't fully comprehend the effect of leaving the lights on at night. In our own lives, we get a bill at the end of the month, and maybe we see that it's higher than the month before. Maybe we complain a bit about it, but ordinarily, that's the end of the matter."

"It's extremely difficult to bring about a significant shift in thinking and acting from what appears to be a minor statistic," Mulcahy said.

"It's human nature to avoid spending too much time in the abstract," Bala said. "Numbers, schnumbers, right?"

"That's another one of the tricks Kodak learned," Bonhoffer said. "Breeze and his team knew that people feel bad when they learn about excess carbon dioxide in the air. But they needed a way to create a link between that feeling and the fact that the more energy we waste, the greater our carbon footprint becomes. Guess how they did it?"

"They brought Al Gore in for a speech?" Moulton said.

"Actually, that's not too far off," Bonhoffer said. "Kodak drove their effort to change the culture by taking every opportunity to remind their people how important the matter is to the plant's future, to the company's future, and to the earth's future, as well. They implemented a 'winning and inclusive culture initiative,' which communicated with the entire enterprise through a host of forums and channels that included posters, meetings, and the employee intranet. A cornerstone of this initiative was Kodak's commitment to diversity. They want everyone to know how much they value diversity of people and thought, and that getting everyone involved so that his or her ideas can be heard is a powerful thing.

"For example, they deployed an 'Update' newsletter and an 'Environmental Annual Report' to publicize their corporate goals to reduce the plant's environmental impact on both the neighborhood and the overall global climate. Their intranet's home page regularly features a variety of the plant's environmental activities, successes, and awards, and their poster campaigns provide energy facts and savings opportunities. Banners and signs are conspicuously displayed, too, all of which publicize goals and celebrate recognition awards by various regulatory agencies. Everyone in the plant knows that the company they work for is committed to environmental soundness, and that that commitment is reflected through participation in activities and organizations like the EPA Climate Leaders, the California Climate Action Registry, Energy Star, and the DOE Save Energy Now program. To boost these messages, Kodak strives to link them with as much national and world media attention on climate change as possible."

Energy Bill of Materials

"Clearly," Mulcahy said, "changing the culture is only the beginning. The real work has yet to begin. How do we get the payoff for giving people a new set of glasses to see energy consumption and their relationship to it?"

"After the corporate culture has turned around such that everyone is on board and understands what's best for both themselves and the planet," Bonhoffer said, "your team needs to create a bill of materials for your energy resources. An energy BOM is a detailed list of the types and amounts of energy that are used to create a given product at a specific time and place. Creating an energy BOM enables you to attach costs to your energies in specific ways. The last thing a plant wants is to make its lowest contribution products in the highest peak hours. If you can't see how much it costs to use a given resource, then you don't have the information required to prevent that, and you certainly don't have the data needed to develop revolutionary innovations."

"Totally," Moulton said. "No changes, no improvements."

"You've got to see the exact impact that consuming a specific type and amount of energy has in the overall scheme of things," Bala said. "And to do that, you need to capture energy at increasing levels of detail. Once that happens, you can analyze how you're using energy to create your product."

"How do we build this BOM, Joan?" Mulcahy said.

"One word," Bonhoffer said. "Metrics. You can't see a clear picture of your usage and costs until you first juxtapose your costs against the energy conditions of any given time. To create an energy BOM requires your team to accurately measure energy usage in real-time. Fortunately, products are now on the market that enable plant operators to get the energy BOMs in real time and associate them with the dashboards running their ERPs."

"That way," Bala said, "the data is more relevant and context sensitive, right?"

"Think about it," Bonhoffer said. "Merely to introduce a kilogram of water to the process system requires energy. And if it leaves the system with more heat in it than when it was introduced, then it's wasted energy, which results in unnecessarily higher costs. We're talking about separating the components and putting them into the drivers to find out the actual impact of each one in the overall manufacturing process. You need the sort of monitoring and metering that feeds the backend analytics in real time so that process owners can tweak their processes on the fly."

"From what I know," Moulton said, "this is not typically what you see out there."

"Typically," Bonhoffer said, "you see some sort of allocated cost. A company gets its 'energy bill' at the end of the month, then allocates it back to the business based on man hours or tons or some other archaic type of attribute. And you know what happens, then."

"In the face of that method's ineffectuality, the powers that be feel powerless," Moulton said. "'I can't reduce my man-hours, but neither can I reduce my resource consumption. Yet something's got to give!'"

"It's absolutely imperative," Bonhoffer said, "to see that you're making a decision around cost at this very instant. I know it sounds crazy, but years ago, plants were designed to work with an energy source whose cost would remain the same for the life of the plant. Now we have a situation where users face a potentially different price for power every 10 minutes. Decisions like these make verifiably chunky contributions or damages to the bottom line. Knowing when and where to implement a grade change to another product in the next 30 minutes, can mean the difference between whether the cost of that product drops to make a positive contribution or jumps up a notch to take a bite out your profits."

"A good way to visualize this concept," Mulcahy said, "is to see every element and every raw material in your bill of materials as being transformed into something that you're trying to sell."

"And the cost of that transformation is proportionate to the cost of your energy," Bala said.

"You're getting the picture," Bonhoffer said. "Corporate has a goal—they want to translate it into goals for all of their plants. Achieving them starts with bringing the whole company on board. Only after this can you begin to think about things like energy BOMs. It's lean thinking everywhere, increasing efficiency and reducing energy use. Creating BOMs is only part of the whole."

Stopping Sloppiness

"Establishing a means to drive out waste and create continual improvement," Bonhoffer continued, "is a plant's ultimate aim. But it can't get there by simply snapping its fingers. It needs to grow in stages, and this requires assessment."

"Now you're bringing us back to the kaizen," Moulton said, "aren't you?"

"You can't fix a problem without a solution," Bonhoffer said. "To find a solution you have to troubleshoot. That, essentially, is the method any scientist worth his name would deploy, right?"

"Of course," Bala said.

"The word kaizen," Bonhoffer said, "means to take apart and put together again, with improvement. It's a way to break down and analyze a process or system. In this case, we want to break down and analyze the processes we use to consume energy, and then rebuild those processes such that the system is substantially more streamlined and effective.

"What I'm about to propose is a combination of ideas from both Breeze and Streed. Kodak modeled their kaizens on Toyota's Lean System. Their approach resulted in demonstrable improvements. Streed, on the other hand, has developed his own ideas, some of them influenced by the work of a guy at Ohio State named Dr. Bowersocks. Streed's methods have achieved measurable gain, as well. We stand to reap benefits from both these schools of thought.

"A plant can't just start performing kaizens. First it needs to be at a demonstrable stage. Part of Streed's method involves considering these stages in detail. For any enterprise, at any location, there are levels of competency that can be categorized and measured."

Bonhoffer's good with the whiteboard. It really helps her and the others to grasp the ideas right away. As she continues to speak, she scratches out a rough chart, with four rows.

"Stage I," she said, "reflects an entrepreneurial startup. Streed used the example of someone opening a soft drink distribution concern. All this person does at Stage I is buy soda from K-Mart and resell it to workers in remote areas. As the business grows, the owner buys more soda, more often. Pretty soon the owner needs a truck and two or three employees. Since the behavior at this stage is very predictable, her supply chain and energy-usage is well under control.

"At Stage II, the business has expanded and is now far more interactive with its customers. It requires systems and processes that provide information to predict and respond. Later, at Stage III, the business has grown so much it has had to integrate. It now has a continuous flow kanban, meaning it has a method of control that schedules needed product to arrive as close to the beginning of a production run as possible. At Stage III, a company receives feedback from both its vendors and its customers, which makes things complicated. At Stage IV, the final stage, to manage its full suite of operations, the business has achieved a virtually integrated customer and vendor supply chain, with automated systems and the works."

STAGES OF DEVELOPMENT: TOWARD THE KAIZEN AND ENERGY BOM

 ## STAGE I: STARTUP
- Low Overhead/employee count
- Manual systems
- Supplychain entirely visible from single vantage

 ## STAGE II: YOUNG BUT GROWING
- Expanded customer demand
- Increased sales outlets
- Implementing systems to manage supplychain

 ## STAGE III:
- Mature

 ## STAGE IV:
- Advanced

"A business at Stage I," Bala said, "can't perform kaizens in the traditional sense, can it? It doesn't have multiple plants, each with a plethora of departments and chains of command."

"So it's not until a company reaches Stage II or III," Mulcahy said, "that it will understand what a bill of material is, or the cause and effect relationship of working on things the way we're thinking. A company has to develop a certain level of procedural sophistication before kaizen-like methodologies stand to affect its overall operations."

"This brings me to another point," Bonhoffer said, "that Streed was eager to stress: a company's overall capability is only as good as its lowest performance. It doesn't matter how good its general manager is, until every department functions at Stage II, minimum, he can't be effective at getting any of these things done."

"This reminds me of the capability maturity model as it relates to software," Bala said. "Level I describes brute heroics. A business is doing the best it can using brainpower and talking to other people. Level II relates to defining processes, meaning a business has actually defined that it *has* a process. Level III is a nuanced version of Level II—its processes are measured and integrated."

"Incidentally," Mulcahy said, "it's also the stage where new processes and measurements can be introduced with relative ease."

"Until you have the ability to manage and control your environment," Bonhoffer said, "you won't be able to perform kaizens whose results are accurate enough to create an energy bill of materials with confidence.

"Streed correlated these stages of a business's development to the stages a business needs to implement a successful energy management program. This is where his ideas conflate with those of Breeze and his team at Kodak. Anyone care to wager a guess as to how that might happen?"

"A plant that wants to gain control of its energy consumption at the most basic level needs to prevent its people from being sloppy," Mulcahy said. "Right away, they have to stop needlessly wasting energy."

"The men I spoke with," Bonhoffer said, "suggested that when you walk into a shop that lacks an efficient energy management program, the first thing you'll see is sloppiness. It's as if everybody's carrying giant buckets of energy, kicking half of them over and sloshing them around like they don't even know they're there.

"Breeze's team frequently visited facilities with very sophisticated controls that no one really knew how to use. They were never properly commissioned or set up from the start. Those that had been set up properly were later neglected. At other plants, the instrumentation sensors had failed. In some cases, opportunities to control the humidity or dew point within certain areas got bungled because of sloppy usage. The overlap between heating and cooling necessary to achieve the right dew point was nearly always excessive. The plant was pumping energy in to heat the room, while at the same time it was using massive energy in to cool it back down. Had they better understood their needs, they could have simply minimized the overlap between simultaneous heating and cooling."

"My guess," Bala said, "is that the next stage would entail getting better information, which the plant could then use to gain deeper granularity of process."

"And then," Mulcahy said, "once you've got the granularity, you develop and nuance an energy bill of materials—"

"—which you then use to implement design changes that will result in the big payoff we're all looking for," Moulton said.

"So let's say you stopped all these sloppy behaviors," Bonhoffer said. "Then what would you do?"

"Can't you just expand that same mindset?" Moulton said. "'The Force' is everywhere, right? Water hoses are running. Lights are on. HVAC systems are blowing away. Do we really need the temperature to be this warm or this cold? What are the tolerance levels for non-value added components such as summertime air conditioning, stuff that isn't a 'real' part of the product?"

"You wouldn't believe how often people fail to consider things like this," Bonhoffer said. "Exhaust systems, for instance. Can you drop to slower speeds during off hours, or even shut down? Many areas that were once 24/7 operations are now working in two shifts, or perhaps only one, and yet the systems still run all the time. Talk about wasted buckets of energy. Entire vats of energy are being squandered."

"And yet they complain they can't get their costs under control," Moulton said.

"From there you need to go to another level still," Mulcahy said. "We need to ask questions about the necessary resources that work behind the scenes. For example, a lot of water runs through heat exchangers. Just how much am I using on a daily basis? On an hourly basis? Virtually every manufacturing operation uses water in some way or another—how much energy is it entering with, and, just as importantly, how much is it leaving with?"

"Energy management," Bonhoffer said, "is a name for a much broader topic—the effective use of resources throughout a plant. No matter what it is—water, heat, dry air, electricity, oil, whatever—we need to be asking, 'How effectively am I using this resource?'"

"Thoroughly conducted kaizens will reveal these weaknesses in short order, I suspect," Bala said.

"That's why Breeze and his team regularly conducted multiple kaizens," Bonhoffer said. "When I talked with him, Kodak had already performed over 20 this year alone. The Kodak site has everything from office areas to research labs to heavy industrial manufacturing. Their processes run from energy intensive stuff to light manufacturing. To ensure they understand the process better and to develop the proper focus, they do about four weeks of planning, conducting team meetings once a week for an hour or two before the actual kaizen."

Measuring Usage

"A critical aspect of every kaizen is measuring usage," Moulton said. "But I don't quite get how you measure the amount and intensity, say, of electricity being consumed in a database center hour by hour."

"There's a lot more to it than simply gathering numbers," Bonhoffer said. "For example, Kodak has a real-time energy information system, which they deploy to its fullest capacity. One vital feature of this system lies in its ability to effectively disseminate the data it collects. In addition, you also need a control system that can sense the energy data and take some control actions. That way, your people can focus on mission-critical control actions.

"Kodak provides wide-open access to the data so everyone in the facility, from senior management to folks on the floor, can see what's going on. Good measurement demonstrates that each person's actions impact energy usage. The results come back right away in the form of positive behavioral changes. Breeze can't overstate just how vital this technique has been to Kodak's success.

"For instance, their manufacturing processes frequently changes from one type of film to another. The kaizen team determined that between those product runs they could employ variable speed fans for more efficient energy usage. The fans could slow down when the first product run finished and then speed up again when the next product line started. But there was a perceived risk in doing that. The system has to maintain certain pressure gradients. The logic built into the automated system slowed down the fans all together and then ramped them all back up, and the people on the floor worried the automatic system would create a gradient that was too sporadic. So, instead of automating right away, they ran manual tests.

"After a few weeks of running trials, when everyone felt comfortable with the process, they set it up so that whenever they weren't making product, the system would automatically shift into conservation mode. It simultaneously demonstrated both the impact on energy usage in that building and the benefits resulting from the change by carving off a nice-sized piece of their costs. Not only did this make everyone happy, but it also motivated them to manage their risks elsewhere."

"How did they determine that there was a problem to begin with?" Mulcahy said. "They must have taken measurements of some sort."

"In this particular case," Bonhoffer said, "the meters attached to the apparatus were sufficient. What wasn't sufficient was how those meters were being used. For a long time, they only read them a couple of weeks into each month. Breeze's team said, 'Listen, doing it this way is like trying to manage how fast you're driving by looking at the picture you took of your odometer three weeks ago.'"

"Is that when they changed to a real-time system?" Bala said.

"You can attach metrics software to specific machines," said Bonhoffer, "to find out how much of a resource goes through them at specific times in the day. With the results visible at an energy-usage console suddenly everyone could see everything. Not only could they determine average usage for the last 30, 60, or 90 days, but they could also see it on a daily basis. At any time of the day they could see whether they were running above or below average, figure out why, and implement the needed adjustments. Within minutes of going into conservation mode, for instance, the operators could see that they had lowered their consumption by 20%. Before, all they had was large-scale statistics on a spreadsheet. Suddenly, the value of the small, incremental steps that might otherwise be neglected was right before their eyes. "

Visualization

"Were there any other ways to help people see the impact of their actions in the moment?" Mulcahy asked.

"For instance," Moulton said, "you mentioned the kanban. Did your experts go into them with any detail?"

"Eric Streed is a big believer in the kanban," Bonhoffer said. "Their main idea is to use only what you need, when you need it, which entails scheduling products to arrive on the line according to detailed specifications. Manufacturers accomplish this is by using a signal system to indicate whether more is needed, or less. This is how they control speed. And when you are the master of speed, you are frequently the master of energy, as well. The signal system can be electronic or physical. Either way, it maintains a continuous flow of operation that prevents you from running out of material or having too much of it.

"We want to think about how the kanban can affect the way we manage our energy resources. We perform kaizens and build energy BOMs. We measure the time between grades, derive new energy parameters, and determine whether it's best to use natural gas, or electricity, or hog fuel, or whatever."

"In short," Mulcahy said, "these tools tell us what we need, how much we need, and when we need it. Now we've got to make those numbers a reality."

"Without them," Bala added, "a kanban is useless."

"But with them," Moulton said, "the kanban will enable us to run right up to an exact point without exceeding specifications."

"And," Bonhoffer said, "we can stop and start our processes on demand to best suit our exact needs. Streed had a great example of how even the most basic incarnation of the kanban has the power to positively transform both people and processes. He went to visit a paper mill whose senior VP of Manufacturing was obsessed with output. But as soon as Streed took a look around, he saw clearly that the mill's real constraint lay in the shipping finishing operation, which people typically ignore. The finishing operation couldn't handle the mill's output. It doesn't matter how much you produce, if you don't have an outlet big enough for it to flow out. What happens when you try to pour a gallon of paint through a straw in 30 seconds? Streed's suspicions were confirmed when he learned that the project leader on the floor had slowed back the paper machines because the output was impossible to manage at finishing. To increase the speed would have plugged everything up beyond manageability.

"Streed estimated that the mill was losing opportunities of over a million dollars a month, just because they were pretending they didn't have a constraint and were creating massive overrun. So what he did was give the project leader and the general manager a new operating and planning model.

"Streed took them all the way back to the order patterns," Bonhoffer said. "They also changed grades more frequently, to set up a tact time that aligned with the constraint and yet maximized the operation's profitability. Once they understood their needs, Streed and his partners were able to deploy a kanban right on the line, using the guys on the machines themselves.

"Here's how it worked: they created a flag system that enabled them to control the speed of the machines. First, they reduced the speed of the least profitable machine, so that everybody could understand the principle. A man was placed at the end of the line of machines, visible to everybody up and down the line, with red, green, and yellow flags. When the first machine had processed a set number of rolls, the flagman raised his yellow flag to announce it, so that everyone else could adjust the pace. Green flags signaled everyone to speed up, and red ones told them to stop. Essentially, the system allowed people to see which machine was slowed back and how much, and when the process was able to resume as usual."

"Totally primitive," Bala said, "but totally effective."

"It engaged all of the workers in the process," Moulton said, "in such a way that they could see their impact on it. Instead of sitting there frustrated that there was no room to put anything, they found themselves in control of a continuous flow process."

"Of course, later," Bonhoffer said, "when the capital came through, they implemented an automated kanban."

"We could also apply this concept directly to our energy management," Mulcahy said. "We have to learn to think about energy in these very basic, manual terms—red, green, and yellow flags. People need visible trigger points that say, 'I've got to be thinking now about what's going to happen next.' The kanban provides them."

"Yes," Bala said. "Not only do kanbans help to know what we need to do, but also they show us why we're doing it. They say, 'We are all part of the solution.'"

"Energy issues, really, are no different from quality issues," Bonhoffer said. "If the quality of your product starts to go off, your testing provides an early warning, from which you can make corrective adjustments. If you're filling an order to capacity, you know when that order is filled. You know when it's not useful to keep up the production, too, and you know that you don't get points for making extra product unnecessarily. If you are, you've got a process that's fundamentally flawed. It's exactly the same with energy resources."

"Most people," Moulton said, "regardless of whether they're in operating environments or in an office, prefer to know their boundaries and how to approach them. Like you said, John, an effective kanban does this. If a rate change needs to happen at noon, and it's 11:33 now, but you've also got a 15-minute grade change to account for, the kanban tells you that."

"Everyone understands the most and works best with trigger points and visual clues securely in place," Bonhoffer said. "Really, that's the challenge: make your energy visible by making what you do visible."

KPIs

"You've tackled measurement and visualization, which means that you're probably going to get at key performance indicators next," Mulcahy said. "We're deep in this, now, looking at the minutiae. We want to know which signs we need to heed and which we can ignore."

"Is there a KPI pyramid somewhere in this mix?" Bala said.

"Before you hit your KPIs," Bonhoffer said, "you want to vet your KRAs— your key result areas. If your KRA is energy reduction, then you look at your KPIs. The KPIs in energy management, according to my resources, are a matter of individual ownership."

"That makes sense," Moulton said. "The focus of this thing from the start has been on bringing individuals into a state of intimacy with the way their actions impact the resources they use."

"Individual ownership can have levels, too," Bonhoffer said. "For instance, it can begin at the department level, as a departmental goal, then drill down to individuals in the department taking responsibility for their actions and hence their resources."

"A department's goals are going to be site-specific, right?" Bala said.

"Breeze talked about this," Bonhoffer said. "Your KPI in one facility could be from BTU per square foot. At another location, it could be energy usage per unit of product made. It could also be more general, in the sense of absolute reduction targets for a given work area. As Team Kodak got closer to the goal they'd set—going from two power plants to one—they opened it up to an all-out effort. They simply said, 'We want a 10% absolute reduction goal for every area on the site.' Amazingly, it happened even in areas that were already quite efficient."

"That was Kodak's ultimate KRA," Moulton said. "Reduce our energy consumption to where we can produce the same product from one plant instead of two."

"And that KRA goes from company to department to individual," Bonhoffer said. "The department announces its KRA, then drills down into KPIs for people that have direct influence and capabilities to impact those KPIs."

"Won't your KPIs vary according to the problem-solving stage of a given plant or department?" Bala said.

"That ties in with our discussion about the various stages of a business's development," Bonhoffer said. "Everything works according to a master plan. The KPI for the startup soda distributor might be as simple as gallons of gas used in a month. It could be equally basic for a company as full-blown as Kodak, too, depending on the evolution of their management program. At the beginning, maybe the best they can hope for is reducing their energy by turning the lights off more often, in more places. You simply instruct the security guard to record which lights are off. The goal may be to ensure that 80% are off at the beginning. Later, after you've met that goal, you can bump it up to 100%."

"The point is to make it simple, measurable, and comparable," Mulcahy said. "As you advance through stages, your KPIs will advance with you until you're assessing the variations in usage room by room. That would definitely happen if you were a data storage facility, for instance. Your KPIs would be electricity consumed by Room A2. No matter, what, though, in the end you want to see the range of variability of usage in your department. Once you've done that, you want to lower it by a set percentage."

"Yet another thing we need to consider," Bonhoffer said, "is that no matter how fantastic our energy management program is on paper, it's impossible to implement it in a meaningful way if we don't view it from the perspective of the enterprise itself. Corporate has to make sure the targets they send down fully appreciate things like the difference in costs and usage from plant to plant. You know—in Facility A it cost this many megawatts per ton, but in Facility B it cost that many megawatts. If individual facilities don't have accurate feedback from corporate, the solutions they develop after running kaizens and building energy BOMs won't truly be accurate, either."

"The last thing we need to account for," Mulcahy said, "is this: *the KPIs for each plant must be things the plant itself can control.* We're concerned with the minimum cost of production at a *specific* plant. What is the energy metric per unit of product you create? That is what we want to minimize, and that's why we're examining these KPIs. Anything else is just a report with information about how you're doing compared with the rest of the world."

Energy Management from the Plant's Perspective

"That's a perfect segue," Moulton said, "for discussing the difference between corporate's idea of an energy management program and the same idea from the perspective of the people on the ground. What did your resources say about eliminating the friction between the two?"

"Or maybe we could hope just to ease it up a little?" Bala said. "I don't see how it could be possible to actually eliminate it."

"Breeze's methods appear to have really narrowed that gulf," Bonhoffer said. "No matter how you slice it, a plant has to tell corporate what they need by suggesting a suite of projects to accomplish the goals corporate has given them. In the past, the tension has derived from the disconnect between what the plant thinks is right and what corporate wants. But, again, Kodak got around this one with flying colors."

"Let me guess." Mulcahy said, "Culture change."

"You've got it," said Bonhoffer. "We're beginning to come full circle. Initially, one of corporate's primary objectives was to bring their people around to a new way of thinking by giving them real-time information. This went a long, long way. First, it demonstrated that corporate had faith in them. Information is power. Suddenly, it's like you're privy to all these secrets. As soon as the data went plantside, the people immediately began to think about everything they were doing in a completely different way, which in turn provoked them into asking questions.

"And that's exactly what corporate wanted, to open an ongoing dialog. Communications were at the center of everything they did. For instance, Kodak began to publish a newsletter distributed to all employees, combined with mass emails discussing Kodak's present and future goals. Kodak went to great lengths to explain why they were doing this. It was all a part of their initiative to develop what they called a 'winning and inclusive culture.' At its heart is the assumption that when there is a wealth of diversity of thought, and the ideas of one and all are welcome, the level of cooperation across the enterprise rises immediately and drastically."

"Didn't people groan when they saw all this coming?" Moulton said. "'Oh, no, not more *initiatives*!'"

"Breeze says they didn't hear very much of that at all," Bonhoffer said. "He attributes this to their method of implementation. Rather than coming down on them avalanche-like, they made the shift in related phases. The whole lean philosophy, for instance, was a thing the company had already begun to instill in the employees. Waste was being minimized in all areas, so it wasn't simply a matter of energy conservation. The concepts behind the 'winning and inclusive culture' were molded to apply to the energy conservation effort."

"It sounds like everyone was given an incentive," Moulton said. "They understood what was in it for themselves, too."

"There are eleven thousand people working at the complex," Bonhoffer said. "Their livelihood depends on its economic viability. The plant's interests, to a great extent, are theirs, as well. The results of their overall effort were huge. From 2006 to 2007, they saw a 16% reduction in both energy and CO_2 emissions. And, they we were able to go from the two power plants to one. Between reduced fuel costs and reduced operation and maintenance fees, Kodak boasted in excess of $20 million in savings."

"And that's an annual number?" Moulton said.

"Correct."

"That pays for a lot of meters, doesn't it?" Mulcahy said. "What about when it gets to be hands-on? What happens when an operator sees an energy spike?"

"Thanks to the open communication channels," Bonhoffer said, "every major department or division has a designated focal point in the energy office. The operator simply contacts that person with the details. Everybody can see the raw data, so it's not just the operators who can raise their hands. It could be anybody, management, whoever. People are widely encouraged to ask questions regardless of the situation, especially if something doesn't look right. If someone raises a hand, the situation gets investigated."

Process and Architecture

"I want to take a quick moment," Bonhoffer said, "to reiterate that the energy management principles we've discussed thus far constitute a comprehensive architectonics within which definitive processes are at work. When you look at each component, from the definition and history of energy management to the principle agents needed to implement needed changes, to the action items themselves—revolutionizing the culture, instigating kaizens, building energy BOMs, measuring usage, and creating ways to visualize processes and usage such as the kanban—you see that none of them function in mutual exclusivity. They are all connected, and one follows naturally from the other."

"Thanks for reminding us, Joan," Mulcahy said. "It's important we don't lose sight of the forest for the trees."

"You know," Bala said, "seeing it this way helps you to understand that your program can only be as strong as its weakest link. If one aspect of it isn't holding weight, the rest will soon follow."

Energy Management Technology

"One thing I've noticed to be conspicuously absent from this discussion is technology," Mulcahy said.

"The reason," Bonhoffer said, "is that energy management technology has not been 'productized,' even though many tools exist. Kodak had 600 electrical distribution meters along with 600 non-electric utility service meters that needed to be integrated into its energy information system. These were for other utilities, such as steam, chilled water, brine, compressed air, process water, nitrogen, and natural gas. To process the data collected by the meters, they had to build a fairly large system with numerous interfaces. There were four different types of building automation systems, including the Rosemount, Siemens, and Emerson, along with some SQL-based historians.

"According to my notes, there were five different kinds of distributed control systems, or DCSs, used to extract the utilities data gathered by their meters and tags: the Fisher Provox, Westinghouse WDPF, Ovation, Mod 300, and Emerson Delta V.

"The tags system is separate from the meters," Bonhoffer continued. "Kodak needs a 250,000-point tag system, over 100,000 of which are defined and increasing. You can put a tag on a main steam or electric line and record the actual flow of steam or electricity that goes through it, along with its quality, and derive how much it costs you, right down to the second. Twenty-three workstations enable the people at Kodak to identify and diagnose problems they find. They also have licenses for 150 concurrent web users, so that as many as 150 people can simultaneously access their energy usage data through the corporate intranet. There were multiple copies of the DCS and Building Automated System interface, too, plus interfaces for power prices, so the system actually has a total of twenty-seven interfaces installed. And one other thing: they have more than 180 iView pages, created from SAP iView portlets embedded in pages from their SAP portal to help facilitate locating and analyzing the data. This is the same SAP portal where employees can view regular pay statements and report attendance exceptions such as vacation and or sick time, helping to make visiting this portal part of their regular routine.

"In any case, with the exception of the meters and tags, while much of this technology is cutting edge, it's not customized for the purpose of being deployed in an energy management program. On the whole, companies are creating and gathering the information they need to make things happen by integrating existing software techniques.

"I want to point out, as well, that, in the past, telematics has played an important function in data acquisition and control systems. Most of the time, these have been either fiber optics or wireless. The plants would prefer energy retrofits to be as seamless as possible, so wireless is an important medium for the demand side energy management devices to speak with each other and the base station. Zigbee for intraplant, and gprs/cdma for interplant are playing important roles here."

Enduring Challenges

"In some of the other areas we've looked into," Bonhoffer said, "such as asset management, there were quite a few issues we still need to address at the corporate level. That's not really the case here, as far as I can tell. We have a single long-term challenge—to continue collecting as much information as possible, and then distill it so that our people can act upon it.

"Streed says the primary way he challenges his people is by asking them to continually examine the tags they use and the way they use them. A typical mill has upwards of 10,000 tags. Are all these tags appropriate, and if so, to what extent? Why were they installed to begin with? Were they intended to help the business or to manage energy specifically? Streed doubts it. It's his feeling that they were put on by process control engineers interested in reducing variability or other process control issues. Our concerns, however, lie in the realm of holistically improving our business."

"That's what this energy management program is about, after all," Moulton said. "Are we making money, or are we not making money? If not, why? How can we make more? By reducing costs. How can we reduce costs?"

"Considering all the trade-offs," Bonhoffer said, "the only people that can answer that question are the people in the plant. So of those 10,000 tags, there are probably 100 of them that are truly useful for energy management. If we want to control energy costs with greater accuracy, we need to figure out what tags we need to monitor different equipment so that the data gets fed through the corporate intranet. That way, our kaizen teams would have a scoreboard that displays the exact energy consumption for an entire facility across our facilities."

"That's perfect if all we're talking about is the big picture," Bala said. "What if we want more granularity?"

"That was exactly Streed's next point," Bonhoffer said. "Unless we begin to look at that data by department, and then by the components that are running at the time, the big picture won't be as useful as it can be. We already know what our orders are. We know the plan for running them, and we're measuring whether they're running to plan. Even if we only simply apply another tag to the inbound bus, we should be able to get a pretty good sense of what our energy consumption is per ton, per hour, for each grade, or, at the very least, per ton for the overall facility."

"This is really good stuff for showing how we can get more and more granular," Moulton said, "which in turn will enable us to allocate more and more. We'll gain in accuracy because we'll be able to actually see 'The Force.' When it spikes, we'll see it. When it drops, we'll see that, too. "

"It definitely suggests attaching more tags to each major asset area," Mulcahy said.

"The better we can do all this," Bonhoffer said, "the easier it will be for people to adapt their behavior to meet the facility's needs on an ongoing basis."

Best Questions about Energy Management

"Okay, Joan," Mulcahy said. "Imagine the Board of Directors has given you an hour to go into a plant and assess the maturity of their energy management program. What are the questions that would best enable you to make that assessment?"

"Luckily," Bonhoffer said as she began to write on the whiteboard, "I was prepared for that question."

TOP QUESTIONS FOR A QUICK EVALUATION OF ENERGY MANAGEMENT MATURITY:

(?) Can you measure energy consumption in both kw and $ on a departmental basis?

(?) Do you have your energy results on line for all to see? How long?

(?) What kind of electrical tariff's is the plant on? Does it have access to wholesale power?

(?) According to what timescale to you trend your data?

(?) At what granularity are you monitoring energy?

(?) What is the delay between when energy usage data becomes available and when that data is acted upon?

(?) What training has been delivered to people about the way they can impact energy management?

(?) What is your approach to encouraging continuous improvement?

"The first question is tricky," Bala said. "Really, you'll know almost everything you need to about a plant, depending on where in the spectrum the answer falls. For example, you'd hope he won't, but a plant manager could feasibly give you an answer like, 'What trend?' At which point you'd know you the plant was in trouble—there is no energy management program. On the other hand, the manager could say, 'Good question. Right now we're doing trending of the larger buildings for the key energy usage, including electric, chilled water, and steam. In some cases, those are available through our web portal on a 15-second update. All of our buildings are monitored according to the trends, and the longest lag time is 30 seconds. Actually, that's our mantra around here: "Trend the data, trend the data, trend the data." We tried that old way, of just looking at a table of numbers, and it didn't get us anywhere! How else can you expect to identify anomalies, opportunities, weird patterns in usage that haven't been unexplained, and things that just plain don't look right? Trending the data is how we consistently discover opportunities for improvement.'"

"That sort of answer kills six birds with a single stone," Moulton said. "It provides you, that is, with answers to most of the questions on the list."

"Exactly," Bala said. "You know perfectly well that this plant is run like a tight ship. You know that the granularity is ultra micro. Kaizens are run. Kanbans are up. BOMs are exploding everywhere. You know that everybody from the captain to the deck-swabber is trained and informed, which means that the delay time between when data becomes available and when it's acted upon is negligible, and you know that there is a keen emphasis on continuous improvement. All that remains to do after that is to find out the specifics to the other questions."

"Yes," Bonhoffer said, "as opposed to putting the screws on the man to learn just how far out in space he and his crew are."

"I think we've got this down," Mulcahy said. "All that's left now, if I haven't forgotten anything, is to quickly go over any possible energy management opportunities that might be recommended to a plant just beginning to implement a new program."

Energy Management Opportunities

"So what's your general advice on getting a program of energy management right?" Mulcahy said.

"Understand your data." Bonhoffer replied. "Which means knowing where the energy is being used and how. Once this happens, you can establish some attainable real-world goals. Until you've done that, you don't stand a chance of rallying support for anything. Try approaching the senior VP of Operations by saying something like, 'We want to reduce energy.' She'll tell you to go get her a macchiato. It will be much, much easier, on the other hand, if you walk in and say, 'Here is our plan to reduce energy consumption at these three facilities, here are the milestones, and here is the bottom-line objective.' In that case, she's going to have her assistant bring *you* a macchiato and ask you to sit down in her most comfortable chair for a nice long chat.

"Of course, if you've done that much, then you've probably developed a fairly extensive plan, including micro and macro strategies and a list of contacts within the organizations that you intend to work with.

"When you've been given the green light," continued Bonhoffer, "you'll implement the plan and engage a continual process of evaluation, using the KPIs that fit each area, respectively.

"Another thing—it's critical that you be able to sustain those results. It's even better if you can continually beat them. For the sake of morale, it's important to recognize your achievements, whether they mark three-day, two-week, three-month, or year-long pushes. You have to make sure to recognize people for their contributions to the overall effort. This will be a multi-disciplinary team, so you can spread the love all over the company.

"Lastly, it's equally important to consider how many areas you can improve without any real capital. Never forget to make use of what you've already got, finding ways to utilize the old stuff first. Breeze and Streed both talked about this repeatedly. If you do all these things right, you'll have a few large victories on your board, and countless small ones."

"All right," Mulcahy said. "Thanks for some great ideas and examples, Joan. Last one out, be sure to turn off the lights."

Chapter Ten
Quality Management

....

Contributing Author:
Manfred Schulz, SAP

"Welcome again, everybody," said Bonhoffer, as Mulcahy, Bala, and Moulton took their seats around the conference table. "I've just returned from an illuminating question-and-answer session on the floors of several manufacturing plants and am ready to deliver my analysis of the issues and solutions surrounding quality management."

"So, what's on the minds of people running quality management projects today?" asked Mulcahy.

"Plant managers today are under more pressure than ever before when it comes to maintaining quality. With mass producers cropping up all over the rapidly industrializing third world, it's harder than ever to compete on quantity and speed," Bonhoffer said. "In order to maintain a competitive edge, some companies find it better to compete on their ability to provide quality products. And the regulatory hurdles are getting higher—lots of metrics that manufacturers have to meet today weren't so stringent in past decades."

"Quality is such a nebulous word—what does it really mean in terms of today's manufacturing processes?" asked Bala.

What Is Quality?

"After my conversations with folks who deal with this every day, I'd say quality is not terribly well-defined, although there are some fairly standardized measures associated with it. First and foremost, quality is meeting or exceeding customer needs," Bonhoffer said. "Essentially, the customer has to get something that matches the expectations set by marketing and sales, and the customer's prior experience with the product."

"From there, it gets fuzzier. We all know that quality is a big part of corporate branding. Remember Ford's slogan, 'Quality is Job 1.' But it's been difficult to nail down a solid definition. The closest we have is the ISO standard 8402, which defines quality as 'the totality of features and characteristics of a product or service that bear on its ability to satisfy stated or implied needs.' Sounds great, but there are some holes in it.

"Whose needs does the service or product address? Who are its customers? Customers for a product or service produced by a company could be internal or external. The needs of an end-user could differ vastly from those of a third-party supplier.

"Defining needs is tough, too," continued Bonhoffer. "The ISO has added seven footnotes to its definition, which include the stipulation that 'in a contractual environment, needs are specified, whereas in other environments, implied needs should be identified and defined' and that 'needs can change with time.' Needs can be defined in terms of safety, usability, availability, versatility, compatibility with other products, reliability, maintainability, overall cost, or environmental impact.

"Then there's the issue of how to assign an acceptable level of quality, or AQL, or the maximum percentage of nonconforming products that would be acceptable. These numbers could be vastly different across industries. Say that a manufacturer's production system produces a quality product if the AQL is 0.1%, which means only one in 1,000 products contains defects. That might be fine for something like a book or a chair. But what if 'only' one in a thousand toxic waste containers breaks? Not acceptable.

"A lot of quality experts say that the only acceptable quality level for any manufactured product or service is 100%, or zero defects, and that any failure to do it right the first time is not tolerable. That's not a universal opinion, but it is one standard.

"Another definition of quality involves holding down the level of variation from the parameters defined for the product—physical dimensions, weight, composition, and the proper relationship and functioning of all of its parts. Of course, these parameters originate from a number of sources—customers, regulators, and from within the company.

"Another definition concerns how many of these products get rejected on the production line, or, worse, returned by customers, because they are defective, or don't meet parameters or customer needs. Companies look at the total amount of rejections, returns, or re-work orders per batch. That's part of the story, but you don't just want to run a process based on the alarms it's setting off. You want to get to the root of the problem before there is a problem— that means controlling the amount of variability in what your production machinery produces. There's a measure for that called SQC, or Statistical Quality Control, but we'll get to that."

"So I guess the quality management of some of these low-cost producers could be defined as pretty poor?" offered Moulton.

"Exactly," Bonhoffer said. "Quality generally costs more. If you look at *Juran's Quality Handbook*, which we quality managers refer to as 'the Bible,' you find a definition of quality that's related to income. Better quality means greater customer satisfaction and, hopefully, better income for the producer. But the investment you make to achieve that improved income is usually greater, so up-front costs are higher."

"Okay," said Mulcahy. "So basically, quality management can be defined as taking the necessary steps toward meeting or exceeding customer needs, meeting or exceeding internal specifications, and limiting returns and rejections?"

"Yes, but there's one more factor that's recently grown in importance," Bonhoffer said, turning to the whiteboard and quickly scribbling a few lines. "It's the idea of creating a quality culture in your organization, and fundamentally integrating quality control into your process, rather than making it something that interferes with production."

"So, quality management can be seen as a cost center or an impediment to production?" asked Bala.

"It has been seen that way," said Bonhoffer, "but increasingly it's perceived as important to the entire company, something that's instilled in every employee, and not just the responsibility of the quality management staff."

"So, everyone drinks the same Kool-Aid," said Mouton.

"And it's all the same color and has the same proportion of sugar to water in every serving, and it goes down real smooth," said Bala.

"I would stop short of saying a quality culture should be reinforced as a cultish obsession, but it is very important," said Bonhoffer.

"Now that we have a working definition of quality management, let's talk about how we figure out if it's effective—what are the metrics and KPIs?" asked Mulcahy.

"I thought you'd never ask," said Bonhoffer, erasing the whiteboard with a flourish.

Key Performance Indicators in Quality Management

"There are a few standard key performance indicators or KPIs in quality management. I'll go through them from the bottom up, starting from the perspective of the floor personnel and going up to corporate management.

"It's important to remember that the management of quality is actually a continuous improvement process. That process is captured in ISO 9000, which is a family of standards for quality management. ISO standards are one of the most common sets of KPIs you'll hear about. As an example, I'll show you some of the main points of ISO 9001."

ISO 9001: A SET OF PROCEDURES THAT COVER ALL KEY PROCESSES IN THE BUSINESS, INCLUDING:

 monitoring processes to ensure they are effective

 keeping adequate records

 checking output for defects, with appropriate corrective action where necessary;

 regularly reviewing individual processes and the quality system itself for effectiveness

 facilitating continual improvement

"Going back to this idea of 'quality as a brand,' a company or organization that has been independently audited and certified to be in conformance with ISO

9001 can publicly state that it is ISO 9001 certified or ISO 9001 registered," said Bonhoffer. "This doesn't mean you're making a guarantee about the quality of the product—it means that someone has independently certified that you are applying consistent business processes.

"Okay, now we'll look at two variations on the continuous quality management process, as it is applied in process and in discrete manufacturing.

"In process manufacturing, where you're dealing with a homogeneous material, you take out samples and extrapolate the test results across the entire batch. It's also common to take time-related samples—the first sample after one hour could return a satisfactory result, but the next few samples could be out of spec.

"It's critical for companies to have a good understanding of their defect rates per material or number of bad units per batch, or test results for a batch that deviate from specifications, otherwise known as Number of Out-of-Spec Results. In discrete manufacturing, like an automotive plant, for example, you take a sample of 100 out of 1,000 parts and measure certain dedicated characteristics on each part or sometimes simply count the number of defective parts. The number of deviations from specifications is the Number of Out-of-Spec Results or defect rate, respectively.

"This is usually measured or collected by inspectors on the floor. The inspectors perform tests, record values, and check whether these values fall inside specifications. If they detect a deviation, then they trigger remedial actions.

"Anything that returns a certain rate of defects over a certain period of time is known as Number of Out-of-Spec Results in regulated industries. It is usually referred to as a 'scrap rate' or 'defect rate' in discrete industries. Often, this is expressed in terms of parts per million—remember those test tubes from high-school chemistry class?"

"I remember accidentally blowing stuff up," said Bala.

"When you're on the floor as part of the quality management team, keep in mind that we generally don't want things to blow up," said Mulcahy.

"It's important to remember that these samples are also taken to determine if your equipment is 'in control,'" Bonhoffer continued. "You determine this either by extrapolating the number of defective products in your sample set, or by taking a time sample of readouts from the machine's indicators to determine whether the machine is operating within an acceptable range of whatever you have defined as 100% quality. You're trying to figure out whether the material you *haven't* sampled has a high probability of being within the limits determined by the testing. This is the function of the SPC chart, which I'll explain in a minute.

"The generic measure across both process and discrete industries is essentially derived from the ratio of Accepted Lots to Rejected Lots—pretty simple, right?" Bonhoffer said. "That's the essential measure on the operations side. But what about on the corporate side? When do the suits get to run some numbers? Don't worry—yes, Bala, there is an algorithm, and it's called cpK, the Process Capability Index. It's a subset of an approach called Statistical Process Control (SPC), which was invented by a physicist named Walter Shewhart in the 1920s. SPC uses statistical tools to observe the performance of the production process in order to predict significant deviations that may later result in a rejected product. Here is a handout showing an SPC chart.

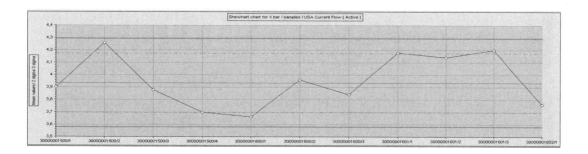

"Instead of inspecting each item and accepting or rejecting it, SPC looks for two types of variations in the manufacturing process—one is 'normal variation.'

"Shewhart found that over a wide range of conditions, the mean of a set of measurements is proportional to the standard deviation of those measurements. The Shewhart chart is the plot of the locus of the variation of the measurement. He developed eight different rules that would alert quality inspectors to a problem. To implement a proactive quality program, these rules have to be run in real time, not used retroactively.

"Quality managers also need to be watchful for a second type of variation," Bonhoffer continued, "known as 'special causes,' which are farther outside the range of acceptability. Since most items on the line are likely to fall within the normal variation tolerances, it's much easier and more effective to spot the special causes. It allows quality personnel to focus on what really needs changing and what not to change.

"cpK is a measure of process capability that looks at the number of measurement values, calculates standard deviation, and creates an algorithm that returns a result. It only looks at normal variation, not special causes. Generally, a batch of data needs to be obtained from the process. The batch should include the normal variety of production conditions, materials, and people in the process so that a mean or average level of specification is met, plus a tolerance of several standard deviations. For example, we could say, 'each box of chocolate must be filled to within one inch of the top of the box,' but if we have a degree of tolerance around that, we could deviate ⅛ of an inch up or down and not have the product flagged as a problem. With a manufactured product, it is common to include at least three different production runs, including start-ups, to determine what the mean should be. Process capability can be understood as the relationship between six standard deviations and the required specification."

"Great—what's 'the so what?'" asked Mulcahy.

"The 'so what' is, you are looking for a degree of variance from your Number Out-of-Control, and that tells you what the outliers are," said Bonhoffer. "It tells you the risk of producing an item that will need to be reworked or scrapped if your process is not altered."

"So, we can calculate whether or not there is an acceptable level of risk of producing defective products and from there determine whether it's worth fixing the process compared with the profits we stand to gain or lose from continuing the process as it is," Moulton said. "Obviously, of course, everyone always strives for zero-defects production."

"Yes, but they need to understand the cost implications if that extremely ambitious goal of zero defects is to be realized," said Bonhoffer.

"Is there a way for the guys on the floor to understand that there's a problem?" asked Mulcahy. "Are any of these KPIs baked into the systems on the floor so that they know to change or stop the process as soon as a KPI is not being met?"

"In an ideal world, all these indicators and systems would be linked so that everyone is on the same page at the same time—though cpK is usually calculated after the fact, not in real time," said Bonhoffer. "This is a good opportunity to illustrate why it's important that systems, from quality management to production to manufacturing, be tightly integrated. There are serious financial impacts from defective products—the U.S. Food and Drug Administration (FDA), for example, requires that recalls be reported immediately for regulated industries such as the pharmaceutical industry. There is reputational risk, and known defects can also create all kinds of problems with warranties. Management is acutely aware of this and is always on the lookout, but production people aren't always aware of it. If the systems were better integrated, everyone would be more aware."

"So, quality management is not just for the quality management people," said Mulcahy.

"Right," said Bonhoffer. "And production and income targets are not just for management. It's all about sharing the goals. There have been some efforts to support this through technology. The manufacturing industry and its software suppliers have tried to come up with standard notifications and coded information for defects so that an operator of a machine on line A and a line manager on line B, who would ordinarily describe their problems on the line differently based on their different experiences and knowledge bases, could enter a defect or problem code and the overall system would understand those codes and calculate them into the cpK or other KPIs. Another way to capture data is to create codes that refer to qualitative attributes like color—A1 represents yellow, A2 is pale yellow, etc. These codes, of course, are pretty useless if they are not used uniformly."

"I'm still hungry," said Bala. "Feed me more algorithms, please."

"Well, I certainly have some acronyms," said Bonhoffer, "which represent methodologies that may involve algorithms. There are a few quality-evaluation techniques that derived from specific industries that you may find useful; these are called CAPA and 8D.

"CAPA stands for Corrective and Preventive Actions. It's actually a subset of Good Manufacturing Processes, also called GMP, which were created by the U.S. Food and Drug Administration (FDA).

"CAPA has its roots in pharmaceutical manufacturing and can be generally applied to anything process-oriented. CAPA is a system for handling deviations, and software can be built around it. If an inspector detects a problem, he can enter that into CAPA software, which then creates a workflow. Then, everyone else down the line sees that action needs to be taken. Generically, you could call it Problem or Deviation Management. The idea is that you incorporate this in a continuous improvement process that strives to prevent the same problem from happening again."

"So this gets communicated to upper management, usually through software, right?" asked Mulcahy.

"It does if you use the right software, and that software is implemented properly throughout the organization," said Bonhoffer.

"Which totally happens all the time," said Moulton, rolling his eyes.

"You guys are sharp and saucy today," said Bonhoffer. "But you're jumping ahead to the 'Challenges' part of our discussion. First, let's look at another acronym that's a little closer to home at Wolverine: 8-D methodology.

"The U.S. government pioneered the 8-D, or eight disciplines, continuous-improvement methodology in World War II, and it was later adopted by the Ford Motor Company, and thus has become a standard in many process-oriented, assembly, and heavy industries."

Bonhoffer turned to the whiteboard and wrote the following:

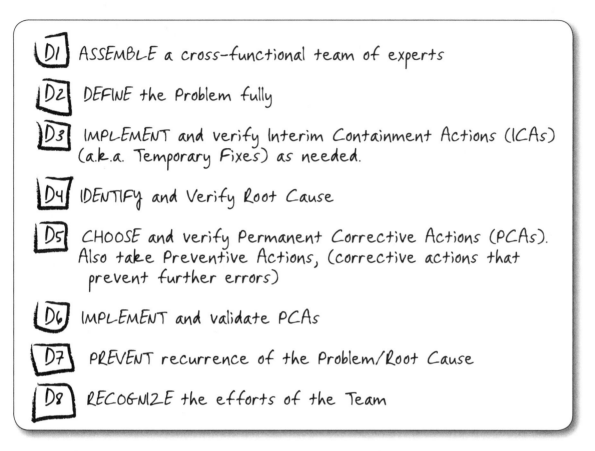

D1 ASSEMBLE a cross-functional team of experts

D2 DEFINE the Problem fully

D3 IMPLEMENT and verify Interim Containment Actions (ICAs) (a.k.a. Temporary Fixes) as needed.

D4 IDENTIFY and Verify Root Cause

D5 CHOOSE and verify Permanent Corrective Actions (PCAs). Also take Preventive Actions, (corrective actions that prevent further errors)

D6 IMPLEMENT and validate PCAs

D7 PREVENT recurrence of the Problem/Root Cause

D8 RECOGNIZE the efforts of the Team

"Don't get too caught up in all the acronyms," Bonhoffer said. "The important thing here is that CAPA is a common term used in process industries and 8D is commonly used in discrete industries, but they mean virtually the same thing.

"Moving up the organizational tree to the corporate level, KPIs break down into two levels. At the highest level are the standard models all you MBA types are familiar with: the balance sheet—'am I making more than I am spending?'—and return on equity. Below that level, things get kind of interesting because the approach varies a bit by industry.

"In discrete industries that thrive on customer-driven orders, the KPIs are measured largely from customer complaints. Ideally, incoming customer complaints can be directly traced back to production defects.

"In more process-oriented companies, a major corporate KPI is number of rejections per product. Say there's a food company that produces 50 different batches of yogurt a day in a 24-hour, three-shift production. All of the batches are tested, and each will have a 'release' or 'reject' stamp from the quality department. As I mentioned before, the companies watch for rejections as an indicator of whether their process capability meets the KPI. Let's say that for each month, the company produces 6,000 batches and their standard is that only one batch out of 6,000 should be rejected for any reason. Each batch that passes through the quality-control lab is part of an inspection lot. Each batch will receive a release or reject code. That is an indicator of how good your process is and how good your produced quality is."

"But do these suits care about whether the pH balance is off on one out of 6,000 yogurt batches? Isn't that a little too much information for them?" asked Moulton.

"Upper management doesn't necessarily want to drill down to that level; it's true," replied Bonhoffer. "They do want to know, as quickly as possible, the immediate impact of these fine-grained issues. They need aggregated data in order to know that there is a risk, the scale of that risk, and the extent of outstanding problems so that they can make a decision about whether they need a budget for a project team to resolve the problem. Ideally, the software you're using would provide both aggregate and drill-down data, so the corporate-level people immediately receive the big picture of a defect's financial impact and can also find out exactly where and why this defect is occurring."

"Isn't this all a little obvious?" asked Moulton, stretching and leaning back in his chair. "You either meet your targets or you don't. You set a goal of a certain number of rejections, you calculate how much that could cost you, you make changes to the line or adjust the model, and you move on."

"Well, it would be straightforward," said Bonhoffer, "were it not for two things: number one, the company is not in control of a lot of these goals and targets. For regulated industries like food, beverages, cosmetics, pharmaceuticals, and life sciences, compliance with regulations is paramount."

"If you don't meet regulatory standards, the implications are a lot worse than one of your production executives taking it on the chin at the next board meeting," said Mulcahy.

"Right. If the FDA comes to your factory and finds a glass break in a sterile environment, you could be shut down," responded Bonhoffer.

"I'm going to dish up another acronym for you, Bala. There are metrics to help with this—the FDA incorporated a standard called Good Manufacturing Practice (GMP) into its Code of Federal Regulations (CFR). These are practices that help companies ensure transparency, visibility, and high-quality standards. They are so stringent, in fact, that any product not properly documented throughout its lifecycle—regardless of whether testing proves it to be—is considered 'contaminated.' The European Union has its own standards as well. These are very demanding procedures if all of the work has to be done by hand, so there is another regulation called 21 CFR Part 11 that allows quality control people to use electronic signatures to sign off on the steps of a process instead of doing it all manually."

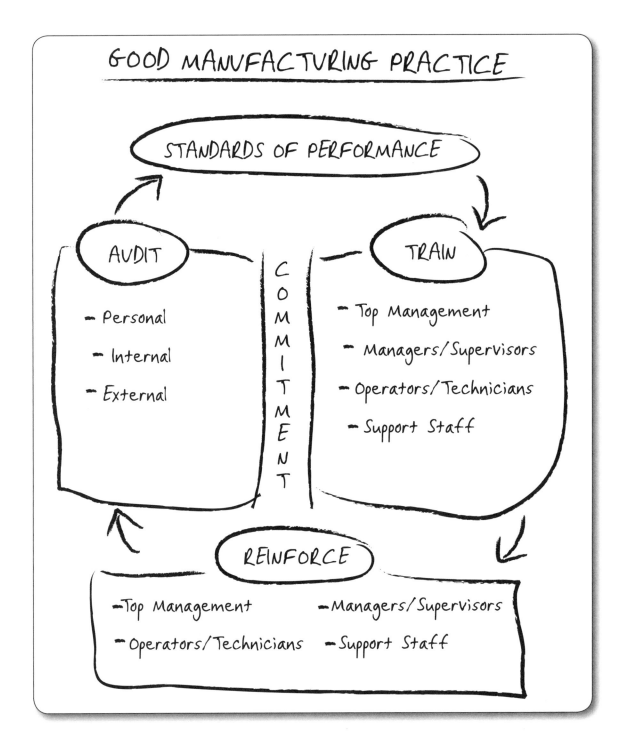

Central Problems in Quality Management

"You'll find it helpful if I give you a little background on Quality Management Systems," Bonhoffer said. "It's important to understand how we got to where we are.

History of Quality Management Systems

"Back in the olden days," she went on, "managers, quite frankly, placed quality second in importance to throughput efficiency. The policy was to squeeze out the most product in the smallest time window for maximum profit. In the 1960s and 1970s, all of the investment in the latest technology was poured into this goal.

"Quality inspections were usually done on paper, or on a piece of software that was disconnected from the production applications and from enterprise resource planning software, which we refer to as ERP. Quality managers were in their own universe, and the onus was on them to make their reports known to upper management—they were not integrated."

"Their methods became... unorthodox," deadpanned Moulton, in his creepiest Marlon Brando voice.

"Actually, their methods were fine—it was just that they weren't considered important enough to be integrated into the broader system," Bonhoffer said. "Here's another acronym—LIMS: Laboratory Information Management System. That's the name used by process-based industries. In discrete industries, LIMS is variously referred to as Quality Control or CAQ, for Computer-Aided Quality. This was a system that managed the whole cycle of sample creation, inspection, and recording. The LIMS would then evaluate the batch against the specifications (master data) and the operators would be able to check tolerance violations. They were very sophisticated systems and their designers and operators were very proud of them. Now, what do you think the problem was?"

"Hello – lo – lo?" Moulton called, imitating the echoing cry of a lost hiker alone in a canyon.

"Exactly. They were isolated and not connected to ERP, maintenance, production planning, or SPC systems," Bonhoffer said. "So a lot of useful information about future plans did not get incorporated into the batch testing, nor did the quality management data get linked into the forward planning of the company in a timely manner. This was not such a great problem until countries with low wages and, as it turns out, low standards, began to aggressively enter the market.

"Competition from low-wage countries got really hot, really fast. They could produce goods in mass quantity far cheaper than their North American and European counterparts. But as we have seen in the news, this productivity had its price—millions of cheap, defective products were released on the global markets, and they had to be recalled at great expense and embarrassment for the companies that outsourced production to these factories.

"But, there was a silver lining to this dark cloud. Those plants that had invested in LIMS and had effective quality management policies now had an opportunity to differentiate themselves on quality. So, the requirements of the software became more stringent."

"So, everything is fixed now and we can all go home?" asked Bala.

"Not quite," Bonhoffer said. "Efficiency was still very important, and as long as these systems were not linked, companies could not maximize efficiency and maintain their optimal levels of quality. Now the integration of quality data into the whole process, contemporaneously and in-sync with other applications, became more important."

Islands of Communication:

"I feel some middleware coming on," moaned Moulton.

"There is more than one way to solve this problem, but yes, software is a big part of the solution," said Bonhoffer. "Two basic ways of doing it are to link in all the disparate applications under a composite application—we don't really like to call it middleware anymore—or you can capture the data in some of the more comprehensive ERP systems, such as those from SAP, which eliminates the need for a separate LIMS in most plants. Another advantage of using a comprehensive ERP system is when multiple systems in multiple plants create a single product, like polyethylene. In polyethylene production there are three reactors, three blenders and a number of silos, and it takes 45 minutes to make a batch, but the system only keeps track of the material on a process-order basis. This might be comprised of many batches from different reactors and different lines, and the time stamp that is ultimately produced is generally set to reflect the activity for one day. The time stamp cannot be used as the sole determinant of when and where defects happened in the process. That's why you see manufacturers recall entire plant outputs when there's a problem—they can't figure out where the problem originated because the information is not linked."

"But haven't we heard this before?" asked Bala. "The whole problem of islands of data, islands of communication, can be solved with software."

"There's a lot more to it than just implementing software," said Bonhoffer. "As we've seen, having a quality management system sit outside of all the other applications isn't very useful. The quality assurance people don't know the production schedule, or they have to transfer files and upload them or, even worse, manually reenter them in order to get quality data to correlate with other data in the enterprise. Not only is this cumbersome and slow, but it's a huge opportunity to introduce errors. On Wall Street, the propensity to accidentally add a couple of zeros to a cell in a trading application is called 'fat-finger syndrome'—someone thinks he's buying 1,000 shares and he finds out it's 100,000 shares when he gets the confirmation back.

"The same thing could happen in quality management, with equally unpleasant results. Even when all the data is entered correctly, communication islands can cause a big delay between detecting a problem and correcting it.

"Another big problem on the floor is that the quality management processes might be performed by machines, such as high-throughput infrared spectral meters and the like, which operate on the production line. Many of them are not linked into the LIMS, or the ERP system—their data is printed onto a report that someone has to retype into the LIMS and ERP systems."

"Meaning an increase in head count and the possibility of more fat fingers," said Moulton.

"The problem is not limited to software and machines," said Bonhoffer. "The processes behind the software are sometimes not integrated, even when it would make a lot of sense to do so. For example, asset management and quality management processes are often not closely linked, but the two departments have to communicate when it's revealed that a defect in the process is the result of an incorrectly calibrated machine."

"Speaking of fat fingers, I can see a lot of fingers being pointed at each other when that happens," said Mulcahy. "Is that a problem on the floor?"

"Oh, yes," said Bonhoffer. "Often the schedules of quality inspections and production are not coordinated. So a quality inspection holds up the production process, and then the production operators complain, 'Hey, now I have to stop the line for quality reasons.' It doesn't have to be that way."

Solutions for Quality Management Improvement

"Okay, so now we know the problems. What about the solutions? From a process point of view, quality inspections should be seamlessly integrated," said Mulcahy.

"There are a few implications of that, and I'll summarize them under the heading of Total Quality Management," said Bonhoffer. "That means imbuing each department with a clear sense of the way your company defines quality and appropriate measurement and analysis. For the quality management personnel, it means fast or automated data entry, sample taking, and measuring, with no double entries. It's also important to have master data maintained in one system, into which all the other systems link, at least for that information. It's even better to have processes aligned and coordinated between asset management, quality management, and the production schedule, and to keep track of those in the same system, or at least to synchronize the various systems. And when I say 'system,' I am talking about the 'information system' of people and software combined, not just software."

"Doesn't it seem like there should be a way to create better products and better processes from the beginning, so the QM guys don't have to foot all the responsibility from the start?" asked Bala.

"It's like we've done a Vulcan mind-meld," smiled Bonhoffer. "That was going to be my next point. The concept I want to introduce is: Quality by Design. The quality management process and the applications that support it exist not only to deliver functions to support quality inspections, but also to provide functions that ensure the quality of design. When you develop a new product or find a problem in the field, you must be sure that in the production process, in the ramp-up, the quality is met per design, not per test. You cannot test quality into a product; you have to ensure quality per design."

"Sounds great—how do you do that?" Mulcahy asked.

"Ready for more acronyms?" asked Bonhoffer. "The essence of quality management is understanding critical factors that affect quality and cause defects. One of the most important factors involves the failure of components and the causes of defects.

"We can understand these best through FMEA: Failure Modes and Effects Analysis. FMEA investigates the relationships between different components in a process and examines how the failure of one could affect others farther down the line.

"This methodology was developed by the U.S. military and was put into use by Ford Motor Company in the 1980s to try to figure out why the Pinto would sometimes explode.

"To continue on the automotive theme, take an example that is near and dear to our hearts here at Wolverine. If the brakes on an earth-mover fail, you know there are plenty of other parts besides the brake pads and drums—cables, hydraulics, and myriad other parts connected to the brakes—that could cause them to fail. An FMEA would diagram the relationship between all these parts and determine three things."

Bonhoffer turned to the whiteboard and wrote:

FAILURE MODES AND EFFECTS ANALYSIS (FMEA)

The probability of occurrence (P)

The severity of the occurrence (S)

The inability of controls to detect the occurrence (D)

RISK PRIORITY NUMBER (RPN) = P X S X D

"A simple FMEA scheme would rank the three indices from 1, for lowest risk, to 10, highest risk," said Bonhoffer. "The overall risk of each failure would then be called the Risk Priority Number, or RPN. In the case of D, Detection, the 1 would mean the control is certain to detect the problem and 10 would mean there is no control or that the control in place is utterly ineffective. Using FMEA, you can prioritize the RPNs of each failure mode and determine what needs to be fixed most urgently."

"So is FMEA universal?" asked Moulton. "I've also heard of HACCP. What exactly is that?"

"It's a close cousin of FMEA," replied Bonhoffer. "FMEA is mostly used in the discrete industries, such as automotive and medical-device manufacturing whereas HACCP, which stands for Hazard Analysis and Critical Control Points, is mostly used in the food and beverage industry, but its essential points could be applied to almost any manufacturing process."

She turned to the whiteboard and wrote:

HACCP: HAZARD ANALYSIS AND CRITICAL CONTROL POINTS

> **PRINCIPLE 1:**
> Conduct a hazard analysis.

> **PRINCIPLE 2:**
> Identify critical control points.

> **PRINCIPLE 3:**
> Establish critical limits for each critical control point.

> **PRINCIPLE 4:**
> Establish critical control point monitoring requirements.

> **PRINCIPLE 5:**
> Establish corrective actions.

> **PRINCIPLE 6:**
> Establish record keeping procedures.

> **PRINCIPLE 7:**
> Establish procedures for HACCP perpetuation.

"I'll walk you through each of the principles," she said.

"Principle 1: Plants conduct a hazard analysis to determine the food safety hazards and identify the preventive measures the plant can apply to control these hazards. A food safety hazard is any biological, chemical, or physical property that may cause a food to be unsafe for human consumption.

"Principle 2: They then identify critical control points. A critical control point is a step, or procedure in a food process where a control can be applied and, as a result, a food safety hazard can be prevented, eliminated, or reduced to an acceptable level.

"Principle 3: Next, they establish a critical limit for each critical control point. A critical limit is the maximum or minimum value to which a physical, biological, or chemical hazard must be controlled at a critical control point to prevent, eliminate, or reduce the hazard to an acceptable level.

"Principle 4: Establishing monitoring requirements for each critical control point comes next. They need monitoring activities to ensure that the process is under control at each critical control point.

"Principle 5: Next, they figure out corrective actions to take when monitoring indicates a deviation from an established critical limit. A plant's HACCP plan must identify the corrective actions to be taken if a critical limit is not met. Corrective actions are intended to ensure that the company never winds up sending a defective product to market.

"Principle 6: Establishing record-keeping procedures comes next. The HACCP regulation, as applied by the U.S. Food Safety and Inspection Service, for example, requires that all plants maintain certain documents, including a hazard analysis and written HACCP plan, and records documenting the monitoring of critical control points, critical limits, verification activities, and the handling of processing deviations.

"Principle 7: Keep it going. This means you ensure that the plants do what they were designed to do; that is, that they are successful in ensuring the production of safe products. Under U.S. regulations, plants are required to validate their own HACCP plans."

"Can you boil it down so it's more generic, Joan?" asked Mulcahy.

"Basically, you find the critical choke points in your process where, if something goes wrong, everything past that point will also go wrong,"

Bonhoffer said. "You determine what needs to be measured at that point in order to prevent the wrong thing from happening, and then you define an action plan—what you do if the temperature is too high or if the bolts get screwed on backwards."

"It sounds like you're talking about a link between a production process and a quality management process," Mulcahy said.

"Right, you're creating a Quality by Design framework as well as a diagnostic framework. You ideally want to design a process with a full acknowledgement of possible failure points, and you also want visibility and traceability back into the process when something about the product doesn't come out right," Bonhoffer said. "We're not just talking about creating quality *products*—we're talking about quality *processes*. You set your process up so that you already have a pretty good idea of where it can break, and what variances are possible within the process, and then you set up statistical models to determine to what extent they are permissible."

"This sounds similar to APQP. Is it?" asked Bala. "I don't think we've discussed enough acronyms yet, so I want to throw that out there."

"I would consider FMEA to be a subset or deliverable of APQP, which stands for Advanced Product Quality Planning," said Bonhoffer. "APQP was established in the auto industry, mainly to streamline and standardize the prototyping and early product-development processes, but it can be, and probably should be, extrapolated into the mainline production process. It's really about ensuring that the product you set out to create turns out to its specification. Generally, Toyota's 'Zero-Defects' process is considered to be the leading example of APQP.

"Another deliverable of APQP is a control plan, which contains all the process steps and critical points in the process you've developed. I call it a living document, first because it's constantly updated during the design process, and second because all the process steps and critical characteristics you want to test when designing a product are also the ones you want to monitor during production."

"So how do all of these aspects relate to each other?" asked Moulton.

"Here's an example," said Bonhoffer. "During the development of a new product, you go through various phases and through an iterative process of testing until you discover the most critical quality characteristics and process parameters that you have to control. These data are obtained by multiple quality methods, such as FMEA or HACCP.

"The data are collected and structured in the control plan, which is used during product development phases, such as design, prototype, and ramp-up.

"In the end," she continued, "you should have a clear picture of what to test or monitor, and when and how to set the tolerance limits and warning limits, and what to do in case of a deviation. This total picture is called Advanced Product Quality Planning (APQP), the goal of which is to eliminate the defects before they can occur.

"Quality by Design means that through the design of the process, including the production and testing plan, the probability for errors gets minimized."

"The Six Sigma methodology for process improvement, which I am sure a lot of you are familiar with, also applies here.

"Motorola developed the Six Sigma methodology in the late 1980s and it has spread across many industries since then. Similarly to some of the other concepts we've looked at previously, Six Sigma emphasizes continuous efforts to minimize variation in process outputs, manufacturing and business processes that can be measured, analyzed, improved, and controlled, and the belief that process improvement can happen only with the commitment of everyone involved in that process, from top brass to the custodians.

"Six Sigma has as its standard 3.4 defects per million opportunities (DPMO). All of the efforts associated with Six Sigma revolve around improving operations until they match or exceed this standard. The 'Six' refers to the process being six nines to the right of the decimal point, or 0.999999, or 99.9999% defect-free."

"Okay, so if this process can be generically applied to anything, how is it applied in manufacturing?" asked Mulcahy.

"Well, in a process industry you look at temperature variation in an oven or kiln and you see if those variations exceed the defined upper or lower limits because that might lead to undesirable changes in the composition of the material," replied Bonhoffer.

"There are two approaches for Six Sigma execution. One is called DMAIC, and one is called DMADV.

"DMAIC stands for Define, Measure, Analyze, Improve, and Control. This is what you'd use to improve an existing process. Define is first. You define and develop a charter, define the process, map the process, and understand what you're trying to measure with respect to the voice of the customer, which is sometimes abbreviated VOC.

"Now Measure. You start to measure and collect data. This includes baseline data on defects, if they are available. Then you perform some statistical analysis and calculate the current process sigma, or deviation from 3.4 DPMO, and you draw up the process maps. In the Analyze phase, you try to identify the potential causes that lead to the variation. You try to establish a cause-and-effect relationship, and from there, you move on to the Improve phase, where you start looking for possible solutions to the root causes, and you set out plans to implement those solutions. From there, in the Control phase, you try to control the process through training and keeping your practices up-to-date.

"DMADV stands for Define, Measure, Analyze, Design, and Verify. If you are building a new product or developing a new process, this is what you use. You'll be defining, measuring, analyzing, and designing the process or product, and verifying it.

"It is essentially the same methodology as DMAIC, except that it is less emphatic about the process as the end result since it is essentially experimental. But it allows you to develop that process."

"Is it typical for plants to actually achieve Six Sigma?" asked Moulton.

"I found that most plants operate between 3.0 and 4.0 DPMO," said Bonhoffer. "It depends quite a bit on how the process is defined and how the targets are established."

"How do plants collect data for Six Sigma?" asked Bala. "I mean, at what level of the process is the data collected—is it from the Historians on the floor or from the higher-level systems at the management level?"

"Great question," Bonhoffer said. "It does vary quite a bit. Many companies use the same applications they use to calculate SPC, where they study the process against upper and lower safety limits and against specification limits, and they analyze how many times the product falls outside those limits. Then they look for the root causes. So, all of the Historians and QM applications are contributing to the Six Sigma analysis in that model, collated in the SPC application."

"Why is Six Sigma so popular?" asked Moulton.

"I think it comes down to the success that Motorola and numerous other big manufacturers have had with it so far," said Bonhoffer. "It does a good job of letting the customer define what quality is and then works backwards from that point. It allows you to analyze the whole process at a very high, but comprehensive level. It lets you to institute a process in a very structured way that is repetitive and defect-free. Then you can figure out where the waste is, and from there, you can figure out how to eliminate it so that your costs are lower and your predictability is higher. That cuts right to the bottom line, and ultimately, that's where you want to be most effective in the final analysis."

Questions to Ask in Quality Management

"If we're going to send our team out to battle for quality, it's important they know what their weaponry will be," said Mulcahy. "What are the top questions they'll need to ask when they head into the plant?"

"When I walk onto a floor," Bonhoffer said, "I definitely want these questions answered:

> (?) CAN YOU TRACK QUALITY PROBLEMS DOWN TO ROOT CAUSES?
>
> (?) HOW DO YOU ENSURE TRACEABILITY IN CASE OF CUSTOMER COMPLAINTS?
>
> (?) HOW MANY INTERFACES AND DIFFERENT SYSTEMS DO YOU USE IN PRODUCTION?
>
> (?) DO YOU HAVE A QUALITY POLICY IN PLACE, WITH COMMITMENT BY YOUR EXECUTIVE MANAGEMENT?
>
> (?) DO YOU HAVE QUALITY KPIS AND QUALITY GOALS DEFINED?
>
> (?) HOW DO THE PEOPLE COLLABORATE WITH EACH OTHER? WHICH TOOLS AND SYSTEMS DO THEY USE?
>
> (?) DO YOU PERFORM PROCESS OR PRODUCT AUDITS ON THE SHOP FLOOR?
>
> (?) DO YOU HAVE DASHBOARDS WITH KPIS BASED ON REAL-TIME DATA?

"Number one: 'Can you track quality problems down to root causes?'

"Do you really know where your quality problems come from?" asked Bonhoffer. "Can you find out the root cause of the problem quickly? If the obvious problem is that 'the screws we're producing are coming out too long,' you would ask: Do you have methods in place to find out why the screws are too long and a means of changing the process? If they say, 'yes, but I need to investigate over three systems and it will take six weeks to eliminate it,' that's a bad sign.

"Look at the case of Topps Meat, a company that had almost $9 million in annual sales. When an *E. coli* outbreak hit their product, they went out of business, because they couldn't provide the FDA an answer as to how *E. coli* might have infiltrated their product. It wasn't because of their response to the inquiry; it's because there *was* no response to the inquiry. They didn't have the tools to pinpoint the problem.

"Number two, 'how do you ensure traceability in case of customer complaints?'

"If a customer complaint comes in, you have to be able track down the root cause using a batch-where-used-list—there may be a bad raw material that got into multiple products or distribution centers. You have to be able to tell exactly where it came from. 'Did I have *E. coli* because of bad raw material, an impurity in the production process, or what? Which batches are affected, and to whom were they delivered? We know Batch 1 went to customer A, because they complained, but we also have to figure out if customers B, C, or D got Batch 1. None have complained, but we have to recall it preemptively.' What if the raw material has also gone into Batches 2 and 3? This would go a lot smoother if you used an integrated system that provides the tools and data and transparency to get to such decisions to ensure a fast recovery—can you do it in three hours, or is it going to take three days?

"Number three, 'How many interfaces and different systems do you use in production?'" Bonhoffer continued.

"How many 'islands of communication' do you have? The more you minimize interfaces between systems, and better yet, consolidate and integrate the systems, the better off you are.

"When you go into a quality management department, you should ask what their interfaces are like with their product development or prototyping development. I don't just mean software, I mean how keyed-in to the early, pre-production cycles are they? How often do they sit together in the same room? That gives me an indication of how well the process works, because if the quality managers are in sync with their product development people, then they are really practicing Quality by Design."

"Number four, 'Do you have a quality policy in place, to which your executive management has fully committed itself?'

"Management has to be committed to quality policy and all the employees need to know it. This commitment needs to be articulated through quality goals and KPIs that should be clearly stated and distributed to everyone in the process. The level to which these standards are articulated tells you a lot about how seriously the topic is taken at this particular company or plant.

"Number five, 'Do you have quality KPIs and quality goals defined?'

"Do they have solid and consistent quality objectives and KPIs, such as, 'we will strive not to exceed more than 3% scrap each month or more than three customer complaints per month?'

"Number six, 'How do people collaborate with each other? Which tools and systems do they use?'

"Do the quality management and production people sit together, do they share information through the same systems, or are they exchanging certain paperwork by hand?

"Number seven, 'Do you perform process or product audits on the shop floor?'

"Ask them, 'What tools do you use?'" Bonhoffer said. "When they conduct audit management, do they do audits of both the products and the process? It's important that they do comparative investigations. Do they investigate according to certain questions and benchmark them? It's very useful if they are able to say, 'We were in Plant A, let's compare its results to those from Plant B. Why does it seem like the process is better in Plant A?' If you have a system for conducting these comparative reviews, you can easily figure out what you can do better.

"Number eight, 'Do you have dashboards with KPIs based on real-time data, affording the possibility to visualize your data from the standpoint of production, quality, and maintenance? Do you get the necessary alerts when quality rules are broken?'

"You must have reliable and reasonable KPIs that reflect a real understanding of the capabilities of the departments. Some KPIs are not reasonable or would not really help maintain quality on the floor. The best way to get a sense of control around all those KPIs is to summarize them in a dashboard that lets you see all of them at once."

"That's great, Joan," said Mulcahy. "So, when we get out there, to whom should we direct these tough questions?"

"I'd start by asking the operator on the line whether the quality checks are organized centrally or whether they are decentralized along the production line," Bonhoffer said. "And if he said, 'All samples or pieces that we inspect are brought to the central Quality assurance lab,' I would go to the QA lab and ask them how often they have out-of-spec results or defective materials.

"If he said the quality checks are decentralized, I would check the work centers for the in-process inspections and I would ask, 'How regularly do you perform quality checks? How often do you do the checks, and how often do you have out-of-spec defects or results?' That would tell me how well their process is functioning.

"Next, I'd ask the production supervisor or production manager, 'Are you performing SPC in your plant?'"

"Does the answer to that need to be 'yes'?" asked Mulcahy.

"Well, they need to be able to tell me which characteristics of their various products are critical to quality and where most of their problems or defects are derived from," Bonhoffer said. "SPC is a good way of summarizing that. You'd be surprised how many companies can't tell you why they have so much re-work and so many scraps—the reason is usually that they don't look, or lack the tools to look for the root causes of the high number of rejections."

"What are some of those causes?" asked Mulcahy.

"Partly it's a lack of subjecting the production to any kind of statistical analysis. But it also goes back to this 'islands' problem I mentioned before," said Bonhoffer.

"So, overall, how would you describe the characteristics of a good quality culture?" asked Mulcahy.

"First, I would check to see how good the collaboration is between the departments, as I mentioned before," Bonhoffer said. "Second, I would want to see that people are not only trained so they can perform their immediate task but also in the general guidelines of Total Quality Management, or TQM. There's a quick way to get an instant sense of that—go into a break room and see if all the guidelines are printed out and posted on the wall, prominently, where people can see them. If so, you have at least a first indication of a company's commitment to quality."

Perfect Plant Playbook

"Why don't you take us through the Perfect Plant Playbook," said Mulcahy, "to give us some solid points on how to implement what we learned today."

"I'd like to break this into two playbooks that serve two aspects of the quality management department's needs," said Bonhoffer. "One is the technical or software aspect and the other is the human factor. Both focus on the same goals: improved transparency and improved communication.

"First, let's talk about solving the technical problems. The main word to keep in mind is 'transparency.' You can create data transparency in five key ways:

"First, reduce the number of redundant data entries. You can do this by automating the data entry or by using composite applications that smooth over the interfaces between disparate systems, eliminating double entries and fat fingers, or you can consolidate more of your quality management functions in an ERP application, which is probably already being used by corporate.

"Second, it's crucial to work from one set of master data, in a database that all systems can access. You need to bridge the islands of communication between the LIMS, maintenance, production, ERP, and SPC systems. That means that each system uses the same code for each item or process, and there are no information gaps between the systems, and no repetitious updating.

"Third, once you have done this, you can create a dashboard customized for each user role—one for management, one for a line operator, and so on—which, on the surface level, shows the data most relevant for each user to do his job but can also allow drilling down into other areas. This is especially helpful when there is a problem with equipment or quality.

"Fourth," continued Bonhoffer, "you need integrated processes encapsulated by a single system, if possible. It's not as effective to simply authorize users to have access to five different systems. It's much more effective to have the ERP and manufacturing systems tightly integrated because that opens the door for better alignment between management's goals and production's capabilities.

"Fifth, continuing on that note, systems integration allows for a common definition and understanding of KPIs. If the production manager can easily see the quality issues that happen in the laboratory, not only does he see them sooner than if he waits for the quality manager's report, he has an opportunity to look inside his own process that may give a clue as to why there is a high defect rate. If systems are integrated and KPIs are shared, some of those political boundaries can be broken down."

"One additional point to consider," said Bala, "is that this software campaign doesn't have to consist entirely of heavy-duty enterprise systems—a simple and effective way to break down barriers would be to set up a wiki where people could log unusual events in an informal way, or perhaps create an SMS system that allows people to informally submit quality ideas or complaints. It doesn't have to be heavy-handed."

"But software integration doesn't solve everything, does it?" asked Moulton.

"Right. As I mentioned before," Bonhoffer said, "software integration is not terribly meaningful unless there is effective communication between the humans using it. That means you have to break down the silos between the departments. Software integration takes care of some of that, but not all of it. I would suggest scheduling common meetings between plant maintenance, quality, and production managers on a regular basis.

"At these meetings, you'll want to coordinate processes across these departments and agree on common symbols, terms, and goals. I'd even suggest setting up meetings between different plants on a fairly regular basis so that best practices can be determined and shared between people who may not ordinarily be in touch with each other."

"What all the employees want is more meetings," chuckled Moulton. "How do we keep these things from going off the rails?"

"The best way to keep meetings from getting in the way of your work is having your software integrated and presenting a clear picture of current events so that you don't waste time chasing down information before anything substantial can be discussed," Bonhoffer said.

"Before I finish, I want to address the concept of Total Quality Management," Bonhoffer said. "The most important thing is for each employee to understand that her own commitment affects the success of the entire quality operation. So, how do you enforce that? One suggestion is to give each employee on the floor a brochure, perhaps attached to a little trinket or give-away, that reminds her of how important her commitment to quality is."

"Refrigerator magnets?" Bala asked.

"Sure, why not?" said Bonhoffer. "In isolation, it would be a trite and hollow gesture, but in conjunction with a smoothly run overall quality management process it could be enough to remind the employees that this is something they need to be committed to every day. It's essential that they all understand how interconnected their jobs are with the overall success of the plant and that they understand why these KPIs are being visited upon them. They need to understand that Total Quality Management is something the company adopts as a whole, not just something that they hand off to quality management. It also means other departments need to take on the mantle of quality management too, by providing the right information and having access to the right information."

"Thanks for the great information today, Joan," said Mulcahy. "All right, troopers, let's rally ourselves to go out there and instill TQM on our floor."

Bala and Moulton began to chant "T-Q-M" as they filed out the door.

Chapter Eleven

Visibility, Compliance, Opportunity, and Risk in the Perfect Plant

Contributing Authors:
Paul Boris, SAP
David Katona, SAP
Dan Knight, Cisco Systems, Inc.
Stewart McCutcheon, ACSIS
Bimal Mehta, SAP
Ian Ryan, SAP

Bala strode into the room with a pair of diving goggles on his face. "Good morning, people," he said with a grin. "You're probably wondering why I'm wearing these amazing, technologically advanced infrared goggles."

Peter Moulton raised his hand. "Because we're going to talk about visibility?"

"Absolutely correct, young sage," Bala said.

The Perfect Plant Vision

"Let me start," Bala said, "by trying to describe the optimal operating situation for a manufacturer running a perfect plant. I want to show how important information visibility is to that vision.

"To solve most problems in a plant, you need to obtain, correlate, contextualize, and analyze information from people, process control systems inside the plant, and systems in the corporation outside the plant, such as

ERP. With all of that information in one place, new insights are possible, as well as new forms of automation. These, in turn, can lead to reduced manual interaction, as well as improved performance in finance and compliance.

"First, the perfect plant leverages the investments you have already made in your enterprise applications. You've all sat through presentations where some vendor comes in and tells you his company is the One True Way, and you have to rip out all the old point solutions and replace them with their all-in-one system. That's a tough sell, and for a good reason. Despite any inherent inadequacies, there's a lot of value in the systems you have already installed and built into the minds of the people who are deeply familiar with them. 'And besides,' the logic goes, 'they work today, and that new system will take weeks or months to become productive.' Visibility is about creating an information intermediary that gets the most value out of what you already have, by displaying the right information to the right people, at the right time, in the right format, so that the job gets done faster and better," said Bala.

"Second, the perfect plant vision recognizes that not everyone has to drink from the fire hose—we don't all need to see all of the same information all of the time. That means we have a backbone of deep, rich information behind custom interfaces for each job role. 80% of the time, the guy on the floor operating the drill press or the transmission pipeline does not need to see anything except a red button for 'stop' and a green button for 'go.' Maybe 15% of the time he needs broader visibility into the work being done around him. That is, he needs to understand that things are speeding up or slowing down, running well or breaking down, and that he may need to get assistance. The rest of the time, maybe 5%, he must know that his capacity will need to be increased for the next few weeks, and that he'll need to change his work routine. So he's given access to supply and demand information when he needs to see it. Wouldn't it be great if that information ran in 'stealth' mode underneath his typical interface so that he could access it only when it was needed? Or better yet, popped up automatically just when he needed it?

"Similarly, a manager doesn't need to get a Blackberry message every time the valve opens or closes, or the drill press is turned off or on. But what if there was an extenuating circumstance? What if he was under the gun about mass balance or first-pass yield? He'd want to know right away whether his pipeline was running full-tilt, because he can't afford to wait until the morning meeting to find out what happened the day before. Then he could drill down and get that answer, using the same information intermediary as the floor operator. He wouldn't have to call somebody on the floor and not get his call returned, because they're too busy putting out fires that have nothing to do with his request or the real problems they are facing as a team.

"Those scenarios typify the value you can get from visibility and role-based portals. That means nobody has to wade through dozens of screens and menus to get the information they need, and depending on what their role is, they are typically only looking at information that pertains to what their role is 80% of the time. But if they need to access any information they have permission to see, they can, and they don't have to spend 15 minutes slogging through screens to get there.

"Third, we are now in a global manufacturing era. The supply chain of customers, partners, manufacturers, assembly, logistics, distribution, and sales and marketing may all be in different countries. A different company working in a different country may cover each of these aspects of the chain. Additionally, employees are dispersed throughout a single plant floor, off-site, and traveling around the world. They still need access to the right information at the right time. An infrastructure that can facilitate these communications has become increasingly important. You need secure access to real-time information from the production systems, as well as all of the tools and applications you need to effectively collaborate. It's important that you're not tied to your desk or operator station. You need the same access and capabilities if you are out on the plant floor or visiting a supplier halfway around the world. An integrated IP network helps you do that because it connects everything from devices on the plant floor to enterprise systems, all based on the same common standards."

"Essentially," Bonhoffer said, "everyone gets the information they need to do their jobs, but not any more than they need. But if there is some reason for them to look up more information, they can, and easily. In fact, depending on the problem, the system might actually guide them to the most important information first."

"In addition," Bala said, "one of the other big themes you'll hear a lot about is traceability. The scenarios that Joan described in her talk about Quality Management, where companies were shut down because they could not explain how food products got contaminated, really comes back to this idea of traceability.

"As I said, today's supply chains are widely distributed across multiple partners and geographies. The plant you're operating is but one node in a long chain of events, and everything that happens along the chain has an impact on everything that follows it. Any fluctuations that happen will have a wider impact on the network.

"In the perfect plant, you can detect a quality or inventory problem at any point in the process, send out alerts in both directions—to suppliers as well as to all downstream supply-chain participants—and prevent bad-quality batches from getting into customers' hands even as you remove any inventoried waste products from the chain."

"But that doesn't really happen now, does it?" Moulton asked.

"Not very often," Bala said. "But I can show you the tools and give you some good examples of companies that are either making it happen or coming very close to doing so.

"I want to point out that visibility in the perfect plant isn't just about staying the course and avoiding pitfalls. It's also about revealing new information that can help you do your job better. Imagine doing for the information systems in your plant what the open plan was supposed to do for interpersonal communications in the office. Hierarchies and closed doors need to be broken down in many plants. Maybe the people on the manufacturing floor will have a view into the product planning cycle that they didn't have before, because now it's so much easier to access that information. Maybe our front-line operators, instead of complaining about the performance of the machines, could actually break the mold and be the ones to initiate a capital request for new equipment–they are the ones dealing with that machine day in and day out, so who would know better than they? It's about striking a delicate balance between bombarding people with information they don't need or care about, and providing simple, straightforward access to several layers of information about the plant."

VISIBILITY IS:

- Not just risk management — identify opportunities

- Centralize data/common data model so ERP and manufacturing data interact usefully

HELPFUL FOR

- Compliance
- Risk
- Business optimization

Bala turned from the whiteboard and wiped his goggles with a handkerchief. "Before I go on about the details of implementing visibility, let me step back for a moment and define visibility in terms of what it helps you do in the plant.

"There is a tendency to identify visibility as the solution to a set of scary problems where there is asymmetry of information and something bad is going to happen as a result—and it definitely is that. But visibility isn't just about avoiding disaster. It's also about seeing opportunities that you haven't been able to see before. If you can visualize information on a single layer, rather than having to dig around for it, you'll see correlations in whole new ways. In a commodity environment, having the ability to provide order fulfillment information in real time may be a competitive advantage. What about the value of the production, test, and performance data collected in a high-tech manufacturing plant? What kind of value can downstream customers derive? Think of the opportunities for the aerospace and defense contractors who have all the parts specifications prior to their arrival in the facility, for example.

"Manufacturing people have drawn an arbitrary box around themselves as to what is possible. Visibility helps extend, and in some cases, dissolve those boxes so that real-time, pertinent information drives innovation and brings people closer to the work they are actually doing."

"Everyone's talking about the environment these days," Bonhoffer said, "and 'green' manufacturing. How do we cope with that, and where does it fit in with all this visibility we're gaining?"

"Environmentally responsible manufacturing is actually good for the bottom line," said Bala. "If Lean is the relentless pursuit and elimination of waste in all forms, then what's the difference between Lean and green manufacturing? Reducing scrap and waste, recycling by-products and co-products that can be sold rather than discarded, and reducing energy consumption are all Lean goals as well as green goals. It's hard to find a big difference between effective and efficient manufacturing processes and green processes when you describe the intended results.

"Enhanced visibility across the enterprise will enable organizations to become greener. Using third-party predictive analysis tools and other production optimization techniques, a company can see what its carbon emissions will be by the end of a production run if it maintains a given set of process parameters. With these tools, the company can say, 'If we maintain this yield, we might go over our carbon credit. Maybe we need to go onto the carbon trading exchange to buy more credit.' Or, it could be the other way around. 'If we maintain this rate of production, we'll be below our emissions cap. Let's sell off some of our extra credits.' Without the visibility provided by these tools, these types of considerations would never be possible."

"The people in charge of EH&S," Moulton said, "can also make decisions based on current trends of yield. They can ask questions like, 'To what extent is it financially and environmentally beneficial to stay below these limits?'"

"Another way that increased visibility can enhance an organization's greenness," Bala said, "pertains to who they choose to work with as partners in the supply chain, and how they deal with them along the way. For example, the Port of Los Angeles is about to enact some severe legislation that will force contract truckers to switch to low emission or biodiesel vehicles. An organization whose product goes through that port may want to evaluate the emissions of their distributors, and they can do it by simply requesting the data from them and then including it in their overall analysis. For some companies, knowing the emission levels of a provider could become a key factor in deciding whether they will work with them. Once companies have data on hand, they can perform analyses and make the best decision. Big companies like Wal-Mart are already asking their suppliers to be green. And because they are so big, they have the power to do so. They can dictate the level of greenness in the supply chain by demanding to know the exact substances in their products along with the emissions that are released in their production and transportation.

"In the end, it's imperative to remember that what you can't see, you can't measure, and what you can't measure you can't improve. Once you've obtained data, then you can establish boundaries, protocols, goals, and so forth. Visibility provides organizations with the opportunity to improve how they do business across the board, whether it's EH&S that is doing the analysis, S&OP, maintenance, or operations. Visibility, in a nutshell, is lean, mean, green, and efficient, but it also leads to innovation and a greater sense of investment in your work."

"Okay, Bala," Mulcahy said, "that's a great description of the pie-in-the-sky future of the plant. Now let's use our x-ray specs to drill down into the gritty reality of visibility in the plant."

The Visibility Challenge

"Let me tell you how bad it is out there in terms of all the information we've got to wade through," Bala said. "I'm sure you already have some idea, because you know how many applications you have open on your screens in your offices. Across the plant, and across manufacturers, it's far worse."

Disparity of Systems and Data

"I'll give you a couple of hard, cold facts about the lack of visibility in plants," Bala said, turning to the whiteboard.

THE CHALLENGE: DATA DISPARITY

- TYPICAL MANUFACTURING PLANT:
  10-50 SFA APPLICATIONS

- MULTI-SITE MANUFACTURER:
  40-700 SFA SYSTEMS ACROSS ENTERPRISE

- USUALLY NOT CONNECTED — PLANT-TO-PLANT
  OR PLANT-TO-ENTERPRISE

"The typical manufacturing plant," Bala said, "has between 10 and 50 shop floor automation, or SFA, applications. And, as you know, an increasing number of manufacturers outsource aspects of their production to partners. A typical multi-site manufacturer will have anywhere between 40 and 700 SFA systems. I even spoke with one company that catalogued 5,000 different sources of data across their six manufacturing sites. And if you think these systems all operate in lockstep synchronization, think again.

"In many ways, you can think of the manufacturing business as 'virtualized.' Most manufacturers no longer own their entire means of production. That makes for a very complex supplier and partner network. The trend started in electronics with companies like Selectron, but it's spread into all the other industries, including auto manufacturing. BMW, for instance, has a vehicle that's more than 90% outsourced.

"That would all be fine if the software had kept up with it, but it hasn't, and that's why we now have hundreds of point solutions operating at 50 factories that you don't necessarily have a lot of information about. With today's product cycles and stricter regulations, this is a major vulnerability."

Disconnected Components in the Plant

"Now," Bala said, "I'll give you a sketch of the disconnected components that plague firms from the plant floor to the head office, and show you the kind of damage they're doing."

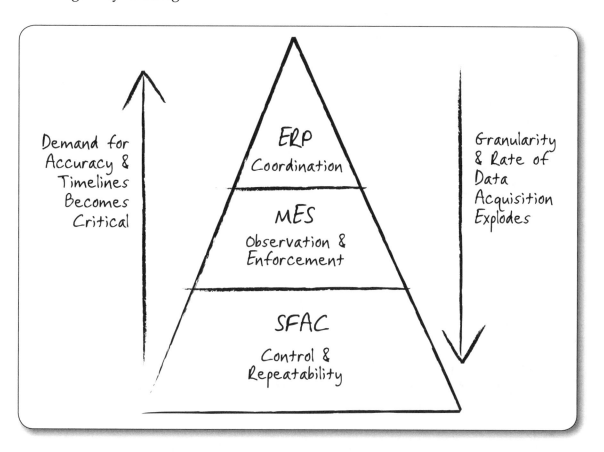

"Many firms have some sort of Manufacturing Execution System or MES—Peter already went into great detail about that—and it sits there, doing a good job of managing the shop-floor systems and the controllers and robots, and so forth. But that's only partial functionality as far as the whole-plant ecosystem is concerned. As Peter pointed out, most MES systems only cover about 30% of shop-floor functions, and that's not including the information that comes down from the corporate ERP system or automated general ledger. These MES applications tend to run in isolation from each other, so if you want them to speak to each other, you have to perform a lot of manual integration in an informal, unorganized way—call it 'sneaker-net'—and when someone finally creates enough of a justification to programmatically integrate them, it is a point-to-point integration that has no hope of surviving an upgrade and no capability to grow and change with the business demands. Worse yet, our corporate standard for MES is actually four different versions of the same package that barely resemble each other, due to each site's mission-critical modifications over the last three years. Quite frankly, a lot of these systems become 'the devil you know,' and the only reason plants continue to use them is because they have no real options other than a tearing them out and starting from scratch.

SHORTFALLS:

- ➤ Packaged MES only provides partial functionality
- ➤ Execution Systems not easily integrated into business
- ➤ Plant, Business & SNO information not fully contextualized
- ➤ Customization of Businesss Application can result in additional cost moving forward (at plant and enterprise)
- ➤ lack of comprehensive Platform to enable composite applications
- ➤ Lack of ability to support disconnected environment

"Many execution systems," Bala said, "are not easily integrated into the business side, because they were never intended to be run by corporate. So while they're great at managing directives about production, there isn't a lot of intelligence built into these applications that can adapt when business needs change. That cuts into agility and response time when the call for change comes down to the floor. The latency associated with the lack of integration, the time it takes to do the manual updates and data loads, often results in lost opportunity, and sometimes in lost product, due to faulty information flows. Also, when you're running multiple systems on the production floor, often with a dedicated infrastructure for each, it's extremely difficult to integrate these systems, and that results in an inflexible infrastructure within the plant.

"Plant, business, and sales and operations planning information is not contextualized. Often, you can't see the relationship between your international sales projections for next quarter and the burst valve that brought your tank down for three weeks—but you can bet there is one. What happens if that expedited order suddenly changes to a credit hold, or you just received a request for grade-b product and no longer need to scrap or regrind that production run, but can drum it off and sell it to a happy customer? If your systems are not integrated, you don't have the ability to coordinate that kind of a response.

"Customizing your business applications, such as HR and ledger, for your specific industry, or the characteristics of a certain plant location, is expensive and doesn't serve you well in the future. It's a one-off point solution that isn't extensible."

"But it happens a lot," Mulcahy added, "because managers don't see another way to build an application that makes sense for their particular deployment."

"A disconnected environment is very difficult to support," said Bala. "It may seem obvious to say so, but such environments persist more often than you'd expect. It's next to impossible to push out updates without driving up the man-hours, and you need local experts to handle support for custom installations. That's not cost-effective.

"The lack of visibility muddles the view in both directions. It's not just about corporate being blind to the realities of the floor, either. A lot of folks on the floor have been doing the same thing the same way for years, so they tend to be resistant to some executive brandishing some new piece of software for them to learn. People don't know how to approach them. As a result, the IT department's goals and objectives, and its vision of the perfect plant, gets further and further away from the plant-level vision. Change management becomes a yearly, ground-shaking event, rather than a gradual, smooth process of improvement and growth for everyone involved. The only path to change seems like a revolutionary, year-zero kind of change, where people's ownership of processes and their feelings of job security are threatened."

"And you will know us by the trail of dead, disused applications," Moulton said.

Costs of Poor Visibility

"Let me give a few examples of where poor visibility started to break the bank," Bala said. "In the early '80s, General Motors created a groundbreaking process—electrically deposited undercoating. As forward-looking as the technology was, they had little, if any, feedback from the field, and, as a result, found out far too late that the floor pans in thousands of vehicles were corroding. The problem was so large that Canadian dealerships had to stock a 'floor-pan replacement kit' for the affected vehicles.

"In another example, Hudson Foods suffered a product recall due to e.coli contamination that ultimately forced the company out of business. In August 1997 they recalled 20,000 pounds of beef patties, only to have the USDA identify contaminated material outside that batch. One week later, the recall was expanded to 1.2 million pounds. The final blow came one week after that when the recall was expanded to include 25 million pounds of product. This ultimately contributed to the collapse of the company. As Joan pointed out in the previous session, 10 years later, Topps Meat Company suffered the same fate—you would think they'd have learned."[1]

Traceability across the Global Manufacturing Supply Chain

"Business was tough enough when a company owned its entire means of production," Bala said. "But that's no longer the case. In the last 5 to 10 years,

---

[1] http://www.fsis.usda.gov/News/Recall_040_2007_Release/index.asp
   http://www.fsis.usda.gov/OA/recalls/prelease/pr015-97.htm

the manufacturing world has gone global. The problems of poor visibility still exist, only now they are magnified because today's supply chain is distributed across multiple companies and facilities across the globe. We live in a world of 'instant' everything—people want immediate access to information in real time. We expect that kind of information visibility from shipping and logistics companies, which manage a global supply chain in their own right. People are beginning to expect it from manufacturers. The problem in manufacturing is that we globalized before we properly integrated the information of all the players, so we often don't have consistent or reliable information about the status of a product at every step of the way.

"Ultimately, no matter how complex and efficient your value network, you are responsible for the satisfaction and safety of your customer. That means you must both demand and implement the tools to create visibility into all of your supply chain partners, up- and downstream from your plant. There's a saying in the industry that will be a mantra for us today: 'The only thing worse than missing a shipment to a customer is missing it and not knowing it.' It won't do any good to point fingers at your suppliers if something goes wrong—your reputation will still be hurt."

"What can we do about this sorry state of affairs?" Mulcahy asked.

Process and discrete industries

"We need to get to a state of total traceability for both process and discrete industries," Bala replied. "You can think of traceability as a product's genealogy. Where did it come from? Where was it made? Where did its parts come from? Who supplied them? The closer a company gets to that level, the more competitive it is.

"In the process industries, you're mainly looking at batches of material. You want to be able to say, 'I made a batch of 1,000 pounds of chemical A, and I want to know all the ingredients that went into making it. I want to know that this batch of raw material supplied by Vendor A was put into batch number 101 of this product XYZ.' In pharmaceuticals that's extremely important—a product needs to have a 'pedigree' so the consumer has confidence that the product is what it claims to be. Their health is on the line.

"In discrete industries, you trace the parts genealogy based on serial numbers. You want to be able to go all the way down to the smallest component level and check the quality history and pinpoint specific problems.

"Then there's the question of shipping, logistics, and distribution. Even after the final product is made, you need to know where it is at all times. Is it in a warehouse when it should be on a shelf? Is it on a rail siding somewhere? Is the packaging correct? Did the right product go to the right person?"

Pressure to go lean

Bala continued, "At the same time that we're seeing manufacturing become a global, multi-enterprise operation, we're also seeing a lot of pressure to go Lean, and to keep inventories as low as possible. If your supplier's plant goes down, that may have a much more immediate effect on you than it would have in the past, because you're not keeping as much in inventory."

"So if you don't have visibility into what's going on in this broader enterprise, you're at the mercy of upsets that you never see coming," Bonhoffer said. "But how do you improve this situation?"

"I'll give you an example," Bala said. "There was a process business that used to maintain a 25-day supply of raw materials to manage unexpected raw material plant outages, or to guard against an unfavorable change in weather conditions that would prevent shipments from arriving. A big reason for this buffer of time was that they didn't know what was going on with the supplier, so they couldn't react quickly if there was a problem. The company heard about the advantages some of its competitors were getting from barcode scans and Radio Frequency Identification (RFID) tags. As a result, they started to instrument their supply chain—including their suppliers as well as the company-owned plants. They now have real-time access to what's going on in the inventory, not only in their own facilities, but also in those of their trading partners. Now the company knows when it or its partners have issues, which means they can react. Increased visibility gave the business confidence to drop its raw materials inventory down to eight days.

"Traceability allows you to provide assurances to customers with much greater confidence. Rather than make a too-conservative or too-aggressive commitment, because you aren't really sure if you have enough inventory or whether your suppliers are up to the task, you could, at the first point of customer contact, look up all the inventory levels and confidently make an aggressive delivery commitment."

Tracing other assets

"Traceability also allows you to track assets other than the product itself," Bala went on, "such as packaging, equipment, or shipping containers. Sort of like the link you see on Amazon.com, 'Where's my stuff?' You'd be surprised how many manufacturers have a hard time answering that. To correct this problem, companies are installing RFIDs and other sensors on everything. It's on the shipping door portal at the warehouse. The inventory management system talks to the ERP and other data systems in the enterprise, so that if a forklift is about to place the wrong product in the truck, alarms go off immediately.

"Another scenario involves inventory again. Just as companies stack up a lot of inventory to account for raw materials discrepancies, they also stack up a lot of asset inventory, such as railcars, totes, and shipping cylinders. They do this because they can't always be sure where all their assets are. They spend their way out of the problem and increase their asset costs, rather than invest in the technology to track assets with precision.

"Traceability also helps with recalls. A mass recall order costs precious time and money, especially in competitive fields, such as computers, where product cycles may be shorter than the time it takes to execute a recall. With good visibility, it's much easier to do a 'surgical recall.'

"Imagine finding out from your raw materials supplier that they have a defective raw material. Rather than issue a blanket recall and tell everybody, 'Hey, you have to send back all of this product, because we don't know exactly which batches are defective,' you can issue a surgical, focused recall because you've tracked and traced the process. You know *this* raw material went into *that* finished product, went into *that* delivery, went into *that* distribution channel, and went to *that* customer. Your supply chain partners, vendors, and distributors are getting alerts through widgets installed on their computers, phones, and PDAs, saying this raw material was defective. Any one of these people can then go into the application and say, 'Where is that raw material?' It shows the raw material inventory that you still have in stock that is defective, and you immediately place a hold on it so that you don't use it. Then you find out you've already made some finished product with that raw material, and some of that's in inventory, so you put a hold on that. And then you find out some of that product's already been shipped to a customer. Since you have your traceability platform integrated with Google Maps, you pull up a picture that says *this* raw material is now in *this* finished product that's in *these* locations. It's at *these* distributors, it's in *this* finished product—and you can, through your integrated supply chain, place a hold on that product, which is no longer even in your facility."

It's more than cost

"That sounds great, Bala," Mulcahy said. "But aren't most outsourced supply chains a lot more low-tech than that? And isn't their low-tech nature actually part of their value proposition? Companies are really between a rock and a hard place. On the one hand, they're told to 'be lean, be efficient, cut costs,' and on the other hand, they are pilloried for outsourcing work to low-cost sources who do shoddy work, put dangerous chemicals in the product, or maintain dangerous or inhumane working conditions. Companies look pretty stupid standing in front of the press, saying, 'We didn't know!' How do we get beyond this?"

"In the next wave of globally distributed supply chains," Bala said, "manufacturers will be looking for a lot more from their partners than low cost. As I suggested earlier, companies will start selecting their outsourcing partners based on their ability to provide the information they need to produce a level of confidence and satisfaction with the products that their customers demand. Some companies, such as Nike and Cisco Systems, have made a lot of headway by demanding deep visibility from their suppliers and outsourcers."

"What about companies that already have an established network of suppliers?" Moulton asked. "What can they do to improve visibility?"

"Like most of the problems we've talked about," Bala said, "the solution is a combination of human effort and technology. First of all, companies must start writing better service-level agreements with their partners. If you say, 'Just make it low-cost, I don't care how you do it,' then you're asking for a great deal of pain down the line. So whether the solution means seeking new partners or renegotiating with old ones, those SLAs have to cover the level of information you need to achieve extremely granular traceability.

"The next issue is enforcing those agreements. Sometimes, in order to make those margins on their low-cost services, some of your suppliers may not be able to afford to put in a totally automated, real-time RFID system. You then have to make a decision about whether it is cost-effective to install that system at your supplier, or provide some kind of lighter portal-type application, into which operators can enter the information you're looking for, such as a certificate of analysis. If you do that, you have to know you can trust people to enter accurate information in a timely fashion, and be sure that they are only sharing that information with you, and not with your competitors. That means you either need to have someone from your company, or a trusted third party, supervising that facility on a regular basis, or moving in permanently on-site. And your contract has to be structured so that the outsourcer is rewarded for accuracy and accountability as much as it is for speed and thrift. Otherwise, you are likely to be told only what you want to hear."

"No news is not necessarily good news," said Moulton.

Performance Goals and Accountability on the Factory Floor

"Now, let's go back to the factory floor," Bala said. "I'm going to talk a lot about software integration, which is a big part of the solution for a lot of the visibility problems. But it's important to remember the human element in all of this. The bottom line is that the operators on the floor are making or breaking the company, because they make the products. So they need to understand they have some agency or importance within the organization.

"An operator working in a control room in a refinery is a big-time economic decision-maker. The decisions he or she makes can have massive impact. But if he is only presented with information that tells him what to do and what not to do, without showing him why, in terms of the bigger picture, he feels robotic and detached from the process.

"I know we've used this expression before, but it holds true in visibility as much as in execution and quality management. If you simply make people 'feed the beast' by putting screens down on the floor and making them enter data and collect data without feedback, they don't know how they're doing and there's no empowerment. If you want initiatives in applying technology and new methodologies in a plant to succeed, the operations people and the plant people need to feel like they're getting something out of it. Surprisingly few companies do this. But it's something you have to invest in, or you won't get the results you want. That's why a window into planning and strategy information from the operator's console has to be there—it should not be a case of involuntary bombardment. Instead, think of it like a window that can be open or shut—sometimes you want to see what the traffic is doing, but most of the time you don't want to hear it. The presence and the role of that window need to be reinforced with training and a broader sense of involvement in the company's goals."

"And it needs to go both ways," said Bonhoffer. "I imagine you want to let process engineers see manufacturing issues and manufacturing people see product planning issues. Throwing new sets of eyeballs at the problem tends to dramatically reduce the friction that's causing those problems."

"That's exactly right," said Bala. "Visibility also allows connections to be made between focus areas and departments that seem like they should be joined at the hip, but in fact are not typically synchronized the way, for instance, that energy management and planning are. For example, it's not uncommon for a facility, where energy costs are a concern, to work with local suppliers and either buy and sell credits to get the best pricing, or throttle production to consume at optimal times.

"In one example, from the Air Products and Chemicals industry, company A buys and sells energy credits and ties that information to customer demand and logistics to determine the best possible production plan—one where profit is optimized, customer demand is appropriately fulfilled, and energy credits are consumed in the most effective fashion. The remaining credits are sold back into the grid at a potential profit.

"In another example, a foundry needs to schedule its pour operation to take advantage of off-peak consumption rates. However, if the wrong material is poured, it can negatively impact the finishing and assembly operations that follow downstream."

Standards and the Data Warehouse

"Now we're going to look at the roots of the problem and at a possible solution," Bala said. "I'm going to start by saying something that may surprise people from the corporate end of things. In terms of information standardization, I think it's fair to say that manufacturing is well ahead of the business world.

"At the enterprise level, we're trying to create services between enterprise applications so they can each provide useful information and functionality to places outside the domain for which it was originally built. But the plant has lived with that situation for a lot longer, in a more extremely distributed and disparate environment. As a result, a variety of standards have been initiated. Manufacturing, by virtue of necessity, has had to have some form of distributed services and standards defined so it could actually manage its environment. This why manufacturing is *ahead* of the enterprise in having defined a set of useful services that connect everything and are reusable."

"If manufacturing has more established standards than business processes, why do we need this meeting about visibility?" asked Bonhoffer.

"The problem with visibility in manufacturing is not that we don't have standards," Bala said. "We have tons of standards, such as OPC, which allowed the PLCs from different manufacturers on the plant floor to communicate with each other and with an MES. There's ISA S-95, too, which mediates between the MES and ERP to achieve correlation between order management and execution. There's also S-88 for batch process control. The ISA is also developing standards for security, with SP-99, and wireless systems, with SP-100, which will be particularly important as more factories run on converged IP networks, and corporate network and business systems become integrated with manufacturing systems.

"Although I'm going to cover standards more deeply in my next talk, I do want to say that just because we have them doesn't mean that they interoperate very well. There are gaps between them. Complicating matters is the fact that many control systems use proprietary standards."

"A friend of mine used to say, 'Standards are like toothbrushes. Everyone knows they need to use one, but no one wants to use anyone else's,'" Mulcahy said.

"There has been a culture of adding more and more systems to do specific tasks and not replacing them until they break down, partly because making them work together seemed so unachievable," said Bala. "Standards don't actually resolve all the information that you might need from the enterprise for the global context, or even just from a manufacturing view perspective. Standards don't leave much room for hypothetical situations, like the scrap factor or the sudden delivery of a lot of quality information. Combine the proliferation of standards with the idea of a 'virtualized plant' that is comprised of global suppliers and partners, and you're talking about a lot of information in a lot of different formats.

"A plant needs to be able to reach outside itself for information. And so it needs to have a model of the world that starts with the orders in corporate and extends through all the suppliers, the owned and outsourced plants, and then extends out through distribution. That said, however, a plant can't be beholden to the availability of that information from a supplier. If a supplier goes down, the plant still has to be able to run. If the corporate ERP system is being fixed, the plant still has to produce. The plant can't shut down simply because of a disruption in their electronic connection to the corporate office or the world in general."

"What could possibly help resolve this issue of standards proliferation and data inconsistency across the enterprise and manufacturing domains?" Moulton asked.

Bala mimed opening a door. "Enter the manufacturing data warehouse, my friends," he said. "Here is where we construct a model of what's inside and outside your plant.

"The key ingredient in a data warehouse is metadata, or basically, data about data. It affords a layer of abstraction to which your ERP and MES systems can write, and if it's well built, then it also comes with adaptors for the various standards we have been talking about. What that does is call all of these disparate elements and corral them into a service that's available to applications and users that may be outside the domain of origin.

"Say a marketing director in the USA wanted to find out what was happening with fulfillment of orders with the distributor in Europe. The marketing director's sales application, probably Excel or something Excel-based, would call the data warehouse, which would then contact the inventory system in Europe. Both the sales and inventory apps, which could have been created by different firms at different times using totally different protocols, can at minimum speak in XML, which the warehouse understands. Plus it has built-in adaptors for an ever-increasing number of applications the manufacturer uses. That means that an interface need only exist between the data warehouse and each application, rather than running a spaghetti system of direct APIs between every conceivable piece of software, using a huge number of protocols and languages. The warehouse should also be able to spit out data in any of the aforementioned standards, irrespective of what version the data might be on the back end.

"The warehouse also feeds the ERP system and is maintained under the full control of the enterprise, which means that if one of our virtualized plants or a supplier goes down, our data doesn't go down with them, and there are no broken links. This also means that we can store that information and make it readily available for the analysis and the reporting capabilities we will need to feed the compliance and financial reporting beasts, as well as all of our KPIs."

"Aren't we just talking about a messaging middleware bus here?" Mulcahy said. "Haven't enterprises had these for years?"

"It's true," Bala said, "that an enterprise services bus, or ESB, is the backbone of any service-oriented architecture (SOA). But the data warehouse, which is the database and repository of adaptors, as well as the manufacturing platform which does the translating, places a layer of meta-data intelligence over the ESB specific to manufacturing and allows some of that pie-in-the-sky visibility to happen. It also allows you to create composite applications out of the applications you already have. Think of ESB as the electricity, the data warehouse as the batteries, and the platform as the appliance.

"And while we're at it, think of the IP network as the electrical distribution network, because that's pretty much what it is. The starting point to attack against the proliferation of isolated systems is at the infrastructure level. There is a movement in manufacturing towards standard networking technologies such as Ethernet, TCP/IP, and 802.11-based wireless for plant automation systems. This is making it easier to connect and integrate multiple systems, but there is still a lot of complexity due to the number of application-level standards in industrial automation. The use of standard networking technologies, however, provides a networking infrastructure that can support multiple applications over the same network. So at least we can eliminate the duplication of networks and enable increased visibility through remote access, connectivity, and the ability to deliver information in multiple forms, such as voice, data, and video, to people in different locations."

Manufacturing Platform Architecture

"The key thing to know about the platform is that it's data-model-centric," Bala said. "Everything the platform does can be traced back to the data model, because that's what mediates between all of the existing applications that speak different protocols. It also allows the creation of a visual composition environment—instead of hard-coding stand-alone links between applications, you are using a graphical user interface, or GUI, to move icons around onscreen. It's like the difference between using command lines on green screens and using Windows on your PCs."

"That should mean more people at varying levels of technical proficiency can participate in application creation and modification," said Bonhoffer.

"Exactly," said Bala. "Another important feature is the local survivability model. In this crazy-quilt world of distributed manufacturing, it's imperative that there is no single point of failure in the network. If one part of the chain goes down, the other parts must still be able to do their jobs."

"So if the ERP system at corporate is down, you want to still be able to do your jobs at the plant level," said Moulton.

"Yes," said Bala. "It could be very costly if you scheduled overtime for a Saturday to expedite orders and it turns out somebody upstairs has the ERP system down for maintenance. But if you can locally cache or store the data that has come downstream, and locally queue the data that you ordinarily would send immediately upstream, at least for a few hours or days, you can still carry on as if the ERP system were running. You need a robust data model and a functioning data warehouse to do that. It might not run for weeks, or even globally, but in critical areas, it could save you a lot of trouble and money."

"So even though most of the time 'the network is the computer,' you don't want to find out that 'without the network, we're all neutered,'" said Moulton.

"The third key thing about the platform that sets it above the typical messaging middleware," said Bala, "is that it has been engineered to connect to all the manufacturing standards and enterprise historian systems. And if it is a productized SOA, you know you have the support of a software firm that will keep track of the updates and make sure each version of the system has the latest adaptors for your industry. Connecting to those systems also can be accomplished in a matter of minutes, because the connectors have already been supplied and maintained by the platform provider. You don't have to dive into your historian database or map tags. It's simply a matter of adding another dashboard to your screen, and you can map how you want to correlate historian data with any of your other systems."

Best Questions

"Okay, people," Bala said, "we're now at the point where we're ready to develop best questions for visibility in the perfect plant. If you had an hour on the factory floor and could fire away at anyone, what would you ask to help your understanding of whether or not the plant has sufficient visibility?"

"How about, 'Do you have a way of creating composite applications?'" Mulcahy said.

"That's great," Bala said. "If your plant isn't using composite applications, then they'd better have unusually simple or transparent operations. Composite applications can really help you see the correlations between previously stand-alone functions and get a better sense of your enterprise as a whole. How about another?"

"Do you have manufacturing data spread across your plant," Moulton said, "and, if so, can you integrate or correlate it from various systems and have a unified view into the data?"

"Peter, you must have read my notes for today," Bala said. "That's a great one—a unified view of data means everyone is literally on the same page. How about you, Joan?"

"Do you need to contextualize or even hide some information from your users, based on roles?" Bonhoffer said.

"I think you guys are the new experts on this," Bala said. "One of the big foundations for a manufacturing platform is the need for some of the information, some of the time, and the need to not always have all the information, all the time.

"Here are some other pertinent questions. 'Do people have access to the information they need and the ability to collaborate and take action, regardless of their location within the plant or whether they're in a remote location?' If not, it's time to consider your network infrastructure efforts, including wireless networks.

"You'd also want to ask, 'Is there a need to proactively schedule events happening on your shop floor, and to correlate that information with ERP information?' If the answer is yes, there's another tick in the 'Platform' column.

"Try this one, too: 'Is there a need to have workflow capabilities to respond to issues like a machine breakdown—and a need to understand how that impacts your business?' If yes, that could very well be another platform designer.

"Here's a real stinger: 'Can you model a complex business process where the data is spread across multiple systems? Does the act of modeling become a manual process because you're not able to integrate that data and visualize that information in a single layer?' If somebody has to put it on paper and then do calculations, how competitive do you really think you are?"

"Ouch," Moulton said.

"I'm just calling it like I researched it," Bala said. "Next, you'd want to ask, 'What capabilities do you have for closing the loop for automation? What capabilities do you have to link monitoring and alerting to the ERP system and the upstairs planning systems? Do you have visibility into your manufacturing operations and supply chain? Do you have the ability to drill down to the deepest level of traceability required without jumping from system to system?'

"Focusing on incentives and integration: 'Do you have your KPIs defined consistently in a standard way across your sites?'

"Looking at partners and outsourcing: Are you capturing the right level of quality information regarding the components you outsourced? Do you have visibility into your supplier data?'

"And I think the most important one is, 'Is there a culture of collaboration?' A lot of this talk has been about software, but really, nothing will happen unless there is a supportive culture for collaboration."

Perfect Plant Playbook: Visibility

"Before we go to lunch, and I get to take off these goggles," said Bala, "let's talk about the 'Perfect Plant Playbook for Visibility.' I think we can pretty easily draw some strong conclusions about how to achieve visibility in the plant.

"If we go back to the top of the talk and look at the qualities in a perfect plant, we can see how visibility assists each of those points.

"Number one, you want to leverage the investment you've made in your existing enterprise architecture. You don't need to rip out and replace what you've got. You just want to place a layer of intelligence over it, so that useful information doesn't go undiscovered, and so that people are not constantly bombarded with information they don't need.

"Two, you want the shop-floor systems to be firmly integrated with the rest of the enterprise. That means an operator on the floor could see the financial impact of his decisions, and someone sitting up in the office knows the financial impact of a quality problem and gets a warning when it starts happening. The less time spent making inquiries, tapping your feet while waiting for feedback and scratching your head, the more productive your plant will be.

"The best way to do either of the above is to implement a Manufacturing Hub. You want to focus your internal development resources on developing specific, point applications that do what your factory needs to do, not on integration. And if you do develop those applications off of Excel, or use standards, there are software vendors out there who are ready to help you build a lot of value out of those applications. That value really comes through when people who are on another level of your organization can see into those applications, and understand quickly and succinctly how they are providing the information your organization needs to function at its highest potential.

"The manufacturing platform will also help with traceability, by reconciling the events and information happening outside the enterprise with those happening inside the walls of your plant. However, the platform won't provide you any value for traceability if you do not first take the steps to enable traceability throughout your supply chain. That means installing a standardized naming convention throughout your network, supported by electronic means such as RFID tagging and barcode readers. Throughout your supply chain you will need to enforce accountability, because ultimately it's your name on the product. That could mean installing software at the partners' sites if their economic models don't allow them to do that. It may also mean implementing more stringent supervisory controls on those sites. It most certainly means writing an explicit, enforceable SLA with these partners, so there are no unpleasant surprises down the line.

"Lastly, don't forget tribal knowledge. Make a concerted effort to gather the expertise of those who may be headed out the door with a head or file folders full of useful information. That is information that no external software vendor will be able to replicate. I'd suggest looking into collaboration technologies, such as wikis. For the purpose of collecting this knowledge, the simpler the collaboration technology, the better."

With a flourish, Bala removed his goggles and bowed to the applause from the three hungry manufacturing executives.

Chapter Twelve

Architecture, Standards, and Interoperability

Contributing Authors:
Connie Chiu, Cisco Systems, Inc
Ashtad Engineer, Tata Consultancy Services
Paul Didier, Cisco Systems, Inc
Stewart McCutcheon, ACSIS

Joan Bonhoffer, Peter Moulton, and John Mulcahy all took their seats around the conference table as Bala opened his laptop and stepped up to the whiteboard. "For the past few sessions," Bala said, "we've focused on detailed areas of the plant, but it's time to jump back into the world of the big picture. Today I'll talk about some of the general architectural principles that apply to systems inside a plant. Certain patterns appear over and over in successfully run plants. The point of view I take is based on John's ideas and those from several of his friends in the industry."

"In this case," Mulcahy added, "architecture means all the structural elements designed to meet the needs of the plant, including the design and structure of the building, the configuration of the line, the power systems, the water and sewer, and the way that air, heat, steam, and liquids are monitored and moved around the plant."

"All the stuff you're stuck with," said Moulton, "there's not much we can do about those things, right?"

"That's exactly what I thought when I started looking into this," said Bala. "And you're right that we won't go into plants and suggest ways of changing the line or reconfiguring power delivery—those things takes a long time to figure out and usually show up as part of the capital requests that John gets every year."

"So what can we do about architecture?" asked Bonhoffer.

"Most of our previous discussions involved increasing the amount of information that's available to run the plant, getting it into the hands of the right people, providing tools so they can understand the information, and making sure it's easy to communicate with others," said Bala. "Once you understand how things are working, then you may want to change and improve them. We're going to discuss the following questions." Bala turned and wrote on the whiteboard.

> (?) How can you design a plant so that the information needed to run it is available?
>
> (?) What sort of systems increase information and flexibility?
>
> (?) What role do standards play in achieving these goals?
>
> (?) What role does the network play in achieving these goals?

The case for better architecture

"Many people in the plant aren't interested in architecture," said Bala. "They just want the information they need to run the plant. A superior architecture provides that information, but a horrible architecture can provide it as well."

"So then why is it important?" asked Moulton.

"The systems in place may provide production information to run the plant," said Bala. "But when things need to be changed, a good architecture and a complete data set makes it easier to reconfigure the plant and lowers the cost. Architecture becomes much more important in a time of rapid change and evolution."

"Designing the architecture of a plant is an art form," said Mulcahy. "So far, we've talked about helping Wolverine's plants create a vision for where they want to go and how to start moving towards it, yet most plants are designed for operation at a fixed set of conditions. The essence of a perfect plant is the ability to change rapidly to meet known and unknown requirements. You can't do this without complete information—not just production information. The data set you need for maximum production is different than the one you need for quality and is different than the one you need for ultra-high reliability. Creating an architecture that will support efficiency and maintainability throughout its life means providing one that supports the effort no matter what the goals. In order to interpret this expanded focus, the systems must deliver analytics in real time, especially ways of calculating the metrics, the true metrics—indicators of value being created from the customer's perspective. "

"When we're in a plant," said Moulton, "how can we tell if they have a good architecture without asking how they would react to change?"

"Information architecture has to be comprehensive in its approach. First, look to see if the plant's systems were driven by only a single focus, for example, operations," said Mulcahy. "You have to record not only information about the equipment or the facilities, but also about the knowledge of how to run the plant and make the products. This intellectual property can be initially stored in all the people's brains but documented in the models used to run that plant."

"Is that true?" said Moulton. "People will pay to buy a building or the equipment but not the intellectual property in people's heads."

"That's where you're wrong," said Mulcahy. "When people buy a business, they often lock out the key employees, but this can be mitigated by encapsulating the knowledge into the information systems and not depending on a skilled workforce. A long time ago, I worked at a company that made thermometers. Based in upstate New York and long before outsourcing hit, they got excited about moving to a southern state with lower labor costs. Unfortunately, after they moved, they found that, although labor costs were lower, they couldn't easily find people to do the work. A community of skilled people had grown around the plant in New York, and around other plants in similar businesses, forming a pool of knowledge that actually kept that plant going. When the company moved, it lost access to that pool of knowledge and this made the move very difficult."

"But how does this relate to architecture?" asked Moulton.

"The biggest architectural issue is to separate the knowledge from the infrastructure. Although models are important, a project that depends on perfect models or analytics or even overall goals will stall if the basic information is not available. Start thinking of what you'll see when you go into a plant," said Mulcahy. "You'll see people using technology and information systems to run the plant. A good architecture is not only a combination of a sound, reliable, maintainable infrastructure—the network, data collection, instrumentation, sensors, and analyzers—it also includes good tools to create a knowledge management system that captures as much of the intellectual property about how to run a plant as possible. In a plant with a good architecture, you see people using data from the systems to make decisions in a quite unexpected and unplanned way, as well as systems that support the usually planning. This is your first clue that somebody was thinking about architecture and not about a project. The architecture supports collecting information about what's going on in a timely manner, analysis to compute the metrics, and context, such as master data and an equipment list, to help people understand the information. For example, a lot of plants are being asked to use less energy. For many of them, the first step is to understand how they're using energy. A plant with a good architecture is already collecting that data and provides the tools to analyze and present it to all who might need it. Without a picture of where you are, it is impossible to improve in any systematic way."

"So, is a good architecture a knowledge management system?" said Moulton.

"No. It is the combination of an infrastructure and analysis to support the knowledge management system," said Mulcahy. "Ready access to information requires participation of every layer. Bala, why don't you go over the levels of architecture in the Purdue model and the platform versus infrastructure discussion."

"Sure," said Bala. "In the session on execution, Peter introduced the Purdue model, which explains the levels of production software systems in a manufacturing plant. Let me quickly draw it up for you again."

LEVEL 4	Enterprise Processes
LEVEL 3	Manufacturing Operations
LEVEL 2	Automation/Connectivity
LEVEL 1	Shop Floor Process Control
LEVEL 0	Plant Equipment

"Most of the software systems we've talked about are located at level 4 and level 3, the levels that deal with higher level processes, "said Bala. "In the ERP system, you have the orders, shipments, and inventories. The supply chain systems track the materials as they flow toward the plant as well the other resources required to run the plant properly. The warehouse management software keeps track of what's in inventory. As we learned in the sessions on planning and execution, there is an overall plan that the plant attempts to follow, and at some point an MRP run is done to ensure the right materials are on hand to avoid outages, and then this gets translated to a production order or a process order, depending on the industry. All of that was level 4. The MRP run brings us into level 3 and that's where the systems for asset management, quality management, and energy management appear. The execution system helps translate the production or process order into the instructions for the different cells or workstations in the plant. Now we're into levels 2 and 1 where the systems that control the equipment at level 0 make everything happen. So far, so good.

"Architecture is not just production software. Levels 3 and 4 are about software, but to optimally run a plant you need data that show what's happening. How is the work progressing through the plant? If there is a problem at any level, what are your choices for resolving it? What are the implications for rushing an order or delaying one? How do you cope with equipment outages? The details for these sorts of questions come from the systems in levels 2 and 1, but they can only be transmitted to the higher levels if context and connectivity allow. Ideally, each piece of equipment should be able to report its status to the local controllers, which should be able to send information to higher level systems. You also want to be able to see the history of how the equipment has performed and how it has been maintained. People running the plant should be able to see what's coming to them and its effect on the rest of the plant.

"A good architecture has another dimension, too, which is an accurate cost model," said Bala. "A good cost model helps predict where to invest in applications to provide the most benefit, and this list is expanded with superior information availability.

"The cost model of a manufacturing organization has a profound impact on the underlying architecture," continued Bala. "If it's accurate, you'll have a good idea where improvements will give you the most bang for the buck. If it's not accurate, you'll wind up putting the money in the wrong place and you won't get the ROI you (and the financial people) are expecting. You need to put time into building a good financial model as well when looking at architectural decisions."

"That cost information is key. So am I right to say that a good architecture is designed to give you any information you're looking for, any place, any time?" asked Moulton.

"Well, that's what you want," said Bala. "But nobody's there yet. A lot of the current architecture wasn't designed to support this world, and the plant's networks aren't ready. No plant could afford to make everything completely visible and connected because it would require replacing huge amounts of equipment, but it is hard to justify not making information already in digital format available for use. In many cases, plants today have equipment with interfaces that provide data that no one bothers to monitor. In a refinery, the estimate to install a new transmitter is $17,000—but it is hard to justify not monitoring the data from that sensor once you've got it installed."

"So most architectural questions in a plant involve deciding how to support the changes that are sure to begin even before the first product is made," said Bonhoffer. "Since you can't do it everywhere, you have to choose your battles and ensure that a general-purpose infrastructure is in place that will provide the data you need and that makes good financial sense. You may add an application after the first year but infrastructure is seldom changed. For example, if the basic networks are missing, you will not be able to retrofit a plant just to create an environmental compliance report. The converse is also true—if you install an infrastructure for environmental compliance, it probably will not support production very well. That's why creating a good general-purpose architecture requires a lot of thought."

"You're right about the architectural challenge at most plants," said Bala. "And the application and infrastructure distinction is important. For example, for most of us, desktop productivity tools like word processing and spreadsheet applications are infrastructure. They provide raw functionality and everyone knows how to use them. When we create a spreadsheet for a particular purpose and share it with others, it becomes an application and must be supported. In the plant, raw networking equipment is infrastructure that allows communication. Data acquisition technology that provides access to raw information along with analysis tools is infrastructure. Platforms are defined by the relationship between companies—to Microsoft, Intel chips are their platform, but Office is part of the infrastructure; it delivers value without another company building an application on it."

"So, the infrastructure is the enabling technology built on platforms like Microsoft and has stand-alone benefit," said Bonhoffer. "Are software applications also infrastructure?"

"This is where things get a bit fuzzy," said Bala. "Infrastructure is usually a general purpose facility, like a network, basic desktop system, or data monitoring. Applications use that infrastructure for a particular purpose, such as automating a business process."

"What does this have to do with architecture?" asked Bonhoffer.

"When you want to invest in improving your plant, you will be faced with decisions about how to get the most bang for your buck," said Bala. "By investing at the infrastructure level and providing the tools for people to make use of that information, you give people the ability to use it in both predictable and unpredictable ways. That's why infrastructure for data analysis and collaboration is becoming more and more important in plants. When you put more data in the hands of more people, they can use their brains to figure out what's going on. They can combine data from many sources and see trends. You want to be able to store information from many sources and store the context for that information.

"Once people have identified something important, it needs to be available to others who may be interested, and someone needs to maintain and support it. This is where the collaboration infrastructure becomes important. When people figure something out, they may need help putting it in context, such as a model. But then if the model changes, the application that uses it must also change. The tools to move from infrastructure to applications are improving. Aside from the basic tools like Microsoft Office, you have another related form of infrastructure that is allowing people to craft their own little applications called mashups that collect data from many sources and present it in new ways. Sort of do-it-yourself development."

"What's an example of a mashup?" asked Bonhoffer.

"Let's suppose we get a bad batch of raw material," replied Bala. "Some of that product is in raw material inventory; some is on the plant floor about to be used; some has been used to make finished product and is in our inventory; and some has already been shipped to a customer. A mashup could locate where all the material is and notify the interested parties to put a quality hold on the product."

"This sort of thing would only fit if you actually expected your workers to take the initiative," said Moulton. "I can't see this sort of architecture working in a place with a locked down command and control mentality."

"You're right," said Mulcahy. "Investing in infrastructure only works if you expect people to use it. There's another barrier as well. Many of the level 3 systems did not live up to their initial billing and plant managers have been reluctant to invest because of past failures. Most of the time these failures occurred because the software was introduced as a narrow application that could succeed only if very specific goals were met. The software was not intended to be infrastructure that could have been used by many people for many purposes."

"All this still seems rather general," said Moulton. "Can we be more specific about what sort of architecture would work?"

Manufacturing SOA: Increasing Information and Flexibility

"Service-oriented architecture, or SOA, is a much more specific form of architecture that achieves most of the goals that we've been talking about," said Mulcahy. "It's been around for several years in the enterprise software business. People are starting to talk about the idea of manufacturing service-oriented architecture as a way of applying SOA to manufacturing."

"In service-oriented architecture, every system that wants to allow access to information or services does so by publishing a 'service' that others can consume," said Bala. "The idea of encapsulating everything into autonomous, stateless chunks is not new. Software design has been trying to decompose applications into clean calling paths, with object-oriented programming and CORBA and so forth. Services are much higher level, however, and can perform complex standalone functions. What's generated so much interest in SOA, as implemented today, is that now we have a pervasive network and all the technology vendors have gotten behind a standard interface for the services, called web services, to make services easier to discover, understand, and consume. Each web service interface is described in a standard form by something called a WSDL file, which stands for Web Service Description Language. This is the software equivalent of a standard set of plugs and sockets. WSDL describes the structure of the plug and the information that flows back and forth through it."

"So how does this affect architecture in a plant?" asked Moulton.

"Well," said Bala, "if you take a step back from all this technical detail, you can see why SOA is the best way to get all the systems in a plant talking to each other. The infrastructure in the plant can't be ripped and replaced. You have point solutions, best of breed applications, and monolithic applications. Point solutions are usually internally built systems that grow over time. Connections between these custom systems create complex architectures and are hard to maintain over time. The TCO is not attractive at all and they are very hard to understand and maintain from a knowledge management perspective. Monolithic applications are provided by niche market players, and they offer fixed behavior that is often not aligned with your plant's business processes. Those niche market vendors create new versions for each customer site and make their money from customization. Best of breed products sound like a good alternative but the benefits are offset by overlapping functionality and different systems that follow different industry standards. With SOA, you can layer services on top of all of these existing systems—and sometimes the vendors even help out by service-enabling their own applications—so even the incremental effort involved in creating services to get the systems talking won't be all yours to do.

"Services decouple the services provided from the underlying standalone functions applications. For example, today, if you want the information from the plant's systems, you have to code a custom interface, but with services you can request that the software system provide you a complete service. For example, you might want to ask a system managing a tank farm how much on spec inventory of a particular material you have, without concerning yourself about the size and shape of the tank, what material is in which tank, or the chemical properties measured ," said Bala. "In the past this would have taken many calls to the API and a lot of specific knowledge of the underlying system. I heard Intel folks in a recent seminar talk about what they consider the three big advantages of SOA for them. First, because services are granular, they can test parts of a system, accelerating development and making faster progress toward a truly hosted system. Second, they could reuse a lot of the code that they converted to a service, and third, the services themselves were reusable, allowing them to get more value from the data center by using the same services. Writing the new code, they calculated, was about 300% of the effort, but reuse alone justified the intial effort. The idea is that by making an investment in the creation of services, you recoup that investment in the future by lower costs of integration or by the increased value of applications that are easy to create.

"Here's another example of SOA. Let's suppose that we are designing a new label on our product. We want that label to be used not only at all of our manufacturing sites, but also at our third-party manufacturers and distributors. A service could be exposed through the Internet that allows each of these parties to collect all the data they need for the product label, such as product name, hazardous goods classification, and so forth, and to print the label with the right information and in the right format. Then we can all share this same label service."

"People in process plants are generally eager for more information," said Mulcahy. "But when the road to that information is paved with lots of custom integration projects that have to be maintained, require waiting for IT, and have a high probability of failure, the enthusiasm drops. SOA in manufacturing is about making the cost of accessing information reliably as low as possible."

"There's another equally important aspect," said Bala. "We learned from the session on execution that the software created for execution only automated a fraction of what could potentially be addressed by software. Not because vendors don't want their products to do more, but because the execution problem is very diverse. In enterprise applications like ERP, there is more commonality than there is on the plant floor. An invoice for Dell is a lot like an invoice for Wal-Mart or for General Motors. On the plant floor, the range of needs is not so common, so you need an environment that provides tools to construct the solutions you need. Vendor solutions will take you a long way, but there's always a gap between what you need and what the solution provides. Manufacturing SOA makes it easier to fill that gap because services provide the information and then new tools arrive to combine them quickly into new applications. These applications are sometimes called mashups, or composite applications. Let me draw what these look like."

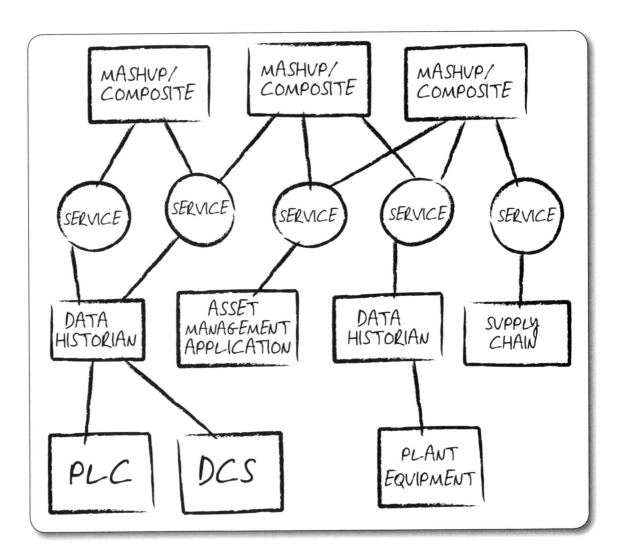

"So services come from all levels of systems," said Bonhoffer. "And then you have some way to combine them into these mashups or composites. But there are a lot of moving parts here. Information coming from asset management systems will be a lot different from that coming from a product management system, or the supply chain. If you have hundreds of services from all these levels, how do you keep track of them?"

"There are many challenges that vendors are working out at all levels," said Mulcahy. "But, like the commercial for digital telephone calls says, it does get better just because it is digital. The need for information is a function of the application and is unrelated to the form. Services are simply a better way to separate and maintain the interaction between modules. Consider what happens today if you need to change out your maintenance or lab system with a different vendor. These systems have certain standalone functionality but are also connected to many other business processes, such as reliability or quality management. If you have the interface broken down into services, then it is clear what functionality you have to support, but if these interfaces are custom coded against an API it is a much more difficult task. In addition, you can test individual functionality without a total build.

"The mechanism is straightforward if a bit new. To support SOA, you need what you just described, a services repository with the right services in it, and a means to discover and consume them. One visual use of services is to create a composition environment to bring services together into mashups.

"It is all about responsibility. If you are responsible for notifying users, you will need to create a service that does this and make it easy to consume so that if you have an event-management infrastructure and need to report something and then have a bunch of other programs and people notified, it is easy to accomplish no matter what system the user is running."

"There's no way to go out and buy a top-to-bottom Manufacturing SOA," said Bala, "but vendors are gradually offering new versions of products that have services available and part of the solution so that individual pieces of functionality can be used. It will be up to each application architect to figure out how to assemble those pieces. AMR Research created a report on Manufacturing SOA that presented one way to organize a Manufacturing SOA. Here are the elements that they identified."

ELEMENTS OF A MANUFACTURING SOA

MANUFACTURING SERVICES ENABLEMENT LAYER

- Operations event/activity monitoring
- Operations process management

OPERATIONS INTELLIGENCE

- Operations service bus

MANUFACTURING MDM

MANUFACTURING COMPOSITION ENVIRONMENT

"The top layer is the manufacturing services enablement layer," said Bala. "The components in this layer are used in the definition of events and services, the management and orchestration of those services, and the synthesis of information for the purposes of performance visualization and analytics. These components include two categories: operations event/activity monitoring and operations process management, or OPM. Especially with manufacturing, real-time event definition and monitoring is critical to composite applications that support key functions such as quality management or reliability. Though a failed business transaction can be detected and corrected retroactively, long-term damage to assets, brand, and even loss of life can result if vital manufacturing events aren't sensed and responded to quickly. Data historians, which we talked about in previous sessions, are a critical foundation for manufacturing SOA. They not only maintain the history and state of the facility, but they also perform analytics to analyze, aggregate, compress, archive, and chart real-time data and expose events requested by the business software. These systems are now huge and, to be useful to the enterprise, they must scale using distributed state-detection machines, designed for complex definition and real-time evaluation of complex events. They perform analytics needed to detect predefined states and events that operate directly on the stream of new incoming data, which frees the business software to manage business processes instead of trying to do high-speed analysis. Putting the raw stream of real-time data and unsolicited events into normal business software without this analysis and aggregation would be like drinking from a firehose.

"Another level in the manufacturing services enablement layer is operations process management, or OPM. Orchestrating manufacturing services has some unusual features, especially the triggering of high-level and slow-running business services from an event instead of by time. OPM relies on the high volumes of complex aggregations and transformations of data from shop-floor sensors and controls, but only responds to the result of these dedicated, scalable historians instead of attempting the processing in the business layer. It's like Peter's slow- and fast-loop analogy. OPM not only needs to link events from the plant, but it also needs to link people as well, since only *people* implement actions required in many manufacturing steps, especially those dealing with abnormal situations. Keep in mind that the maximum bandwidth of a person is no more than 3 hz while, in a large complex, the low level event stream might be in excess of 100,000 hz. Something is needed to distill that data into actionable information, and that's what OPM does.

"Beyond orchestrating manufacturing services," continued Bala, "OPM needs to integrate operational manufacturing processes with BPM systems across disparate time domains, crossing application and enterprise boundaries. Consider the problem of managing quality or customer orders in three redundant data centers around the world. Think about the synchronization, fail-over operation, and restart after failure that are needed—all without losing an order or any data. These are just a few of the problems that can be addressed by decomposition using the more maintainable services environment. The need for this sort of help is especially acute for organizations that can ill-afford the adverse effect to their customers or manufacturing assets or, even worse, their compliance efforts, such as a recall.

"Another level is operations intelligence. Just as you need integrated business performance management to see the benefits of BPM, operations intelligence must provide business context for real-time manufacturing processes. This is orchestrated by OPM to provide event-driven, role-based performance management across distributed manufacturing sites.

"The next level is the operations services bus. Like any information bus, this layer consists of the message management, queuing, dispatching, and arbitration functions needed to broker communications between the various entities that share the bus, including legacy applications such as MES and CMMS systems. However, unlike the traditional message buses, it provides new methods of discovery and implementation in the cloud using SOA technology. Most off-the-shelf enterprise-class message bus technology will struggle to keep up with the volumes and speed of unsolicited events found in manufacturing.

"The next level up is the manufacturing Master Data Management (MDM) level. This level provides a single repository for information about business objects, such as materials, processes, products, employees, customers, suppliers, and assets. It is current, consistent, and accurate, whether it is used inside or exchanged outside the enterprise.

"Some of the key elements of MDM are schema definitions," Bala went on, "data model management, and data synchronization across distributed master data repositories. Key to manufacturing MDM is the recognition that manufacturing master data has multiple masters within each manufacturing site, in addition to coordination points with the enterprise systems that create product definitions. Data synchronization, name space management, and governance processes are necessities that will be supported by emerging operations services bus architectures and federated database management frameworks. At the end of the day, the application that is responsible for the maintenance of the information must be the 'owner.' In many ways, an out of sync master data system is worse than no master data at all.

"I'd like you to also think of the top level, the manufacturing composition environment, as the way forward for creating user-centric, extensible applications in manufacturing.

"We're accustomed to the concept of the integrated development environment that's used to develop run-time execution code for monolithic applications deployed on a single operating system platform.

"Today's manufacturers need a new integrated set of tools to allow us to develop run-time code distributed across multiple platforms, as well as install, invoke, and orchestrate services that are continually evolving on different operating systems and hardware platforms and services play an important part. These tools must also collect and present data and tasks on various user interfaces and devices.

"So those are the levels of automation we see in the Manufacturing 2.0 world. You'll want to compare your notes side-by-side with the way things have worked in the past."

"As you can see, all these layers have a lot to them," said Mulcahy. "In most of our plants, we don't have even the beginnings of this sort of architecture and nothing like the entire vision presented here can be built at once. It can only be created incrementally. It must be implemented in layers. First, put in a decent infrastructure including sensors, controls, historian, and so on. These can be of value even with simple tools like Excel. Then you have to design the first level—LIMS, maintenance, product tracking, batch execution, reporting, and the like. Then you have to put in essentially an enterprise gateway that massages the information and creates the transactions that the ERP system uses and finally incorporate the ERP system that takes advantage of the rest of the architecture. But if we want the most from our investments, we need to create structures like these to allow ourselves to build flexibility and to easily gather information and create applications using services."

Manufacturing Standards and Interoperability

"It would be hard enough to do what we outlined," said Bala. "But there's another key question we must answer to make any SOA work. Imagine you could wave a wand and all these services would magically work. Well, we know the services come from different levels of systems and that at each level numerous vendors are building those services."

"I see the problem," said Bonhoffer. "What are the chances that the information provided by all these services will be consistent? Will some services report in units per minute and others in units per second? Will some use different codings for events and error conditions?"

"Exactly," said Bala. "The first generation of services that arrive will not be semantically consistent."

"How can you get around this?" asked Bonhoffer.

"One way is to put mapping logic in the mashups or composites using the services," said Bala. "This is a horrible way forward because it creates complexity and a maintenance nightmare. A better way is to create a layer of consistent services on top of ones that are not consistent. This puts the mapping and transformation logic in one place."

"That would help, but it seems like a lot of work," said Bonhoffer. "This sort of thing is not what Wolverine is good at."

"There's more to it than just consistent data," said Bala. "You noticed the layers. How will the systems in layer 4 communication with those in layer 3? How will layer 3 communicate with layer 2, and layer 2 communicate to layer 1? Will the people integrating these systems make it up each time they do it?"

"I know you have an answer," said Moulton.

"The answer is standards, and when building an architecture at Wolverine or at any other plant, you need to be aware of what standards exist and how you want to use them," said Bala. "An understanding of standards helps you manage a heterogeneous environment, choose the right outsourcing partner, pick and choose between vendor products, and reduce vendor-lock-in in some cases."

"So what standards are involved and how does it work?" asked Moulton.

"There a huge numbers of standards in manufacturing," said Bala. "The ones that will mean most to us are those that will help improve communication between the levels of systems in the Purdue model. Here are the ones I will explain today."

MANUFACTURING STANDARDS

- ## ISA S95
  A standard for communicating between enterprise level systems like ERP and Manufacturing operations management systems for execution.

- ## ISA S88
  A standard for batch control that helps describe how the shop floor equipment will carry out the work of creating products.

- ## OAGIS
  A standards group that has created standards for messages exchanged in ISA-95.

- ## OPC
  A standard for communicating with process control equipment.

- ## MIMOSA
  A standard through which equipment can communicate about its status and need for preventative and scheduled maintenance.

"The session on execution addressed ISA S95 and ISA S88," said Bala. "These standards provide a framework for communicating between levels of systems. S95 is all about how ERP and other systems in Level 4 communicate with the execution and other operational systems in Level 3. The kind of communication described in S95 standards starts with the ERP system sending a production schedule to the execution system. The S95 standard explains how this interaction would take place. The OAGIS standards describe the specific fields in the messages to be exchanged, and they also do a lot of standardization outside of manufacturing. Then the execution system would report back the performance as the work gets done. There are ways to change the schedule once it has been sent and all sorts of other messages. The S88 standard is focused on coordinating the process of creating a batch of products. This involves the shop floor control systems. at levels 0,1, and 2. OPC is used to communicate between controllers and equipment. MIMOSA is a standard for how equipment can report on its status or on its need for maintenance. There are 10 or 20 more standards are used in manufacturing."

"So, with all these standards you can sort out the problems you identified of how to communicate and of semantic consistency," said Moulton.

"They're definitely a good start," said Bala. "What happens is that you start gradually putting equipment and infrastructure in that supports these standards and at some point you reach critical mass and are able to get closer to the vision of manufacturing SOA. But it's important to understand why their development and their implementation has taken so long to get a head of steam. Look at it this way—there are many more B2B standards widely adopted and used to transact billions of dollars in business every year because it got painful to manually process things like purchase orders, invoices, and other standard business documents. Financial transactions and supply chain communication happened in large volumes. The need to increase efficiency and reduce costs drove the development and adoption of standards."

"So what's driving standardization in the plant?" asked Moulton.

"Efficiency, globalization, and virtualization," said Bala. "The world of globalized, outsourced manufacturing really got going in the 1990s. At first, you provided specifications to a contract manufacturer and they built everything and shipped the products to you. This sometimes was called toll manufacturing. But now the world moves much faster. Companies like Nike or Cisco have huge worldwide supply chains that deliver materials to factories they don't own—virtualized manufacturing. They don't just want to know how many products are created every month; they want to know the yields by the day or by the hour. They want up an up-to-the-minute understanding of what's going on in that factory. Companies who own factories want the same so they can also use lean techniques and more demand-driven models needed to react quickly to changing market conditions. Companies needed to be able to answer questions about how fast large orders will be delivered or to make promises about rushing orders or to deal with disruptions in the supply chain with the least possible trauma."

"But how does it help to be standardized?" asked Moulton.

"Well, here's what has happened without standards," said Bala. "The contract manufacturers provide a window into their operations by creating a portal web site. Or the plant would do the same thing for corporate. The web site would provide information about the operations of the factory and how orders were progressing through it. This is fine, if you have a small number of partners and orders to track. But if you're doing this at scale and globally, you want a flow of information from the plant floor to your master supply chain system where you're modeling your worldwide manufacturing capability and analyzing what's going on and making adjustments. Contract manufacturers get a leg up by supporting this flow of information. Companies executing demand driven models and lean manufacturing across large numbers of plants need this visibility as well."

"So supporting standards will be a competitive advantage," said Moulton.

"Yes, the ones we've mentioned will increase efficiency and automate the flow of information. There are lots of other standards in play that will help solve the problems of efficiency and productivity by helping make a manufacturing SOA work," said Bala. "The point is that as we make incremental changes in the plant, we want to incrementally adopt standards that will fit into a larger architectural vision."

Instrumentation and Data Collection

"So far, we've mostly talked about information that's part of the production process," said Bala. "The systems for ERP do have strong links to the execution systems in layer 3, and knowing what's going on in your production process is key, but there is a wider world of processes both upstream and downstream from production, and those processes, for shipping, logistics, and maintenance, can make or break a plant."

"You're talking about the broadest possible concept of the supply chain," said Moulton.

"It's important to include the challenge of understanding, monitoring, and managing the supply chain in our analysis because the manufacturer is always held responsible, no matter where the problem occurs," said Bala. "The larger challenge of making a plant run better involves all sorts of ancillary processes to the core production processes. In some plants, the bottleneck comes from the containers used to package and ship the product. Regardless of the challenge, if you don't have information about what's happening, you can't manage it. What I want to cover now is how our architectural thinking should include instrumenting processes inside the plant and in partners up and downstream."

"By instrumenting, do you mean installing automatic data collection mechanisms and the means to broadcast their data?" asked Bonhoffer. "That I get, but you're also talking about creating systems at the plant or at corporate to help make sense of that information and help take the right action."

"Raw data isn't helpful unless it's rolled up into the proper level or summary or used to recognize important events," said Bala. "You also need the ability to understand and react to the information and events. This implies software somewhere will capture this data and analyze it. Let's go through some examples.

"Consider inventory levels. Inventory represents an insurance policy that you won't run out of a material. The less certain the supply of the material and the longer the lead time, the larger the inventory. But imagine if you could see into the inventory levels and production schedules and work in progress of the manufacturer that supplied the materials. You could be more confident that the material would be on its way and could react to problems as soon as they started to appear. The people I talked to during my research said that such visibility could reduce the amount of inventory needed by two thirds. But to do this you need instrumentation on the supplier side. As we said before, this instrumentation could provide the information to a portal, but it would be far better if it were provided as a web service or stream of messages so it could be automatically collected and analyzed."

"Isn't that what Wal-Mart was after with its RFID mandate?" asked Moulton.

"Yes, they wanted to make the supply chain more efficient and to raise visibility and also help automate operations in their warehouses and stores," said Bala. "There are plenty of other examples—if you had a bunch of special shipping containers, it could make sense to tag them somehow to better track and manage them in order to reduce the number you needed or to avoid bottlenecks. Or say you wanted pallets scanned as they went onto trucks, as one last check against packing and shipping errors. All of these situations have a similar structure." He drew the following diagram on the whiteboard.

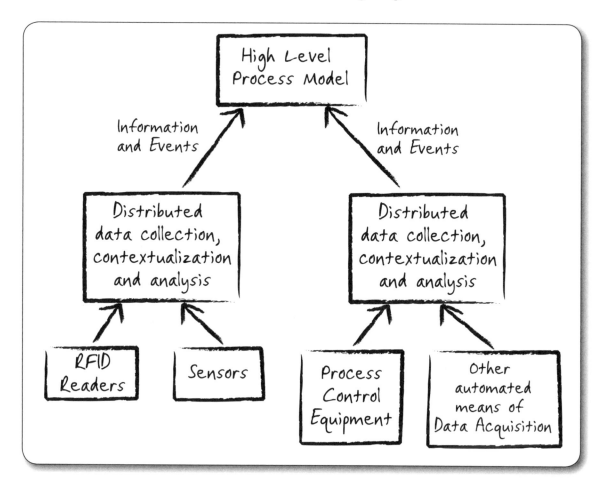

"Tracing products and tracking components is of the most important applications of instrumentation," said Bala. "The ability to trace drugs from the manufacturer to the pharmacy is increasingly demanded by regulators. And, as we pointed out in the visibility session, the ability to track the specific components that went into a batch of products allows you to do a targeted recall rather than a mass recall, which can save a huge amount of money."

"But isn't this advanced stuff for a company like Wolverine?" asked Moulton. "Are we really going to benefit?"

"That's the key question," said Mulcahy. "Just throwing technology out there and investing in instrumentation and visibility for its own sake won't do anyone much good. But there are huge opportunities, not just to make what we do now more efficient, but to do things in new ways. As we visit the plants, we want to raise awareness of these possibilities. The people we meet in the plants have the deep understanding to know when instrumentation can make a difference. We need to educate them about what can be done and see if any good ideas pop out. As we make incremental improvement, we need to move the architecture to be friendlier to instrumentation in general."

Evolving the Network in the Plant

"One of the best ways we can prepare for more instrumentation and other improvements is to take a close look at the network architecture in the plants," said Bala. "When John explained the nature of the network in manufacturing, I was shocked by how different it was from the networks I used at home and at work. Basically, I thought Ethernet and IP networking ruled the world and were used everywhere. In manufacturing that's just not that case, and the lack of a uniform, standards-based network will be a problem that impedes some of the improvements we want to make. As we move our plants forward, it's important that we understand the network architecture we have now and the one we want."

"So what problems did you discover in your research about networking in manufacturing?" said Bonhoffer.

"Let me diagram the different types of networking that happen in a plant," said Bala.

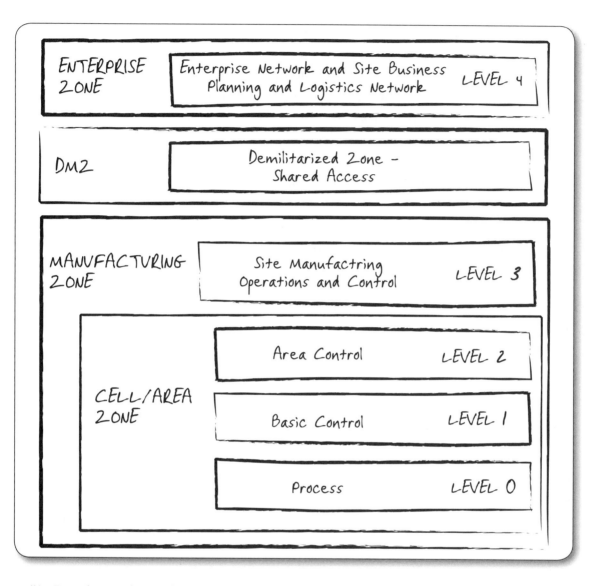

"At Level 4 we have the network we all know and love, the one we use for email and connecting to the internet and voice over IP and so on," said Bala. "This same network exists at the plant site to do the same things. Once you get onto the plant floor, the whole picture changes.

"John covered the basic reasons in the early session on the process, systems, and networks in the plant. The plants have needed networks for longer than Ethernet and IP have been around. Often these networks needed to work at high speed and had other challenging requirements for reliability and performance. These special needs sparked the creation of various special purpose networks, especially as you get closer to the equipment in the cell and area zones. The reason I drew a DMZ is that the plant networks, especially the special purpose ones, were never intended to be open to the world in the way that the Internet is. A lot of that equipment is not properly firewalled, so when you start talking about having the PLCs communicate to the site level manufacturing and the level 4 networks it can create some large worries. The S99 standard is focused on this problem."

"So what is there to do?" asked Moulton.

"We must determine where we need the information," said Bala. "Many of the manufacturers of plant equipment now offer versions of their products that work on industrial Ethernet and IP, so if a specific cell is really crucial we can upgrade that equipment and start the information flowing. There are also new forms of wireless networks based on IP which can transmit information around a plant site."

"Why is it important that Industrial Ethernet and IP be used?" asked Bonhoffer.

"Now we get to the big opportunity," said Bala. "IP is the key because once everything speaks IP, your network becomes a source of information that's gathered in a new way. IP reduces all network traffic into a standard form— IP packets. So, if you have an IP network, you can dip in and start inspecting that traffic—it used to be called packet sniffing, when people did it without authorization, but now it's called Application-oriented Networking or network mining.

"If you understand what's in the traffic on the network, you can inspect packets and determine all sorts of things. The stream of traffic becomes a source of raw data that can be turned into events that have business importance. You can track messages that indicate needs for maintenance or quality failures or alerts. Because lots of different information is flowing together in one stream, you can look for patterns of both success and failure. For example, if a PLC reports a maintenance problem, the networking mining program can recognize this as an important event and can send an alert to the appropriate party indicating there may be a problem with the orders currently underway. Instead of waiting for hours or days to find this out, the impact can be assessed instantly."

"So this is sort of like a network version of the sort of instrumentation we just talked about," said Moulton.

"Yes, but it can go way beyond that," said Bala. "A wireless IP network could be used to support communication to handsets or remote data collection or sensing of the location of equipment or people. But of course for any of this to work, you're going to need the help and expertise of people who understand IP networks—and usually that means people in the IT department."

"The key to those ideas and all that we've talked about today, is that they have to have a business case," said Mulcahy. "We've gone over the space of the possible and the sort of architecture that would be needed to support it. It's important that we know the biggest possible pictures, so we can convey this potential to others at the plant. If we do, then they'll come to us with ideas implementing a slice of the big picture here, a sliver of it there, and we can achieve major victories that build over time into a structure that allows even more flexibility. The key here is to think big and act incrementally. Bala, thanks for a great session."

Part III

Making It Happen

Part III examines the ways that plants successfully transform themselves, moving in incremental steps toward a carefully designed future state, a vision of perfection.

Chapter Thirteen

Transformation Playbook: An Overview of the Change Process

Contributing Author:
Prasad Satyavolu, Tata Consultancy Services

Mulcahy, Moulton, and Bonhoffer took their seats around the conference table while Bala used his colored markers to make a rainbow on the whiteboard, in proper spectral order. Finally, he turned to face his colleagues, ready for his presentation.

"I will assume," he said, "that you share my feeling that the term 'change management' doesn't give us anything substantial enough to grab hold of, sort of like trying to put your hand on a rainbow." Bala began to write on the whiteboard again. "To begin, let's ask a few questions. What exactly does 'change management' mean? What is its significance and what can happen when change is inappropriately planned and implemented?"

- CHANGE MANAGEMENT DEFINED
- SIGNIFICANCE OF CHANGE MANAGEMENT?
- POTENTIAL PITFALLS?

The Philosophy of Continuous Improvement

"For a plant to survive in an economy characterized by continual and unpredictable change," Bala said, "it has to roll with the punches and come out stronger on the other side."

"When a plant fails to continuously improve," Moulton said, "it can't compete."

"Exactly," Bala said. "For a plant, change must be seen in terms of continuous improvement. Before it can improve continuously, however, the organization must build a philosophy to guide its progress. Moreover, once it does this, the organization must also take pains to ensure that all its activities and processes, from corporate practices to basic tasks on the plant floor, are a direct result of this basic improvement philosophy."

"What's the actual source of the philosophy?" Bonhoffer asked. "It can't just be some heady idea conjured up by a smarty-pants executive looking for something clever to say at the C-suite meetings. It needs to be anchored to something solid."

"Because change in a plant is not a mere abstraction," Bala said, "it can never be made for its own sake. Any continuous improvement philosophy, which is really another way of describing 'change management,' must be inspired by the plant's ultimate objective. What are the results the plant wants to attain? What are the organization's stated business objectives? Remember, a plant exists to carry out the corporate strategy, and that strategy must reflect some sort of corporate-wide process that provides value to the customer."

"In other words," Moulton said, "A plant's goal, the philosophy conceived with that goal in mind, and the methods put into practice as a result of that philosophy and goal, must all be in strict alignment."

"As we mentioned when we talked about the plant's vision," Bala said, "running a plant is comparable to optimizing a massive multivariate, non-linear equation. The variant, nonlinear character of this equation expresses the constantly changing needs and demands of the customer, to whom the organization has pledged value. If the plant does things right, that value appears in products with a high degree of quality at the lowest cost. Any plant that wants to provide this value to its customers must meet its stated plan, maximize the life of its equipment, use energy efficiently, stay in compliance with environmental, health, and safety regulations, and adhere to labor union agreements, among a host of other criteria. It must keep a close eye on the stream of arriving orders and supplies, and, no matter what, it must always, always, *always* ship and deliver its product on time."

"What you've just described," Mulcahy said, "is the vision of a perfect plant."

"The perfect plant provides perfect fulfillment," Bala said. "Every product shipped out of our plant must be in perfect condition, from a performance perspective and from packaging and documentation perspectives. What's more, after the product leaves the plant, it has to adhere to a schedule dictated by the customer, arriving at their specified destination in the same perfect condition as when it was shipped. Some may question whether these logistical concerns lie within the purview of the plant's operations. However, it's our responsibility to guarantee the success of the entire process because every part of it ultimately reflects on the plant's overall performance metric. If we ever fall into confusion, we must always return to our vision of the perfect plant. The significance of successful change management goes far beyond the plant's mere survival. When change management is properly executed, the organization thrives. When change is inappropriately planned and implemented, the plant fails to provide the best value to the customer and thus to meet its potential."

"So all successful plants execute effective change management," Bonhoffer said, "and the source of this effective change is always a holistic, institutionalized program driven by a well-conceived continuous improvement philosophy. This is much bigger than a simple plan to change problem X, Y, or Z. It addresses the entire value chain process, every single aspect of a plant's operations."

The Need for Performance Metrics

"That's exactly right," said Bala said. "The next question to consider is, 'How do we achieve the sort of world class performance metrics needed to arrive at perfect fulfillment across the entire value chain?

"I talked to people who suggested that the solution begins with closed-loop feedback systems with respect to customer inquiries, orders, and deliveries. On the surface, such communication issues may appear mundane, but they're far from it. Clear lines of communication lie at the heart of vital behavioral patterns, since they are directly related to other critical processes.

"Communication goes hand-in-hand with planning. We need to consider the ways in which planning processes, whether long term or hour-by-hour, affect the big picture. After that, you look at how those plans are executed, from the ways and means by which we receive our materials and transform them into product, to how we deliver our product to the customer's doorstep in perfect condition.

"When we look at these processes at a very high level, we see how critical it is that they're seamlessly integrated. At this level, communication, planning, and execution are not three mutually exclusive items, but a single symbiotic entity. Without crystal clear communication, plans can run astray, and when plans lack clearly articulated objectives, as determined by the plant's requirements—which, as we must never forget, are themselves based on the customer's need—execution can rarely be anything more than haphazard. At the end of the day, these processes are all about continuous improvement, directed at achieving perfect fulfillment."

Initiating a Program of Continuous Improvement

"Obviously," Bala said, and began to write on the whiteboard again, "it's not enough to tell a plant full of people to be more productive. Frankly, I don't even know what that means."

"Instead, we need to provide everybody with easily understandable incentives directly related to the goal at hand. For instance, people will hustle when they hear that corporate will reward teams who increase the percentage of product delivered on time, or those who boost the percentage of product that makes it past quality control, or those who reduce the number of accidents over a given period of time. Also, people take pride in achieving tangible goals.

"Another factor common to all plants with successful change management programs is inspiring leadership. I'll talk more about this in a few minutes, but for now, I'll simply stress that strong leadership is the focal point of all successful organizations.

"My next point, though it may sound contradictory, is important in terms of psychological impact. The last thing you should do is call your change management initiative a 'change management initiative.' Anyone care to guess why?"

"For many people," Bonhoffer said, "suggesting they change how they do things sends the message that they're doing them incorrectly. A change management initiative would send the message that there's always a problem. That's no way to motivate people."

"Precisely," Bala said. "A much better expression is 'Continuous Improvement Initiative.' Whether you label the initiative or not, however, the most important things to do are, first, develop a concept for continuous improvement that is specific to your organization's objectives, and, second, weave the plan's principles into the entire business initiative such that specific goals are achieved in specific areas across the board. This is much more effective than categorizing a given set of activities under the 'change management' umbrella.

Things like that frequently become flavors of the month without any staying power. Think of it like this: the sea is made of salt water, but when you look at it, you can't say, 'Here is the salt, and here is the water.' In the same way, continuous improvement should not be considered separate from the rest of a plant's activities and processes, but rather an inherent part of them all.

"For example," Bala continued, "if you want to increase productivity, the process will require at least four or five simultaneous activities. You'll look at the entire labor deployment, at your methods of scheduling, and at the way your operators function on various machines and assembly stations. You'll want to isolate your areas of waste, too. And there are questions to ask. How are schedules communicated? Can you improve communication? Does the employee mindset align with the organization's basic philosophy? Do your people really shoot for additional productivity and simply come up short, or are they actually delaying some of the machining processes just to kill time? Does an intervention need to happen in a given department?

"In effect, you'll need to initiate an analysis of behaviors as part of the overall productivity improvement plan. Once you have the data, you can devise a course of action and set up a weekly or daily conference with your floor managers to listen to their needs and concerns even as you highlight your own goals, explaining to them how adopting newer methods will help them to improve, get better bonuses, enhance the quality of their work life, and so forth."

"I like how this approach evaluates the rate of change that's already underway in a plant," Mulcahy said. "In a plant with good continuous improvement, you don't need to change much of your change, so to speak. There is a general culture of awareness beneath all of the processes, so people are constantly searching for and working with the weakest links in the chain. A plant that has never given thought to these concerns, on the other hand, will need more drastic measures to initiate the change, much less to sustain it. At the other end of the spectrum is the plant that's already perfect. It wouldn't need a change management program at all, since the change itself is woven into the minutest fibers of the plant's methodological fabric."

"Now that you all have a firm grasp on the rudiments of this subject," Bala said, "I want to reiterate a few things. We must never forget that a plant exists in the middle of a value chain whose mission is to provide perfect fulfillment—the delivery to a customer of a perfect product in perfect condition. On one hand, you have customers. On the other, you have suppliers. Within the plant itself, you have various stakeholders, to say nothing of your employees, your contractors, and your partners. And, to complicate matters further, all these components work through a mesh of networks that consists of countless people and entities to achieve the same goal."

"I see where you're headed," Moulton said. "We must reckon with the fact that there are far too many dependencies and variables that make up the performance metric of a perfect plant. Within such a crucible, it's virtually impossible to build an information system capable of addressing every possible business scenario, change, and contingency that can potentially happen within a plant."

"The question becomes," Bala said, "how do you deal with such a situation? Not only do we want continuous improvement, but we're also trying to achieve it in an environment of continuous change. For instance, today our supply source may be so close that we receive supplies within a week of ordering them. Tomorrow, though, our strategy may dictate using a supplier located in China. Suddenly our supply lead-time goes from two days to three or four weeks, perhaps even six to eight weeks. This is not a hypothetical scenario—these sorts of drastic changes are happening in every manufacturing plant environment, across every industry."

"How do manufacturers deal with them?" Bonhoffer said. "It seems impossible to build a system agile enough to continuously adapt to new business scenarios and environments."

"What we can do," Bala said, "is build a system flexible enough to accommodate multiple business scenarios, and change within each."

"That's all well and good," Moulton said, "but we can't foresee every possible scenario."

"You're right," Bala said, "we can't. That's why it's so important that agility and flexibility be inherent in your system, and that a culture of deep awareness of the realities sits at its foundation. When your people know they're working in the midst of continual change and that they're expected to achieve continuous improvement, they will be motivated to address and solve problems immediately. Many scenarios can be handled, and new changes implemented very quickly. Other scenarios will be eliminated before they cause any trouble. A great deal of this subject concerns how effectively your people sense the changes in their operating and business environment and how they react to it and proactively work to effect changes in the face of such challenges."

"I'm clear on the basic principles of continuous improvement," Bonhoffer said, "but I'm still a bit hazy on when and where to start. You can't just waltz into a plant and outline the deficiencies and dictate changes to be made. How do you get a sense of the plant's efficiency?"

"Best questions and analysis," Bala said. "To determine the sophistication of a plant's continuous improvement initiatives, you need evidence. The evidence lies in data. To get the data, you've got to ask questions. Once you've got the data, you analyze it."

How Much Help Does Your Plant Need?

"Diagnosing the state of an organization's continuous improvement will occur in stages," Mulcahy said. "Stage one is defining where you want to be and where you are right now in terms of getting there. If you're a refinery, for instance, you might discuss whether your goal is really to be a Solomon first quartile performer. That may not be where you want to go. You may not be ready for it. The last part of this first stage involves estimating what it will take to achieve your objective. We're talking about the big stuff here—time, money, and people."

"This is difficult work," Bala said, "which means it has to be highly structured. Getting the data requires a lot of digging, which in turn requires experienced people who have the energy and the enthusiasm to do it right."

"Stage two entails devising a plan to achieve your objective," Mulcahy said. "This is where the real challenge is, because in any plant environment there is so much that you could do, on so many different levels, that any process you try to improve will only yield incremental results."

Establishing Priorities

"How do you decide where to act?" Moulton said. "It seems like you push a little bit here and move a little bit there, while worrying that none of your other areas of concern drop behind."

"Our old friend Pareto," Bala said, and began to draw a graph on the whiteboard, "who devised the 80/20 rule, also created a nifty device called the Pareto bar."

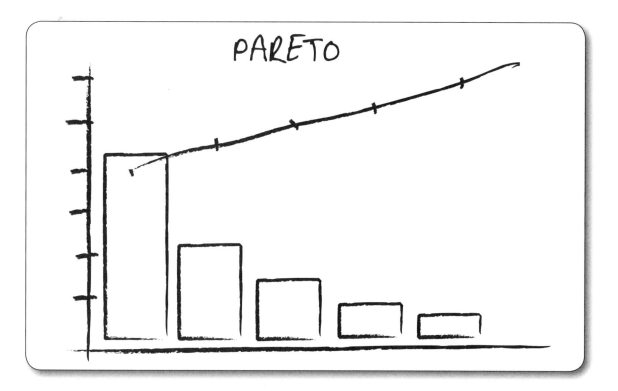

"It's a form of analysis that involves breaking your problems into categories, and then examining them to see which have the most impact. Once you determine which category has the greatest impact, you begin to chip away at it. That category will always return the biggest bang for your buck."

"And to locate those problem areas," Bonhoffer said, "you have to ask the right questions, which is where the digging effort lies."

"Ask the questions," Bala said as he began to write a series of questions on the whiteboard, "then analyze the answers.

1. How is demand this year vs. last year?

2. How are the plant's revenues and output this year?

3. How often does your product ship on time?

4. How have quality parameters improved in your plant?

5. How has productivity improved?

6. What is the overall cost improvement in this plant?

7. What is customer feedback and customer perception of our plant, and what does the data say?

8. If there is a problem, how do you go about solving it?

"These are just a few of the questions that can help you find the areas in a plant that require work. Once you get plant managers talking about these topics, and you know how to listen, their answers will give shape to how the plant operates, where its deficiencies lie, and how you can help them assess their areas of weaknesses and create strategies for change. For example, I talked about how important it is to consider every aspect of the plant's operations, even ones seemingly tangential to its general operations. Timely shipping is one such aspect, since it can provide a window into the organization's financial health. Timely shipping affects customer satisfaction, which is critical to a company's profitability. It also reflects the productivity of a plant's inventory, quality control, and even safety and maintenance departments. A skilled interviewer can uncover details about all these parts of the plant, and the overall communication and vision of the company, just by asking this one question and listening effectively."

"After you've got your Pareto bars," Bonhoffer said, "and are putting your biggest effort into the highest among them, I assume you want to continue to reassess which areas will yield the most improvement for your effort?"

"That takes skill, too," Bala said. "One expert said the process sometimes reminded him of a hammer looking for a nail. Since you probably excel at some processes more than others, those are the ones you'll be inclined to search out for improvement. Unfortunately, they may not be the processes in the greatest need of help. Another of my sources described this as 'a solution looking for a problem.'"

"How does this play out in the plant?" Bonhoffer said.

"Suppose somebody says they have a new solution that will solve all your equipment availability problems," Bala said, "and then proceeds to justify how it will work without first describing the actual problem. At that point, you need to say, 'I see you want to help improve our operating availability. Show me what our availability is now.' If they can't show you the availability of your equipment, it's probably because they haven't truly looked at it. Instead, they ascribed to the notion that the new bells and whistles on this system can solve all their ills. We've seen this sort of thing in the host of scoreboards and KPIs and other such packages that purport to show us how we need to run."

"The solution," Mulcahy said, "must be a function of the need, and the only people who know the need are the experts in the plant itself."

"To avoid this pitfall and get straight to your needs," Bala said, "it's imperative that your analysis is strictly objective. A relentless objectivity will also help ensure you stay within your means. Every organization has limited resources. Straying too far in the wrong direction as a result of faulty analysis is a sure way to get over-extended. Close analysis and critical objectivity will also guarantee rapid results, which are equally vital to a successful continuous improvement initiative. Once you have momentum, your people's faith in the project grows exponentially, and they will rally to the cause. We must never forget that in the end it's the effort of the people that makes the plant work."

"How do you know when you're guiding your effort with unbiased data and when you're not?" Bonhoffer asked.

"In addition to a solid set of best questions," Bala said, "you must have an analysis methodology that starts high and understands the business objectives of a plant, that looks at what the business is expecting on a P&L sheet. You want to see the kinds of revenues the plant should be generating, along with the cost structure of the plant, and so forth. When things are going poorly, revenues will be off. Or maybe revenues are okay, but expenses are too high—it could be energy, it could be maintenance, it could be breakdowns. You'll nearly always see the problem reflected on the P&L sheet."

"After we have a list of problem categories as determined by our Pareto bars," Bonhoffer said, "people will begin to offer solutions to them. How can we know which direction to take?"

"That's where experience helps," Bala said. "People experienced in these matters acquire good eyes and ears and know instinctively how to avoid blind alleys. These are also people who like to feel some heat.

"For instance, engineers at a plant frequently analyze problems on their computers. That's fine, as far as it goes, but a plant or production manager can't do the same and expect to ferret out the best solutions. People in the plant use all five of their senses. In a refinery, if something's not right, they hear noises or feel heat from a furnace that's not firing properly, or they can smell something that's not burning the way it should. There's also a little bit of fear involved, sometimes more than a little, from concern over personal safety or from facing customers when things haven't gone right.

"Sometimes you've got to get your hands dirty. One of the problems in a plant might be out at the loading dock—maybe your rail cars or your boats aren't coming in on time or in the right proportions. Or it could be in the operations area, where the plant isn't being controlled properly and product is constantly off-spec. An experienced manager should be able to use his or her five senses to get to the heart of the real problems."

"Isn't that theory at loggerheads with the notion that our solutions ought to be data driven?" Bonhoffer said.

"On the contrary," Bala said, "this is exactly what it means to be data driven. You must have data to fix those problems. They are the only way to the solutions. But you've got to know where to start. Using your senses and your instinct is always a great way in. If you see the railcars not working they way they should, instead of fighting to make them run correctly by brute force, you can simply run your numbers. The data will not lie. If you're objective, you'll know right away whether this area needs attention, and to what extent. The reason you see a discombobulated railcar system is because a problem hasn't been solved. The best plants have the people who are the best problem solvers. It's that simple."

"This is the nitty-gritty of running a top-end manufacturing plant in the 21st century," Mulcahy said. "Nothing is easy. Everything's a challenge. Continually improving an organization involves more than merely formulating a handsome vision backed up with well-planned processes. It involves the senses and instincts, as well, things that can't be bought on the university campus. You need hard-earned experience."

"Once you've collected your information," Bala said, "you plot it out to assess the gap between where the plant is and what your goals are, so that each necessary change, large and small, can be ranked. Small, fast projects might take priority, especially if they're not dependent on external forces, such as clearance from corporate. Each step must be aligned with an objective to show people how their efforts relate to the goals they've set forth."

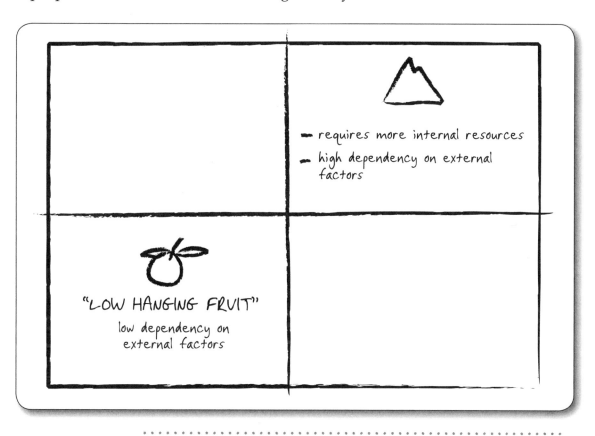

"These steps can be prioritized using a four-quadrant grid," Bala continued. "The Y axis is effort, or internal factors, and the X axis is dependency, or external factors. The lower left quadrant is occupied by 'low-hanging fruit'—quick, easy projects with a low dependency on external factors like clearance and interference and signing off from corporate. The upper right quadrant requires more internal resources, like time and manpower, and has a high dependency on external factors, such as changing supplier or customer relationships.

"Suppose you have a plant trying to improve its overall throughput. The analysis and the solution themes zero in on two initiatives: a physical layout change of the whole plant, and a change in the planning process. With limited resources, the plant must prioritize and synchronize these initiatives to achieve the end goal. With multiple dependencies in such situations, frameworks like this quadrant help leadership make the right decision."

"Where does Pareto figure into this?" Moulton asked.

"Pareto," Bala said, "is a quick and established way to get to some fast decisions. Carrying out a complete root cause analysis of the sort I just described, however, is preferable. Plants where Six Sigma culture exists usually resort to defining a good Six Sigma project. Certainly, a variety of techniques used concurrently will yield the best results. Still, we always want to consider at least three key elements: business processes mapping and analysis, data analysis using a standard performance metric definition set, and organizational culture assessment. In addition, a structured and iterative interview process with the key stakeholders and process owners will help identify the buried issues and also validate solution themes."

"So we need to combine our data and analysis with our intuition," Bonhoffer said, "to evaluate the whole thing from every possible angle before we make decisions. Of course, we never have enough data or enough experience. We just get as much as we can and let our gut guide us along the way."

"What are the things that should scare us?" Moulton said. "Bala, you mentioned people who want to throw a software system at a problem they haven't seen. What about when people try to make a project too big, or when they go the other direction and understate it?"

"One expert talked about how nervous he gets when he's depending on someone who doesn't have a grasp of the problem," Bala said. "He suggested keeping a close eye on your trial balloons—the questions you ask to find out how much someone knows. He felt it's critical for any manager to employ this technique. Ask people questions for which you already know the answer, to see what they understand, what they've accomplished, and how hard they've worked. In his opinion, every top manager does this instinctively."

"Were there any questions that your expert specifically recommended asking?" Bonhoffer asked.

"For instance," Bala said, "you might ask a plant manager, 'Why do you want to make these changes?' If the person answers, 'Corporate told me to,' you would have insight into both them and the plant culture in general. On the other hand, the manager could say, 'Our poor quality standards result in a lot of waste and wasted time, both of which prevent us from shipping on schedule. That, in turn, is compromising our customer satisfaction, which we worry will start to hurt orders, not to mention employee morale.' This answer indicates the manager has a clear vision of the plant's role in the company and the dynamics of its inner workings. More importantly, it helps you set goals and benchmarks for the larger change. In this case, the benchmarks could include quality standards, timely shipping, and improved orders, as opposed to improved quality alone, which might have appeared to be the most immediate issue."

Benchmarking for Discussion, Not Intimidation

"Benchmarking and identifying best practices are critical parts of the goal-setting process," continued Bala. "Ask the plant managers what they consider to be useful benchmarks—perhaps another facility within the organization, or industry-wide benchmarks that are generated quarterly or yearly, like Solomon for the process industries or the Harbor Report for automotive."

"There is a famous product called The Manufacturing Game that works across sectors to set maintenance standards," said Mulcahy. "It's a computer-based game and benchmarking tool used to help change plant culture. There have been some dramatic results reported at DuPont and British Petroleum."

THE MANUFACTURING GAME

In the 1990s, DuPont conducted a two-day computer-based benchmarking study of 140 plants with 33,000 people that aimed to improve maintenance processes called The Manufacturing Game. The main theme of the game is to get people to cooperate cross-functionally to get the right results, as well as the basics of a reliable plant, which involves ridding a plant of defects. The game has been instrumental in creating a culture of change in the way a plant operates, maintains, and improves equipment by working out communication and management systems. In the game, players take on the roles of either operating, maintenance, or business. The players are asked to communicate and accomplish tasks. The facilitators have found that at the beginning when players are unclear of how to do their jobs, there is lots of discussion, but after 30 repetitions of the game, communication is reduced, the processes move effortlessly, and there is less wasted time and fewer wrong moves.

The basic lesson? The more people understand what other roles do, the better the communication, the less waste, and the more efficiently a plant will run.

The game has proven successful in places where as much as 80% of the employees go through the exercise. In Lima, Ohio, a British Petroleum refinery used The Manufacturing Game and was then sold for $179 million to Clark, which turned it around and sold it for $1.9 billion three years later. The value of that process has lasted for thirteen years and through four owners.

"Some of the experts mentioned that as a great tool," Bala said. "But a lot of the time it will be up to the consultant—you—to step in and do the research and make concrete suggestions about standard practices and benchmarks. Make absolutely certain the standards you set forth are actually relevant to the plant and processes and goals at hand. Sometimes the most creative minds look outside their industry to figure out best practices. The aerospace industry took cues from the automotive industry's success with assembly line manufacturing, even though one would presume that the size difference in the product would preclude one industry from borrowing benchmarks from the other. But it can go the other way, too—it might seem to make sense to borrow productivity benchmarks from a plant that makes similar products, but less obvious forces, like distribution chains or raw material sources, could mean that doing so would be comparing apples to oranges. Be careful with benchmarks—discussing them can be valuable in drawing out understandings of processes and goal setting and brainstorming, but laying out benchmarks as absolute standards can be a showstopper. After all, managers' bonuses are often tied to whether they meet specific results. At this stage, the goal is to create a non-threatening environment that encourages people to share ideas and issues without feeling like they have to defend their performance. Even identifying divergences between people's ideas of useful benchmarks can be useful. Think of benchmarks as more of a process than an end goal. Don't forget, we need to go behind the benchmark numbers and identify the best practices and processes that made those numbers happen."

"There seems to be a lot of psychology involved in this transformation process," Bonhoffer said.

"This benchmarking process is a good example of that," Bala said. "Because people tend to resist change when it's forced upon them in a threatening environment, the benchmarking process must not be intimidating. It should actually bring out the human tendency to strive for betterment so that people look at the processes behind the numbers and learn from those benchmarks, which are then adopted into the plant's processes. The key is to keep it non-threatening and to enlist people's support for changes that must be made. One way to do that is to disarm them by making the conversation just that—a conversation and not a lecture full of directives about how things are changing whether they like it or not. As I said before, people do their best work when their ideas are heard and they feel invested in the process."

"Someone might be enthusiastic about changes," Moulton said, "but there are so many other factors at play. Like, 'Who is going to pay for these changes? How much will it cost?' Those issues can be showstoppers for the most enthusiastic of plant managers."

"It takes a skilled and knowledgeable project planner to assess the situation, formulate goals, and produce an outline for the kind of investment required," Bala said. "That investment includes time, effort, and human resources, as well as hard money. This project planner should take into account softer issues like the plant culture. If the people at this facility like to make changes themselves, that should be factored in. If these people aren't creative thinkers, the change assessment must include leadership to make things happen."

Incremental Change — No Big Bang

"Implementing continuous improvement in a plant," Bala said, "is an order of magnitude more difficult than in, say, a publishing house. In a plant, if you make an inappropriate change, you could kill somebody or damage very expensive equipment. One expert I interviewed told me how in his early years he met with a principal scientist in UOP, the firm that developed the great majority of the world's refining technology. 'Your methods are far too conservative,' my expert told him. The scientist shook his head and looked at him with amusement. 'This is a refinery, sonny, not a bank. If you work in a building in San Francisco that sits right on top of the San Andreas fault-line, you better pray that the civil engineers who crunched the numbers for the architect were extremely conservative. Fortunately, the people who work in any refinery we designed don't have to worry about such matters.' And my expert knew the scientist was right. When potential loss of life and equipment are at stake, the manufacturing industry is conservative, which means that continuous improvement occurs incrementally, as opposed to in a series of big bangs.

"Let me give you an example of the havoc that can be wreaked when change is made quickly and relatively thoughtlessly. In Flixbourgh, England, in 1974, they needed to connect a giant hexane line to a smaller one. Of course, the powers that be needed it done yesterday, so the company engineer designed a rubber coupling that went from one line to the other, and then installed it immediately without running any tests. Unfortunately, the engineer was not versed in materials engineering, so he didn't understand that rubber 'work hardens'—when there's vibration inside a copper line, for instance, any contiguous rubber grows less and less flexible until it ultimately breaks. The limits to this engineer's innovation rested in his narrow expertise. If the people who ran the plant had taken their time, they could have assembled a team of engineers with experience in diverse disciplines to collaborate on a safe, long-lasting solution instead of the helter-skelter 'solution' that killed 28 people and injured 36 more when it failed and exploded.

"Fortunately, something positive was born of that terrible accident. The ensuing investigation precipitated a set of safety standards called the Brady

Safety Standard, which in the United States became the 29CFR1910.119 standards. These standards constitute a procedure under which safety is managed in plants handling highly hazardous materials, which would include any plant working with group C or group D material—gasoline, ethylene, and the like. The procedure has been implemented in a number of different ways, every one with a whole suite of requirements designed by law. Basically, they amount to a continuous improvement system, quite like those we see today for aircraft safety, where recommendations are made, implemented, and closely monitored. When an incident occurs, it is thoroughly investigated, and any recommendations that arise in consequence undergo the same careful scrutiny before being implemented. The ISO 9000 is another such continuous improvement process for the management of quality, and Title V includes a similar procedure designed to ensure health and safety while managing the release of factory emissions. There are sure to be others over time, all of which will entail processes of incremental, deep-running, evolutionary change."

Change: A Culture of Innovation through Collaboration

"Next, I want to look at the means by which change is implemented," Bala said. "Change is brought about by innovation. Innovation, in turn, entails traveling into the unknown, and the only way do that successfully is to collaborate."

Here Bala began to write another list on the whiteboard.

INCREMENTAL CHANGE

- CULTURE

- INNOVATION

- COLLABORATION

"The first obstacle you'll encounter if you attempt to innovate in a vacuum is the extent of your own knowledge. The disaster at Flixbourgh was a textbook example of this. The engineer who designed the faulty coupling may have been a very good mechanical engineer, and he may have been a very good chemical engineer, but he didn't have knowledge in the field of material science. Overlooking that shortcoming proved fatal. If you don't have multiple people examining a single problem from various points of view, you can't collaborate, and if you can't collaborate, you can't come up with solid solutions.

"The question is, 'How do you get people from the widest variety of disciplines looking at a given problem?' There are some exciting examples of plants that generated hundreds of ideas and saved millions of dollars by forming teams of people who don't normally interact. This sort of collaboration creates a hotbed of innovation, exactly the environment required for an agile plant to adapt and constantly change. In turn, a change of culture is created in an organization that nurtures innovation through collaboration."

"Are there are methods to foster such a culture?" Moulton asked.

"They can be as simple as putting together an engineer and an inventory guy for a week," Bala said. "Often, however, it requires the use of technology—or at least a means of assessing the way workers interact with technology. Back in the day, the first IT systems would recommend that users complete a task. The users complied for a while, but soon they started saying, 'Why don't you just do that yourself?' So the systems were configured to be more automatic and only informed the user once the task was completed. After some cultural transformation, the users began to say, 'Just do the task and don't bother telling me.' They audited the task but didn't need to be informed each time something was done. The workers were empowered because they trusted the computers and were then free to complete other tasks. This unleashed innovative thinking, since now people brainstormed ways to further use the computers for activities they once performed manually. Change like this can't happen if management doesn't nurture it. If a policy states that the system must absolutely inform users about each completed task, then there will be no cultural change because users don't come to rely on the very technology that's designed to improve production."

"The Web," Bonhoffer said, "is the quintessential means of using technology in the service of collaborative innovation. As Bala said, the idea is to get the largest number of eyeballs looking at a problem to maximize the possibilities of generating the best solution. When organizations exploit blogs, wikis, and discussion boards to their fullest potential, they provide a forum through which the number of eyeballs that can be brought to bear on a given problem is theoretically limitless."

"When you put your latest brainstorm anonymously on a discussion board," Bala said, "you can see what kind of feedback it gets. As other ideas are added, it can blossom."

"These are all pretty esoteric ideas," Mulcahy said. "How do we use them to change our plant for the better?"

"Again," Bala said, "the real key to reaching that goal is to create a solid community out of people who are down and dirty with the workings of the plant, people who have a pressing need to change it and who are the thinkers and the doers. Then it's management's job to create an environment that's innovative because it's collaborative. The prime mover behind any of these initiatives, big or small, will be one or more strong leaders in the organization. I'd like to close our discussion by talking in more detail about this key aspect of the transformation playbook."

The Importance of Strong Leadership

"There are numerous ways," Bala said, "that powerful managers can impact a plant's continuous improvement initiative, both positively and negatively."

"Before you elaborate," Moulton said, "could you define what makes someone both a leader and a manager, rather than merely a manager?"

"That's a vital distinction," Bala said. "The person who is both manager and leader will never ask anyone to do something he or she wouldn't do, and will always be out there leading. This is a person who addresses any problem, wherever it may be. Strong leaders instinctively use their senses and intuition and get on the scene to mix it up with their fellows. They're never afraid to make a call independently, and never sit around waiting for some committee to give them a recommendation. They're not afraid to make mistakes, either. These people also have a great deal of integrity, and most are well informed in broad areas of knowledge. In addition to their areas of personal interest, they know about people, HR systems, performance appraisals, Six Sigma, all the things that are ancillary to a plant's chief concerns. And this as well: these people are personally *strong*. Once of my sources talked about leaders in terms of racehorses—he said that when you bet on horses, you look at all the data. You look at their speed rating, at how many races they've won, at how fast they can do a furlong. But the thing you can never overlook is class—if a horse has been running in a stakes race, which means he's a good horse, and then he comes down to a lower category, such as a claiming race, it doesn't matter how fast he's been running. He's going to win that race, because he intimidates the other horses. Why? He has a lot of personal power, and the rest of the horses know and understand it. People are the same way. When a strong manager comes in, everyone knows it. He or she doesn't have to be physically big and strong or the best looking person in the room. But after two hours, everyone knows, 'This person is strong.' One major quality possessed by all great leaders is an ability to understand their people, and to work with their welfare always in mind. A strong leader in the plant wants to develop his people to their greatest potential."

"It sounds to me," Bonhoffer said, "that if corporate wants to guarantee that its plants have a rock-solid continuous improvement philosophy, it's critical to spend as much time as necessary to hire the right plant manager. Afterwards, corporate needs to listen to that person and do their best to give her everything she needs to achieve her goals."

"The other thing a stronger manager/leader needs is enthusiasm," Mulcahy said.

"The stuff is contagious," Bala said. "When the manager is on the ball, understands all the aspects of the plan, knows where he's going, has a good plan, and is enthusiastic, people eagerly follow him."

"What are the biggest mistakes your sources have seen plant managers make when trying to improve things?" Bonhoffer asked.

"The first thing everybody mentioned," Bala said, "is that they don't have enough contact with their people. A good indicator of your manager's level of personal strength and security is the door to her office. If it's closed, or if the manager has a secretary between her and the office, you can assume that she's probably in trouble. The good ones are walking up and down the hall, or out on the plant floor. It's always a postive sign when you see them out there mixing it up. Another critical shortcoming to avoid in a leader is cynicism. This is contagious, too, only it's destructive, like the flu.

"Good attitude and strong morale are vital to the success of a plant's operations. For instance, there are a certain amount of methodical, repetitious activities that must be done every day, such as checking pumps. You can't put enough instruments on them to do it without human interface. They simply must be checked every two hours to make sure they aren't vibrating. It must be done with the proper attitude, or it won't be right, which is a sure way to invite a catastrophe into the plant. The same dilemma applies to many managerial tasks, which one expert compared to fighting a swarm of mosquitoes. There are a million things that must happen everyday, many of which can become tiresome and repetitious. It takes strong people to remain optimistic and enthusiastic in the face of these difficulties. Before disaster strikes, a certain number of things usually happen in a row, much the way tumblers in a combination lock must fall into place before it can be opened. When people at the top get cynical about their jobs and duties, they tend to overlook these disaster signs. Before the Air Florida plane crashed in the Potomac, for example, or the train hit that bridge in New Orleans, people disregarded various incoming signals and data simply because they'd grown cynical. Every single person I spoke with warned me about this. When it happens at the top, it's spreads like wildfire down the ranks, and before you know it, you've lost your plant."

"What other mistakes can a manager make?" Mulcahy asked.

"They can become what one expert called 'crusaders,'" Bala said. "At a plant he had visited, the manager was exceedingly proud of how 'low' he kept his costs. Over and over, he repeated that he was 'the low-cost producer.' He hired the minimum number of people and paid them the lowest salaries. After about two weeks of analyzing the plant, our expert went up to this low-cost producer and said, 'I've looked at your plant, and I do applaud you. There are many, many good things happening here. However, if I had to put you in a category of one through four, I'd put you at number five.' Naturally, the low-cost man didn't like hearing this. 'Why is that?' he said. 'Because all of those things you're looking at,' our expert said, "are small Pareto bars. The biggest bar is energy, and you haven't even seen it, much less begun to troubleshoot it. You're bleeding energy like a stuck pig. While you're focused on salaries and fringe benefits and other penny-pinching concerns, dollars are flying out of the stacks.' This manager's crusade in the wrong area blinded him to the critical objectivity required to see what issues needed attention.

"Yet another pitfall to beware of is a labor force working with low personal energy levels. One of my experts mentioned a Jesuit priest who gave seminars on how running a plant could be seen as working with people and their energy levels. One of the chief goals at any plant should be to maintain a very high energy level in its labor force. The last thing you want is to find them working at the lowest level, which is a state of apathy. The priest offered an example to illustrate his point. He gave one of the young men on the job a bad review because the man was performing terribly. The next day, the man burst into his office, screaming and yelling with anger. When the priest's colleague asked him what he intended to do with the man, the priest said, 'I'm doing it! His energy level just went up from apathy to anger. Next time I'll move him up to enthusiasm.'"

"Is there a method for elevating people's energy levels?" asked Moulton.

"That's why a strong leader is so critical," Bala said. "Most of them do this sort of thing naturally. Even if they don't, it doesn't take a genius to see when people are apathetic. They're not working hard, not doing their assignments, aren't participating in meetings. The times they do participate, they aren't prepared, and their results are poor. Telling people with low energy to get their numbers up is a waste of time. You need to energize them or get rid of them. However, most people really do want to work. They want to change and to grow. Not only do they want to meet the plant's expectations, but also they want to exceed them. The leaders in your plant will determine how well its people can perform, one way or the other. The great leaders inspire their people to do more. But it's up to leadership to make that first move.

"To repeat, powerful leadership lies at the heart of a successful plant. We started out this conversation by noting that change in a plant is not an abstraction. Any continuous improvement philosophy must be inspired by the plant's ultimate objective, which is to provide value to the customer, in the form of a perfect product delivered in perfect condition with perfect accuracy. Without the right leadership, this can never happen, because the people on the floor running the plant will slip into apathy and cynicism. When you have the right people at the top, on the other hand, people with vision, strength, knowledge, energy, and experience, they will share and transfer those qualities to the people they're working with. A plant with a team that fits this description will soon approach a state of perfect continuous improvement."

Bala closed his laptop and capped his pen, as the others gathered their notes. "We made it to the end of the rainbow," he said. "I guess it's time to see if we can find that pot of gold. Lunch is on John, right?"

Mulcahy smiled. "These past sessions have shown how much you've learned, and you've taught me a lot, too. I think you're ready to help pursue the perfect plant. After lunch."

•   •   •